CIVIL ENGINEERING DIVISION
GENERAL EDITOR: J. R. D. FRANCIS

TRAFFIC PLANNING
AND ENGINEERING

A

TRAFFIC PLANNING AND ENGINEERING

BY

F. D. HOBBS

PAVIORS AND SENIOR LECTURER, DEPARTMENT OF TRANSPORTATION
AND ENVIRONMENTAL PLANNING, UNIVERSITY OF BIRMINGHAM

PERGAMON PRESS

Oxford · New York · Toronto · Sydney

Pergamon Press Ltd., Headington Hill Hall, Oxford

Pergamon Press Inc., Maxwell House, Fairview Park, Elmsford, New York 10523

Pergamon of Canada Ltd., 207 Queen's Quay West, Toronto 1

Pergamon Press (Aust.) Pty. Ltd., 19a Boundary Street, Rushcutters Bay, N.S.W. 2011, Australia

First edition 1974

Library of Congress Cataloging in Publication Data

Hobbs, Frederick Derek.

Traffic planning and engineering.

(Civil engineering division)

Edition for 1967 by F. D. Hobbs and B. D. Richardson published under title: Traffic engineering.

1. Traffic engineering. I. Title.

HE333.H6 1974   388.3'1   74-6393

ISBN 0-08-017926-6

ISBN 0-08-017927-4 (flexicover)

Printed in Great Britain by A. Brown & Sons Ltd., Hull.

Contents

4 Parking   155

5 Traffic and Environmental Management ✓   194

Preface

WHILE the subject-matter of traffic engineering is now well established, within a growing body of theory and practice, it needs to be studied within the wider context embraced by planning and transportation. The practitioner must not only play a part in the formulation of public policy objectives but be both aware and responsive to changing circumstances and, overall, be concerned with the fusion of theory and practice. He must be conscious of the need to preserve and enhance the city as a place to live, to balance the provision of accessibility with mobility and to seek a fuller understanding of the effects of transport decisions on society.

The motor car, once heralded as the saviour of cities congested and polluted by horse-drawn vehicles, is currently the subject of some public disillusionment, mainly arising from its mis-use. While it may provide maximum mobility to the individual owner, it can simultaneously impose grave social penalties, both to other owners and non-owners, by its indiscriminate use, causing congestion, down-grading of the environment and destroying the viability of public transport. The problem is sometimes one of balancing conflicting alternatives but, more often, of meeting complementary needs and evaluating the consequences satisfactorily in economic and social terms. There is a need to perceive demands and satisfy them efficiently at a minimum cost with the least inconvenience. Efficiency and quality, conservation and preservation and new development are not necessarily incompatible once the correct problem has been identified. In an age where resources are more critical their efficient use becomes paramount and may entail moving away from the notion of a maximisation of travel opportunities to that of a minimisation of travel needs, although at a similar level of activity enjoyment.

Technological change and the generation of new opportunities must also be taken into account. Whereas the aim of traffic control is to transform the flow of vehicles from a pattern of individual behaviour into a collective phenomenon, where drivers' actions are curtailed by restrictive measures, a consequence is the degree to which individual latitude and

ix

aberrations are to be permitted. As the system approaches its limits the proximity of other vehicles imposes impossible demands on individual drivers consequent on the closer coupling of their stimulus–response mechanism. Thus, diminishing returns can be expected from each higher level of control sophistication. The general question then has to be resolved as to the stage at which current systems should give way to entirely new transport modes for the overall benefit of communities and individuals within them.

Although the title has been changed the original scope of the book remains unchanged from that of its predecessor, *Traffic Engineering* (vols. 1 and 2). Inevitably, with the passage of time, the emphasis changes in any field embracing human development. Besides the additions of new material, and updating to accommodate such changes, drastic revisions of the original text and order have been made and the work has been combined into a single volume. The book has been written to provide an introductory, rather than a definitive, text of use not only to engineers, planners, architects and geographers but also to other professional and sometimes lay people involved in community development and decisions which often require a substantial background knowledge of traffic planning and engineering.

References in the text have been kept to the minimum but at the end of each chapter there are listed further and often more specialised works which expand on the chapter's contents. In limiting the references care has been taken not to offend by plagiarism, but as, over the years, ideas are disseminated and absorbed the original sources are forgotten and unwittingly assumed as one's own. For all such implied personal credit I ask for pardon and hope that some reward will be a recognition of the influence they have exercised.

My debts are many and I gratefully acknowledge the contributions that have been made by my friends and colleagues, but in particular to many former graduate students who have contributed so much to the development of my ideas and for their ever-patient and wide-ranging discussions over many topics. In addition some of the data, used to illustrate the text, has been developed from past student projects. The final tribute is to my late friend and previous co-author Mr. B. D. Richardson, who died so tragically in a mountain accident in 1971.

F. D. HOBBS

CHAPTER 1

Historical Influences in Traffic Engineering

PRE-NINETEENTH CENTURY

The practice of regulating and controlling traffic has evolved with the development of wheeled transport and the social and commercial consequences of its use. In the first century B.C. traffic congestion was a regular characteristic of travel in Roman towns, causing municipalities to plan for traffic and to enact regulations for its better control. The first orders banning wheeled traffic during the daytime were made by Julius Caesar and, subsequently, Hadrian limited the total number of carts allowed to enter the city. British legislation has developed from the Statute of Winchester, in 1285, which laid down the responsibilities of landowners for road maintenance. Their duties also required them to safeguard travellers from robbery by clearing bushes and undergrowth likely to conceal assailants near the edges of the track. Roman practice had been to build their roads on low banks to give a clear view over the surrounding countryside, and hence the term highway.

Citizens established the rights of passage over another's land. If the track became impassable, they were allowed to divert the route, creating the winding nature of some English roads. After the dissolution of the monasteries, the responsibility for roads passed from the landowners to the parish by the Highway Act of 1555. This formed the basis of highway administration for nearly 300 years, although with declining influence in later years as fines replaced the statutory obligation of parishioners to labour on the roads. Eventually, the fines gave way to a rating system.

The development of the coach, in the seventeenth century, led to problems of road maintenance on the long distance routes which passed through poor parishes. From 1663 onwards, Acts of Parliament established turnpike trusts, responsible for the collection of tolls and administration of what then constituted the main trunk road system, known as turnpikes. By the year 1830 some 2200 miles of turnpikes were administered by 1100 separate authorities, whereas the 105,000 miles of local roads remained the responsibility of the parish.

Generally, the eighteenth century was a period of increasing activity and travel; extensive legislation was enacted, often in an attempt to control vehicle use and regulate the type of vehicle equipment and loading permitted. Roads were often severely damaged by the narrowness of wheel rims of the fast moving gigs and the heavily loaded lumbering wagons, but it was only towards the end of the period that road construction methods and design improved to any extent. The efficiency of operations and better roads meant that journey speeds were more than trebled between 1760 and 1830. It was in this period that William Pitt introduced mail coaches, in 1784, and they contributed to safer, speedier and more comfortable travel. Coach services were operated throughout the land with a route of over 1000 miles between Lands End and Thurso.

The 1835 Highway Act introduced important traffic legislation besides abolishing statute labour and authorising the levying of highway rates. The parish remained the administrative unit but with powers to combine with neighbours. Traffic provisions dealt with obstruction, riding on the footpath, driving furiously and keeping to the left when meeting oncoming vehicles. Other parts of the Act included aspects of development control forbidding encroachments on the highway or erecting machinery within 25 yards of the highway unless concealed by a wall or house.

During the period of intensive railway construction a few mechanically propelled steam vehicles competed with the stage coaches, but restrictive legislation and exhorbitant tolls precluded their widespread use. It was not until the advent of the internal combustion engine and the independent re-invention, by Dunlop in 1888, of Thomson's earlier patented pneumatic tyre that the technical conditions arose which, coupled with economic and production factors, have led to today's plethora of personal vehicles. The basis of local government, established in the last decade of the nineteenth century, has remained with little change until the Royal Commission in Local Government reported in 1969.   Subsequent legislation, albeit different from the recommendations, creates new authorities from April 1974.

In the year 1868 a semaphore signal, showing red and green lights, was erected in Westminster to stop and start traffic. With more than 460,000 licensed carriages in the late 1870's traffic congestion was rapidly growing worse in urban areas and, on London streets alone, 237 persons were killed and nearly 3200 were reported injured in that year. The invention of the internal combustion engine by Lenoir in 1860 and its use in a three-wheeled vehicle by Benz in 1885 was soon heralded as an invention overcoming the hazards, pollution and congestion caused by the horse carriage. The abolition in 1896 of the notorious "Red Flag Act", imposing severe restrictions on mechanically propelled road vehicles, soon led to the rapid growth in car ownership, offering greater convenience in personal travel.

TWENTIETH CENTURY

County registers of motor vehicles were established by statute in 1903, and new speed limits, identification plates, driver licences and lighting requirements were specified.

Roads had to be redesigned to suit the needs of the new vehicles. Earlier waterbound macadam surfaces of the rural road system and the stone set-paved city road surfaces, constructed for the horse and iron wheel, were no longer suitable for the rubber tyres and speeds of the motor car or cycle. Inevitably, the question was raised as to how taxes, paid to a central Road Fund administered by a Road Board, should best be allocated. The decision taken at that time to concentrate on the improvement of surfaces at the expense of improvements in alignment has left us, more than 60 years later, with tortuous and dangerous sections on many of our major routes. With the rapid growth in numbers of motor vehicles came the formation of the Ministry of Transport in 1920 and the steady increase in vehicle revenue, which now makes such an important contribution to the general revenue from taxation.

The rapidly increasing vehicle ownership (330,000 vehicles in 1919 to over 2,270,000 vehicles in 1930) also brought an increase in road casualties (from 50,000 in 1919 to over 185,000 in 1930) and after the Royal

Commissions, in the late 1920's, came the introduction of the comprehensive 1934 Road Traffic Act. This was an attempt to improve road safety and deal with accidents, which had by then risen to 239,000 (total vehicles 2,405,000), by such measures as driver competence tests, urban speed limits of 30 mph and increased penalties for many driving offences.

During the inter-war depression period, resources of men and materials were sometimes directed to road building and a fairly considerable programme of arterial routes and by-pass construction was undertaken, in addition to maintenance and minor improvement. Some comparative

TABLE 1.1.

PUBLIC ROAD STATISTICS IN GREAT BRITAIN

	Year (values in thousands)				
	1939	1957	1962	1967	1972
Kilometres of public roads	290.5	306.0	315.6	326.2	339.2
Number of vehicles	3,149	7,484	10,562	14,096	15,700
New construction and major improvement	17,377	9,100	25,800	280,600	512,900
Maintenance and minor improvement	31,599	51,200	63,700	135,700	169,300
Miscellaneous, including cleansing and administration	9,308	25,000	36,000	67,400	102,800
Road lighting	—	20,200	26,000	32,700	40,300
Car parks	—	—	4,100	8,000	10,400
Total expenditure	£58,284	£105,500	£155,600	£524,400	£835,700

Source: Department of the Environment Statistics.

figures for expenditure are shown in Table 1.1. At the same time, in Germany, the need for long-distance and high-speed road networks was accepted and an extensive mileage of autobahns was constructed. Similar types of road were also built in Italy and the U.S.A. While Britain recognised the need for major national routes in the 1936 Trunk Road Act, little was done to establish a new, purpose-built, trunk system. The now familiar encroachment of cities into surrounding rural areas and their suburban sprawl, often flanking new arterial by-passes, went ahead rapidly and largely unchecked. The Restriction of Ribbon Development Act 1935 sought to control the planning of development, preservation of amenities and access to new major routes which, in many instances, had already become completely built-up. The war brought an end to new road building and also car manufacture and it was to be nearly twenty years before a substantial road programme was again developed.

Post-war acts have emphasised the need for important national routes by the establishment of urban and rural motorways and the further control, use and development of land through extensive planning legislation. Later, Tables 1.2, 1.3 and 1.4 set out some of the more important Acts and list their general provisions.

Trends in Development

Each new development in technology, either of the vehicle or its right of way, has not only led to new travel opportunities and changes in the distribution of spatial activities but has affected social behaviour. The practitioner must be aware of trends in vehicle improvements and technical advances in control and operation for each change poses fresh problems and implications in planning for a new situation. Often the gains from such opportunities have been transitory and before long corrective measures have had to be taken to achieve a more desirable balance. Inevitably precipitate action is taken too late with over-correction resulting in further losses of benefit. It is important to guard against the temptation to see the advantages of one form of transport in a certain context of use as having a universality of application or as a panacea to some vague "travel problem". Transport is a servant of human travel needs and its preservation in a variety of forms and types is more likely, in the long term, to both satisfy and safeguard the diversity of individual needs and remain in scale with the nature of our social and physical environment. Viewed in these terms it is also likely that it will meet the elusive criterion of "economic efficiency".

LEGISLATION

The preceding brief review of British highway history forms a basis for developing the general requirements of legislation. A major aim for the legislator is to ensure that the pattern of development should be one of gradual accommodation to changing conditions, with care being taken to eliminate outmoded laws. The sudden infliction of new measures, marking major changes in the existing legislative pattern, often needlessly incenses the individual, encourages abuse, and makes effective enforcement difficult. Nor must traffic legislation be directed punitively at single sections of road user to correct a situation for which they are not necessarily responsible. Formulation of Acts must ensure clear meaning, individual clauses must relate to a conceptual whole and the subject matter must be capable of reasonable performance for the prescribed conditions. In addition legislation must be acceptable to a majority and also readily enforceable.

Legislation Requirements

The general requirements of highway traffic legislation can be broken down into the following principal categories:

Category 1. Vehicle Regulation: registration, mechanical fitness and tests, equipment carried, size, weight and performance of the vehicle and components, such as tyres, brakes, lights, structure, emissions, etc.

Category 2. Road User Regulation: Licensing of different categories of driver (passenger vehicles, goods vehicles, cars, etc.); accident procedures and reporting; insurance requirements; driver competence tests; medical standards and evidence; drivers' hours of work; cyclists and pedestrian regulation.

Category 3. Traffic and System Regulation: types and uses of devices, signals, signs and markings; definition and control of parking, loading/unloading, prohibitions and definition of street uses, control of access and terminals.

Category 4. Community Protection: planning controls, environmental standards—noise, air and visual pollution; public transport provision, lighting, inquiries, compensation and citizen rights, information services.

Category 5. Financial Provisions: revenue and expenditure control—vehicle taxes, fuel taxes, tolls and other use charges—parking, road pricing, etc.; rates and local taxes.

Category 6. Management and Operation of the Road System: road classifications, public utilities, maintenance controls, safety organisations, publicity programmes and public participation.

Category 7. Control of New Construction: land acquisition, construction planning, new routes and road improvements—publication of schemes and alternatives, public participation and decision making.

British legislation is initiated in the Houses of Parliament in the form of Bills which can be introduced by the government or private members in either the Lords or the Commons, with the exception of Money Bills. A formal first reading is made to present the Bill after which it is printed and circulated. The next stage is the second reading where broad issues are debated and ammendments put down and if the Bill is passed it reaches the Committee stage (whole House, Select or Standing). After clause by clause discussion it is returned to the House with or without amendment. At the Report Stage the Bill is either accepted by the House or referred back for further discussion. Finally the Bill receives its third reading where only verbal amendments are permissible and is sent to the House of Lords. When passed by both Houses it becomes an Act of Parliament after the Royal Assent has been given. Amending Orders can be brought in without amending the Act and Ministers of State are empowered to make Statutory Rules and Orders in amplification of the Act. Advice is given by Departments in the form of Circulars.

Britain is probably more fortunate in respect of uniformity than other countries such as the United States where National Conferences, Reports of National Committees on Uniform Traffic Laws and Ordinances and Presidents Highway Safety Conferences have produced Uniform Codes which are not necessarily adopted by individual states who are often slow and reluctant to accept central direction. While trafficlegislativeuniformity has been attained in this country, interpretation and definition of the law are sometimes difficult and lengthy to establish.

A brief outline of a limited number of the more important Acts are shown in Tables 1.2, 1.3 and 1.4 listed under the various categories described above.

TABLE 1.2.
ROAD TRAFFIC ACTS

Year	Main provisions (categories 1, Vehicle Regulation; 2, User Regulation; 3, Traffic Control)
1930	Classification of vehicles by types, regulation concerning equipment and construction dimensions, loads, smoke, mirrors, etc. Abolition of speed limits on cars and motor-cycles and revised limits for commercial vehicles. Third party insurance made obligatory and new provisions for licensing drivers and ages. Maximum hours of work specified for drivers of public service and goods vehicles and provisions for fair wages. Appointment of Traffic Commissioners in Traffic Areas controlling bus and coach services, public service vehicles subject to annual renewal of licence and justification of service against rivals, mainly the railways, to eliminate unnecessary competition.
1934	Mainly road safety with increased penalties for dangerous driving. Introduced 30 m.p.h. speed limit in built-up areas (roads with street lighting) and instituted a driving test for all new drivers. Special licensing arrangements for heavy goods vehicles.
1956	Extensive measures for improved road safety including a compulsory annual test for vehicles over ten years and stricter regulation on the sale of unroadworthy vehicles and the renewal of driving licences. Dangerous driving penalties increased and include cyclists. Penalties for pedestrians disobeying directions of police on traffic duty. Special ministerial powers to approve local authority parking schemes and charges and experimental traffic control schemes by the Metropolitan Police including towing away of vehicles causing obstruction.
1960	Consolidation into one Act, under seven parts, the more important legislation from earlier and above Acts. Parts (i) general relating to road traffic,

TABLE 1.2. ROAD TRAFFIC ACTS (*cont.*)

	(ii) licences and ages of drivers, (iii) passenger service vehicles, (iv) goods carrying regulations, (v) heavy goods licensing of drivers, (vi) third party liability, (vii) general.
1960	(Road Traffic and Road Improvement Act). Traffic wardens appointed by police authorities and option of fixed penalties for certain offences. New powers conferred on local authorities for traffic control and additional ones for off-street parking. Special provisions to deal with traffic, parking and roadworks in London.
1962	Control of hover vehicles on roads. Increased penalties for offences including an additive penalty system and new proposals on drink and driving, imposition of new speed limits and variations, e.g. 40 m.p.h. urban limits, 50 m.p.h. rural limits and an upper overall 70 m.p.h. Voluntary registration of driving instructors.
1967	(Road Safety). Provisions detailing offences of driving with alcohol (80 mg per 100 ml) or drugs and disqualifications. Safety of goods vehicles, plating system, marked laden weights. Tests for vehicles over 30 cwt unladen weight. Reintroduced special licences and tests for Heavy Goods Vehicle drivers.
1967	Removed the five-year limit in connection with off-street parking in 1960 Act provisions.
1967	(Road Traffic Regulation Act). Mainly a consolidating Act for traffic regulations outside Greater London, traffic regulations in Greater London for experimental traffic schemes; pedestrian and school crossings, street playgrounds, parking places, traffic signs, speed limits, inquiries (replaces much of 1960 Act).
1969	(Transport Act). Regulation of traffic in parking places, parking of passenger service vehicles; fixed penalties and traffic warden powers.
1972	Regulations of cycle racing on highways and restrictions on use of motor vehicles off roadways.

The most recent road traffic acts continue the trend already established of increasing penalties for driving offences and extend the liability of automatic disqualification. Following the London example of introducing traffic wardens and procedures for the payment of fixed penalties for

TABLE 1.3.

MISCELLANEOUS HIGHWAY ACTS

Year	Name of Act	Main Provisions (categories 6 and 7)
1936	Trunk Roads	Establishment of national route requirements. Ministry of Transport to exercise all functions of highway authority for 4500 miles of Class 1 routes, outside County of London and County Boroughs, to be designated trunk roads.
1946	Trunk Roads	Additional 3700 miles Class 1 routes designated trunk roads. Legislation for one-way roads, cycle tracks and footpaths. Preparation of scheme orders and procedures and power to construct bridges and tunnels over and under navigable waterways. Establishment of third class of grant-aided roads with higher grants to existing two classes.
1949	Special Roads	Principal purpose to provide the legal machinery for the construction of roads reserved for special categories of traffic, notably motorways.
1950	Public Utilities Street Works	Introduced to avoid unnecessary and frequent distrbuance of the highway. Provided a street works code of Statutory Powers for mains authorities and undertakers. Deals with notices, arbitration, safety measures and the protection of transport operations.
1959	Highways	Consolidation of existing legislation from previous Trunk Roads and Special Roads Acts. Financial provisions for making up private streets; codes of 1875 and 1892 incorporated in Part IX. Powers of local authorities to make new street by-laws.
1961	Highways (Misc. Provisions)	Actions against highway authorities in respect of damage resulting from failure to maintain highways.
1966	Local Government	Roads classified for purposes of grants and other legislation. Separate provisions for street lighting and grant aid for origin and destination surveys.
1971	Highways	Provisions with respect to construction improvements of highways. Power to stop-up and provide access to premises, provision of picnic areas, diversion of watercourses; construction of bridges over and under navigable waterways.

certain offences, such as breaches of the parking regulations, all authorities have been granted similar powers.

The dangers of rigidity of legislation and the affect of sudden sweeping changes can be shown in the approach to speed limits starting with the abolition of limits in 1930 to the hurried introduction of a 30 mph urban (built-up area) limit in 1934 after a marked increase in the number of accidents. This single speed limit remained with little modification, until the trial experiments of 40 mph speed limits on certain London roads in 1955, despite the fact that it had not been effectively enforced for many years on major roads. More experimental trials are now made before major legislative changes are initiated.

TABLE 1.4. PLANNING AND TRANSPORT ACTS

Year	Name of Act	Main Provisions (categories 4 and 7)
1947	Town and Country Planning	Comprehensive legislation bringing together road planning and social and community planning proposals. Introduced development plans and review procedures. Updated earlier Acts of 1935 and 1943 on control of development and access along classified roads. Control of advertisements on highways and preservation of trees and woodlands.
1959 & 1962	Town and Country Planning	Acquisition of land for highways, largely repealed by Road Traffic Act 1972.
1968	Transport	Comprehensive legislation on integration of transport planning, establishment of four Passenger Transport Areas outside greater London area. Bus and rail services to be co-ordinated by Authority with professional executive. Subsidies from local rates for unremunerative services needed for social reason. Formation of National Bus Company. Integration of freight transport service with formation of National Freight Corporation and National Carriers Ltd. to be part operated with British Rail. Introduced new licensing systems for operators (quality licensing of operators) and

TABLE 1.4.   PLANNING AND TRANSPORT ACTS (*cont.*)

		proposed quantity licensing (authorisation for road bulk deliveries in vehicles over 16 tons and distances over 100 miles).
1968	Countryside	Enlarged functions of the Commission established under the National Parks and Access to the Countryside Act 1949. Conferred new powers on local authorities and other bodies for conservation and enhancement of natural beauty. Amendments of law concerning trees, woodlands, footpaths, bridle ways and other public paths.
1968	Town and Country Planning	New provisions were incorporated in this act for Development plans to include both the survey of planning areas and the preparation of a structure plan which resulted from the Planning Advisory Group Report. Structure plans formulate, in a written statement, the local planning authority's policy and general proposals for the area in respect of land, development and traffic management with respect to regional policies, availability of resources and other special matters. Arising from Structure plans are the detailed preparation of local plans and the procedures for public participation and objections.
1971	Town and Country Planning	Consolidation Act superseding earlier legislation and provisions in others and repealing and dealing with Development plans; General Planning Control; Special Control for listed buildings, trees, advertisements, waste land; Enforcement of Control and Acquisition, Stopping up and diversion of highways; Statutory Undertakings.

In many respects the treatment of transgressors of the law has become more liberalised in recent years with an emphasis on correction rather than punishment, but it has not been carried far enough where road user offenders are concerned. If punishment should fit the crime it is possible that many offenders would respond better to education and retraining, with its widest implications of medical treatment and community service, than to imprisonment or heavy fines.

Administration

The administration of roads has passed through many changes to meet the varying needs of a period. The Road Board was never popular with Parliament mainly due to its lack of control over the Board's financial powers. The alternative system of, in effect, close Treasury control has proved to be disappointing because of its too rigorous limitation on transport expenditure generally and for long, after the war, on roads. Restrictive policies in transport expenditure have frequently borne no relationship to the problem of passenger or goods movement. Output in Britain has lagged behind many industrialised nations of the world and part of the reason for this may well be due to an inadequate transportation system.

Until 1966 roads were classified in Classes I, II and III for the purpose of making central authority grants of 75, 60 and 50% respectively. Unclassified roads did not receive direct support from central funds and were maintained from local revenue. Motorways and trunk roads are wholly the responsibility of central government for their construction and upkeep. The 1966 Local Government Act enabled the Minister to classify roads either for the purpose of making grants or legislation, and after April 1967 classified roads, for the purpose of finance, were replaced by principal roads, basically the former Class 1 roads, and Class II and III roads were amalgamated with unclassified roads. It gave the local authorities greater freedom of choice on road improvements and maintenance policy than hitherto, by providing a block sum for expenditure. This was given in the form of a rate support grant based on previous expenditure on highways and lighting, mileage of principal roads and with increased grants for higher population density. Principal roads were the only group classified for specific capital grants of 75%. As they form part of the major national road network, together with motorways, they have a wider significance than just the area of a local authority and national strategy has to be borne in mind when making strategic investment decisions for their improvement or maintenance. It can thus be seen that, in some respects, the powers of central authority are now being disseminated locally.

While the Ministry has complete financial liability for trunk roads, local authorities are often employed as agents to undertake directed work on them. However, to expedite major works on the inter-urban trunk and motorway network six Road Construction Units were formed of personnel from the Ministry and County Councils. In 1967 major planning work was divided into two parts known as the firm programme and the preparation pool. Schemes of sufficient priority are added to the preparation pool for detailed assessment and are then considered for inclusion in the firm programme for a specific year in relation to the available resources. A separate preparation pool is maintained for the Welsh road programme and the road investment programme for Scotland was set out in Scottish Roads in the 1970's. A preparation list has also been developed for principal roads.

The strategy for main road development in England, until the mid-eighties, followed from a green paper published in 1969, *Roads for the Future*. It envisaged a comprehensive network of about 3250 km of major road with a substantial proportion constructed as motorways.

The main functional types of urban road form a hierarchy as follows: Primary distributors, forming the main road network of the town, are intended to carry all longer distance traffic to, from and within the town. District distributors provide access to the principal functional areas of a town such as residential, industrial and business areas and form links between the primary distributors and the roads within areas. These districts are divided into environmental areas, which are intended to be functionally cohesive, and where environmental control factors such as noise, pollution, safety and visual aspects all predominate in traffic design. Local distributors are the main traffic distributors within an environmental area and link the district distributors to the local *access roads* which give direct access to buildings and land.

Some of the major characteristics of roads in Britain are shown in Tables 1.5 and 1.6 and Fig. 1.1. Tables 1.7, 1.8 and 1.9 compare road lengths and vehicles by categories in some E.E.C. countries and motorway statistics. Figure 1.2 shows the relative distribution of vehicle ages in Britain and Fig. 1.3 the length of haul by goods vehicles.

TABLE 1.5.   RESULTS OF SAMPLE SURVEY OF ROAD SYSTEM OF GREAT BRITAIN
(1957–9)
(converted to metric units)

	Trunk and Class I		Classes II, III and Unclassified	
	Urban	Rural	Urban	Rural
Average width of carriageway (m)	8·84	6·71	6·40	4·57
Percentage 6.10 m wide or less	7	29	42	90
Percentage 9.14 m wide or greater	41	11	6	0
Percentage with radius of curvature				
<152 m	2	2	4	6
152–457 m	4	11	4	7
457–914 m	4	6	3	6
Percentage with gradient steeper than				
1 in 12½ (8%)	2	2	4	5
1 in 25 (4%)	16	15	24	22
Percentage with footpath				
on both sides	69	10	65	3
on one side	21	22	12	5
Percentage with reflecting studs	36	53	3	2
Percentage with speed limit	70	12	75	7
Percentage with frontage development	63	21	69	14
Per 160 km of road				
Uncontrolled pedestrian crossings	40	3	1.2	0
Lay-bys	12	20	0.6	0.6
Pairs of bus stops	210	35	60	9
Per km of road, junctions encountered				
3-way	4.4	1.1	4.3	1.0
4-way	1.1	0.2	1.4	0.2
Other	0.04	0.01	0.09	0.01

Source: P.I.A.R.C., XIIth Congress, Rome 1964.

TABLE 1.6. PERCENTAGE OF BRITISH HOUSEHOLDS WITH ONE AND MORE
THAN ONE CAR

Year	One car	Two or more cars	Households (millions)
1961	29	2	16.6
1963	33	3	17.1
1965	36	5	17.7
1967	41	6	18.1
1969	44	7	18.2
1971	45	8	18.8

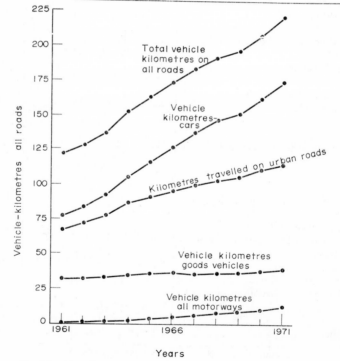

FIG. 1.1. Growth in road travel on roads in Great Britain, 1961-71.

TABLE 1.7.   CARS AND TAXIS PER THOUSAND POPULATION, 1963 AND 1970
(*Annual Bulletin of Transport Statistics for Europe*, 1970, United Nations)

Country	1963	1970
France	165	246
Great Britain	142	209
Italy	77	169
Netherlands	72	177
W. Germany	127	207
U.S.A.	364	412

TABLE 1.8.   ROAD STATISTICS IN EUROPE

Country	Total km of road (1000's)	km of road per vehicle km run	Road vehicles (1000's) 1968			
			M/cycles & auxiliary cycles	Private cars & taxis	Coaches & buses	Goods vehicles
Great Britain	350.8	180	1,325	11,500	56.7	1,634
France	1,482.2	1,003	5,550	10,880	81.1	2,431
Italy	282.0	288	3,270	7,370	34.5	1,049
Netherlands	96.0	221	1,990	2,000	10.0	275
W. Germany	410.0	199	1,312	11,683	41.5	927

Source: United Nations, *Annual Bulletin of Transport Statistics for Europe*, 1969.

TABLE 1.9.   MOTORWAYS IN EUROPE AND THE U.S.A., 1972 (kilometres)

Country	Total km of motorways	kilometres per million population	kilometres length per 1000 km² area
Britain	1,630	29.6	6.76
France	1,650	33.5	2.99
Germany	4,750	79.2	19.10
Holland	970	77.0	27.74
Italy	4,360	82.3	12.85
U.S.A.	72,500	362.0	7.88

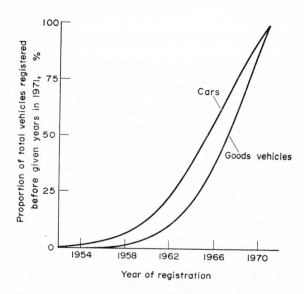

FIG. 1.2.   Cumulative frequency curve of vehicle ages by year of registration.

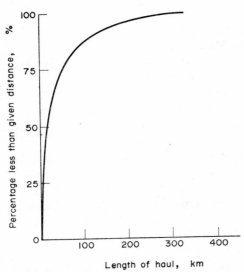

Fig. 1.3. Cumulative frequency of commercial vehicle haul lengths in Britain.

ORGANISATION OF LOCAL GOVERNMENT

From April 1974 local government will operate under a changed structure. The new councils will still have the same basic purpose—"To secure the people"—but will be divided into either County Councils or District Councils in a two-tier structure which differs from the principle of unitary authorities proposed by the Royal Commission on Local Government. In England there are now 47 new County authorities with some 296 District councils. The principal conurbation areas are to be governed locally by six metropolitan county councils. These metropolitan authorities are similar, in some respects, to that of the Greater London Council which remains unchanged by the later legislation. The functions of the upper-tier authorities are regional in nature whereas district councils provide the more local and personal services within an area.

Metropolitan County Councils' services include the following: the police forces, fire services, the Passenger Transport Authority, transport planning, highways and road safety, parking and strategic development, structure plans, parks and recreation, refuse disposal and museums and art galleries.

County Councils, in addition to the responsibilities of Metropolitan County Councils, include services for education, libraries, personal social services and youth employment.

Metropolitan District Councils have control of education, housing, local planning and development, environmental health, clean air, refuse collection, personal social services, libraries, youth employment and markets.

District Councils, within non-Metropolitan County Council areas, are responsible for housing, clean air, environmental health, refuse disposal and local servicing of sewerage. They also assist the County with matters relating to planning, transport and highways, parks, art galleries and museums.

The new authorities have replaced many smaller authorities and, in order to maintain a closer contact at the local level, most former parish councils are retained in the overall system. A number of new parish councils have been created to serve small towns which did not retain a local authority.

Parish Councils, besides retaining their existing responsibilities, have further duties in respect of footpaths and bridleways, off-street parking, footway lighting, parks and open spaces, allotments, swimming baths and cemeteries.

Figure 1.4 indicates the principal areas of traffic engineering and planning and their functional relationships.

PLANNING

Land use and its planned spatial distribution is the basic determinant of traffic demand. Planning presupposes that there are arrangements of activities within a built environment which yield benefits both to individuals and, in aggregate, to the community. The main problems lie in reconciling one course of action with another, particularly in relation to the apportionment of benefits and disbenefits between individuals, groups and the community at large. Besides the creation and conservation

Traffic Investigation and Study	Planning	Design	Operation
Transportation surveys	National and regional development of land and facilities	New Road design including intersections	Capacity
Parking surveys			Characteristics
Traffic and pedestrian characteristics	Integration of transportation Road, Rail, Air and Water	Re-design of intersections and existing street systems	Signs, Markings and Signal Systems
Road utilization			
		Standards	Street Lighting
Road safety and accidents	Environmental Planning	Service areas, parking, pedestrianisation and terminals	Regulation and Control of Traffic
Environmental surveys	Utilization of resources		Traffic segregation
The study and improvement of highway transportation	Community satisfactions and individual needs	Design for safety and economy	Efficient operation of the road system

Education	Enforcement	Engineering
Schools	Legislation for:	Vehicle Engineering
Adult Education	Driver and Vehicle	Highway
Public Press	Licensing	Traffic Engineering
Radio	Police and Courts	Pollution Control
Television	Regulatory policy	Information Engineering
Re-education of offenders		

Fig. 1.4. Traffic engineering functions.

of amenities, a planning mechanism must protect standards and permit the development of resources in both human and material terms. However, the act of planning must not stultify individualism nor impair the need of free expression. The technologist, in the search for a better physical environment, may also lose sight of the social and economic consequence of planning. Cities and people are part of a dynamic process in a state of continuous evolution and without unique solutions to their problems at any point in time. Nor are yesterday's needs necessarily a clear guide to tomorrow's.

Transport, although only a part of this total process, has an important and influential role. The activities of people, by necessity, become separated and, for their enjoyment, communication must exist between each part. The forms of communication stimulate different uses and demands, and technological change may permit the substitution of one form for another. The intensity of use is dependent not only on the attractiveness of the activity but on the available choices of transport and the effort required to overcome the spatial separation. An overall effect may cause environmental damage to both users and non-users or the loss of alternative opportunities.

Activities are spatially distributed at locations dependent on their separation in terms of time, cost, convenience and some intrinsic site value. Locations may range from those specifically determined (e.g. a mine) to those almost randomly selected. Obviously many activities could be sited, with equal preference, in alternative ways and others nearly so. The siting of an industry can be taken as an example of some of the factors which influence location generally, although the weight of any one factor will depend on the nature of the process and the end product. Some form of "profitability" will normally be a principal goal, although this can be profit to individuals, the corporate body or to the state, and may be a monetary gain or some alternative. There must be accessibility to a market and to the wherewithal for production—materials, energy, machinery, components and labour. The scale of production is related to the demands, and each component of the process incurs costs of manufacture and distribution. An initial choice, if all alternatives have been explored, could be an optimum site, but this will only apply at that instant in time, as decisions of competitors, changes in the market and other external influences will alter the state of the system.

Similar instabilities arise with the transport system as the accessibilities, occurring with particular flows, change to reflect the shifts in the demands as individual or groups seek to optimise their activities. Under-use tends to attract traffic and, as this increases, the individual benefits decrease when congestion sets in, site values fall and redevelopment becomes opportune. At this stage, extra capacity is normally provided and the cycle begins again. An individual's ability to enjoy accessibility depends on the price he can afford to pay. A peasant has little time to spare outside the work activity, few resources to provide speedier travel and, therefore, must live in close proximity to work. Those who do not own cars can be deprived of many opportunities to enjoy the range of facilities of car owners, unless the public transport service provides a high level of service to the required localities. Table 1.10 indicates the range of activities available to the different groups using a criterion of journey time by mode.

TABLE 1.10.   AVAILABILITY OF SELECTED COMMUNITY FACILITIES
(Source: Nashville, Tennessee, A. M. Voorhees & Assoc., 1969)

Type of facility	Total available	Number within 20 min travel of residential areas	
		by car	by bus
Hospital	14	10	1
Parks	34	28	0
Colleges and Universities	13	11	3
Libraries	8	6	2

Traffic Generation

The amount and type of traffic generated by a land use can be measured in persons or vehicles per unit area distributed in time. Each land use, whether it be a school, factory, house or park, is a generator of traffic.

B

The traffic may be pedestrian, cyclist or vehicular and, depending on its relationship to other generating units, traffic flows will be developed either locally or nationally and will be distributed throughout the hours of the day, and in varying proportions. Industrial activity can be described by inputs of labour and raw materials or, alternatively, by intensities of use in the form of capital, structure or work force per unit area, all of which can be related to traffic generation. Land utilised for agriculture, mineral exploitation, recreation or building is also an important influence in demand for road space. An essential contribution can be made to the costs and benefits of travel by careful planning controls but social factors are increasingly influential. Many aspects of traffic generation are correlated with such socio-economic variables of the population as age, income distribution, occupations and educational grouping.

Population and Traffic Characteristics

The numbers and distribution of people are affected by total land area available, climate, transport, topography and other factors which influence development and running costs. Of the developed nations, there is a wide range between Australia (1·7 pers/km²), U.S.S.R. (10·5 pers/km²), U.S.A. (22·3 pers/km²), France (91 pers/km²), Japan (265 pers/km²) and England and Wales (325 pers/km²). Whereas in England and Wales about 12% is unsuitable for general habitation, the figure is many times higher in Japan. Within each country there is a distribution of the population in in settlements. Average densities in Britain range from 1,000 pers/km² in the city regions, to 72 pers/km² in mainly agricultural regions and from 7,000 pers/km² in the older seaport cities to 3,000 pers/km² in more recently developed cities or those in hilly areas. In Great Britain, as a whole, there is an absolute range from less than 2·5 pers/km² in remote country areas to over 25,000 pers/km² in parts of the cities. While nearly half the population occupy only 3% of the total land area a similar distribution will be found in the use of the transport systems. A quarter of the total road vehicle mileage is carried on just 2% of the system, 60% on 10% and 95% on half of the available roads. The thousand miles of motorway, $\frac{1}{2}$% of the total, alone carries over 5% of all vehicle kilometres.

TABLE 1.11. THE GEOGRAPHICAL DISTRIBUTION OF THE HOME
POPULATION WITHIN THE UNITED KINGDOM

	Thousands (%)		
	1951	1968	2001 (projected)
England and Wales	43,815 (87·1)	48,593 (87·9)	60,655 (88·3)
Northern	3,130 (6·2)	3,341 (6·0)	3,843 (5·6)
Yorks. & Humberside	4,488 (8·9)	4,804 (8·7)	5,770 (8·4)
North West	6,417 (12·8)	6,755 (12·2)	8,173 (11·9)
East Midlands	2,913 (5·8)	3,323 (6·0)	4,577 (6·7)
West Midlands	4,426 (8·8)	5,085 (9·2)	6,417 (9·3)
East Anglia	1,388 (2·8)	1,637 (3·0)	2,404 (3·5)
South East	15,216 (30·2)	17,230 (31·2)	21,469 (31·3)
South West	3,247 (6·5)	3,700 (6·7)	4,792 (7·0)
Wales	2,589 (5·1)	2,720 (4·9)	3,210 (4·7)
Scotland	5,103 (10·2)	5,188 (9·4)	5,950 (8·7)
Northern Ireland	1,373 (2·7)	1,502 (2·7)	2,056 (3·0)
United Kingdom	50,290 (100)	55,283 (100)	68,661 (100)

Traffic is growing faster on urban than rural roads but capacity constraints, on the most important routes, confines the greatest growth to
minor urban roads and between the smaller towns (i.e. Class II roads) in
rural areas.

Table 1.11 shows comparisons and changes in population distribution.
Great changes have occurred during the last century since the cities and
towns of Northern England, Scotland and South Wales grew up on the
site of raw material areas, and their workers became skilled in mining,
ship building, metal crafts and the manufacture of textiles. This historical
background to city growth has influenced modern planning, by indicating
the need for diversified industrial development. Rapid advances in
automation and the transmission of power, coupled with the development
of new industries in electronics, plastics and light engineering have
changed the geographical dependence and confinement of a city to
a particular area. The new sources and techniques of power generation,

and industry itself, are cleaner and need not pollute, thus removing the necessity for its confinement to certain areas. The rapid movement of people, either by mass means or in individual forms of transport, has replaced the need to house workers in close proximity to their employment. Unfortunately these trends have encouraged further urbanisation, and conurbations have engulfed freestanding towns and cities by growing into vast, sprawling urban regions. The expansion of the Midlands, centred on Birmingham, the London region and the older conurbations not only causes costly congestion and shortages of housing and land but also creates difficulties in the administration and provision of adequate levels of service to the population.

Cities and Transport

The growth and development of cities to their present state is largely a legacy of past social, industrial, and communication patterns wrought mainly by the need to locate workers advantageously to the development and growth of industry. Today, the function of the city must embrace man's whole development not only providing the everyday needs of a place to live and work in safe and amenable surroundings, but the recreational needs of entertainment, sport, the arts and the specialised facilities of shopping, education and medicine. For the well-being and health of the urbanised populations, ready access to the countryside and coast is important. In addition, the whole life of a city can be sustained only through interchange with other regions provided by good transportation facilities. The form in which these transport facilities will be used depends ultimately, in a free society, on consumer choice which, to a limited degree, can be influenced by authority through education, legislation or fiscal control.

Despite the fact that even in a densely populated country, like Great Britain, about 90% of the total area is not built on, land resources still need careful conservation to meet the diversity of uses. While much of our urban environment is of poor physical quality, a long history of development has bequeathed many ancient towns and villages, and some parts of the cities which are of great charm and individual character. These need skilled preservation and conservation from the inroads of development and destruction by the vehicle and yet must be viable. Likewise, the countryside in many areas has settings of great natural beauty which must not be desecrated for some tenuous economic benefit.

Planning for Traffic

There are a few basic situations which can be defined in traffic planning:

1. (a) Existing areas, whether large or small, which have established character and function effectively in social terms, where ordinary road improvements can cause increased traffic generation. There are many examples in this country where damage, or destruction, would result to the whole existing concept. Physical road building can often be avoided by the skilled application of traffic regulation and control to the existing street pattern. Alternatively, other forms of travel facilities can be provided.

(b) Where increased traffic capacity is unavoidable, or where existing traffic must be reduced in part of the network for improvement of an area, relief roads can be built. Their construction may be expensive and cannot be based solely on the normally accepted methods of cost-benefit analysis. It will often be necessary to resort to tunnelled sections and to allow for greater route diversions. Both central and local government must be prepared to initiate such projects in the overall interest and to sustain areas which may not always be commercially viable in competition with newer purpose-built areas.

2. Often isolated buildings and monuments of special merit exist in areas subject to over-use or redevelopment. The major aim will be to avoid their demolition and to restrain traffic to a suitable level by a restoration of functional compatibility. It is more than ever necessary in the pace of the modern world to re-create and establish new areas of tranquility within the restless and noisy environment of the city to improve the overall quality of city life. Again it is difficult to assess these more intangible benefits, but they must be included in assessments even though not directly contributing to increased revenues. However, not every preservation made today is either worthwhile or sensible and new environments must be created for future generations.

The first two situations, by taking account of amenity values, will considerably modify road traffic planning considered in traditional terms. The apparent extra costs must be recouped from the many situations where efficient solutions can be applied without general detriment.

3. Major routes are only suitably built in areas lacking social or physical merit. In some nineteenth-century urban areas of dereliction, the bold construction of modern highways, flanked by compatible land-uses or built on parkway systems through new green belt areas, can act as a focus of urban revival. The regrouping of land for residential, commercial, public and industrial use can commence along the lines of new routes. New buildings can be matched to the scale of the urban motorway, which can be sited to create environmental areas and ameliorate the consequences of bringing incompatible elements together.

4. Many existing residential areas, because of the inadequate provision of arterial roads of satisfactory traffic-handling capabilities, have been turned into peak-hour through routes, much to the disturbance and peace of mind of their residents. Accidents occur; the air is polluted by exhaust fumes; visual intrusion arises and the environment deteriorates. The inadequacy of many layouts is marked by the frequency of cross-roads often without adequate sight lines or even the demarcation of the major right of way. A primary need is for the removal of traffic not associated with the local area and the rationalisation of the numbers and types of junctions. It is also necessary to reduce the widths of roads creating new opportunities for landscaping, parking and play areas. Entirely new footpaths can be located to provide better internal access to neighbourhood shops, schools, public transport and other services and amenities creating new open space for seats and meeting areas. Some examples of modifying earlier road layouts are shown in Fig. 1.5.

5. *New areas.* In new towns and in large redevelopment schemes for existing cities, building development can match the scale of the major roads, and appropriate design for the individual sections of road user can be made from the start of the project, taking advantage of topographical conditions on the site for split-level development, precincts and parking. New transport modes can be more easily designed to suit the basic land-use distribution and novel methods adopted to provide interchange and more efficient travel facilities.

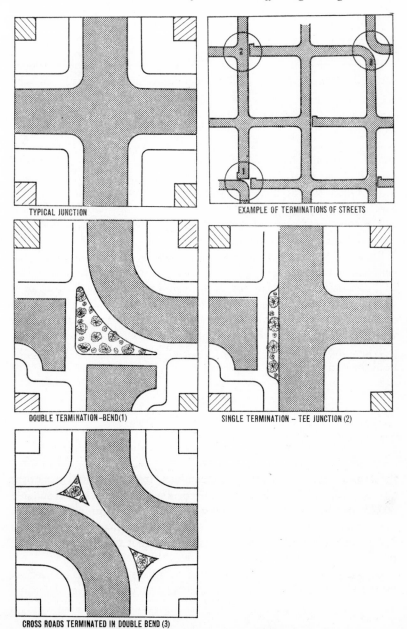

TYPICAL JUNCTION

EXAMPLE OF TERMINATIONS OF STREETS

DOUBLE TERMINATION –BEND(1)

SINGLE TERMINATION – TEE JUNCTION (2)

CROSS ROADS TERMINATED IN DOUBLE BEND (3)

FIG. 1.5. Limiting through routes in residential areas.

DESIGN OF RESIDENTIAL AREAS

Amenity and Safety

The traffic engineer has neglected the design for movement in residential areas. If improvements in living conditions are to be made, and the accident potential reduced, more detailed study must be directed to the smaller-scale problems of urban life. Special care is needed in design to ensure the amenity, safety and accessibility of facilities to all age ranges in the population. The functioning of residential areas is complex, requiring valuable land space for access to buildings and for the maintenance of services (refuse collection, fire, ambulance, health, education and commercial activities). In addition, space must be found for cars, garages, gardens, play areas and other community needs. All these factors must be considered comprehensively, and together, if costs and economy are to lead to maximum satisfaction.

By skilful planning it is possible to reduce vehicle and pedestrian conflicts, developing separated rights of way for the various activities and uses. New footpaths can be located to follow the least arduous vertical alignment and be more direct than the roads, although changes of direction can be sharp and sudden. At road crossings, particularly where children move to and from play areas or schools, subways can be provided most suitably by raising the road levels and thus reducing the need for ramps and steps.

Design

The general design and layout of new residential areas depends on the selection of a density normally determined by land values and this often shows a strong relationship to the site distance from the central area of the city. High densities require a large proportion of high blocks, but suitably spaced to allow light, landscaping, private and communal gardens. Social survey information is needed to determine many aspects of the development, but particularly the optimum ratios of different dwelling types. Some typical figures are shown in Table 1.12.

Densities are generally defined either on a basis of persons per hectare or habitable rooms per hectare. Gross density refers to the overall density, including land used for all purposes, and net density to the area occupied solely for residential requirements. As density is increased, a greater proportion of the inhabitants must be accommodated in the more expensive multi-storey type of building and Table 1.13 indicates some typical values.

TABLE 1.12.   TYPICAL PERCENTAGES OF HOUSEHOLD TYPES

Type of dwelling (no. of bedrooms)	% of total households
1	0—10
2	20—30
3	50—70
4	5—10
>4	0— 5

Once the numbers, types and density of accommodation are deter-mined, the road and footpath pattern can be developed. On a small site the roads will be purely for access, but as sites grow larger provision must be made for main development roads to carry scheduled bus services, and these should not have direct frontage access to residences, unless minibus services are provided to adjacent houses. Community and shopping centres can conveniently be sited near or just off this type of road. Intersections must not be of a cross-road type but variations of the tee, with careful attention paid to sight lines as specified in other sections of this book. Variations in curvature, to develop changing viewpoints, must also be designed with sight lines free from obstruction, in horizontal and vertical planes. Some examples of layout are shown in Figs. 1.6. and 1.7, and include those based on modified Radburn principles, where pedestrian and vehicle are generally segregated.

TABLE 1.13.   COMPARISONS OF RESIDENTIAL DENSITIES

Density type	Persons/ hectare	Dwellings/ hectare	Habitable rooms/ hectare	Dwelling types
Very high	65–100 and >	22– 33 and >	85–125 and >	All dwellings in high rise flats without car parking space.
High	50– 65	17– 22	65– 85	Most dwellings in high rise flats, car parking underground.
Medium/high	25– 40	8– 13	30– 50	Maximum density suitable.
Medium	15	5	19	Mainly terraced housing and small proportion of three- or four-storey flats.
Low	9	3	11	Detached and semi-detached.
Very low	3	1	4	High-income areas.

Parking in Residential Areas

The parking of vehicles is an important aspect of community life today and will continue to be so in the foreseeable future. Inadequate attention to this problem may well mar the outcome in otherwise carefully planned and developed areas, with vehicles being left on roads or their margins and on other open spaces. Off-street surface car parks, apart from being aesthetically undesirable, do not make efficient use of land in residential areas. Where site levels are varying, there are many possible choices of garage and parking arrangements at low relative cost. Roofs of buildings can suitably perform additional functions to that of keeping the weather out. Play areas, adjacent to tall blocks of flats, can be sited over under-

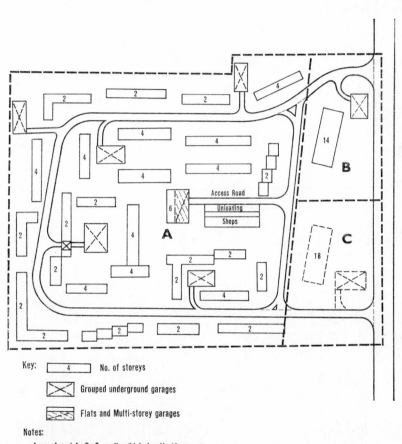

Key: [4]   No. of storeys

[⊠]   Grouped underground garages

[▨]   Flats and Multi-storey garages

Notes:
Areas A and A+B+C medium/high density (C vacant)
Areas A+B+C high density (C Built)
Area B+C very high density

FIG. 1.6.   Layout of residential areas.

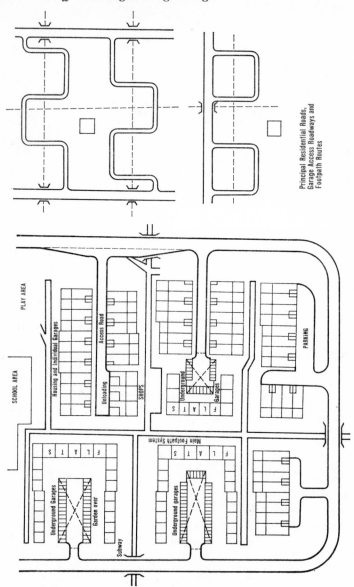

FIG. 1.7.   Diagrammatic illustrations of pedestrianised estate layouts.

ground car parks, and similarly with school playgrounds. Some proportion of parking is limited to overnight only, and dual use can be made with other non-conflicting activities. Terracing slabs between blocks are useful for residents in maisonettes without gardens, and the underside can be utilised for car ports. In these ways, parking can be distributed over an area providing a better service with less overloading of the road network, and reduce maintenance and security problems, while improving visual amenities. Initial costs may be higher, but better use is made of land and more space provided for other activities.

SPACE FOR TRAVEL

The problems of providing urban transportation to cope with the travel demands of passengers and goods is a world-wide problem existing in all major cities. With higher-density developments, there is a greater concentration of demand, making it impossible to provide for universal use of personal transport, both for running space and parking.

Each type of transport develops individual characteristics of convenience, terminal requirements, comfort, speed, safety, cost and utilisation of land. A comparison can be made of the effectiveness of different modes of transport based on the area required per person (A) for a journey of 1 km at the maximum hourly capacity for the system, as shown:

$$A = \frac{w \times 1000}{c \times p}$$

where $w =$ width of track occupied by selected mode (m),
$c =$ capacity in veh/h,
$p =$ occupancy of vehicle, persons/veh.

Values of 'A' range for cars on motorways, with average occupancy of 1·5 from 1·00 m² to nearly 5·00 m² on busy mixed-use streets as shown in Table 1.14. Railways utilise a much smaller area of about 0·15 m², but this increases to 0·30 m² allowing for terminal areas, and for the average journey length.

TABLE 1.14.   AREA REQUIRED FOR TRAVEL BY DIFFERENT MODES

Type of route	Capacity (pcu/h/lane)	Area required for travel (m²)		
		Driver only	$p=1 \cdot 5$	$p=4$
Central area 2- or 3-lane	500	7·3	4·86	1·82
Suburban area 2- or 3-lane	1000	3·65	2·4	0·6
Suburban dual 2- or 3-lane	1200	3·04	2·0	0·5
Urban motorway	2400	1·52	1·0	0·25
Rural 2- or 3-lane	1500	2·43	1·6	0·41
Rural motorway 2- or 3-lane	2500	1·46	0·97	0·24
Footway		0·3		
Standard railway		0·2		
Rapid transit		0·15		

Distance Travelled on Networks

Smeed has developed an ingenious model for comparing the effectiveness of travel facilities in central areas of towns with different sized working populations. It is necessary to first of all calculate the average distance travelled on a selected type of network, and this partly depends on the distribution of destinations. The two types which have been considered are a uniform distribution and a density of destinations inversely proportional to the distance from the centre, as shown in Fig. 1.8(a). It is also assumed in the model that workers live outside the central area with their arrivals uniformly spread round its periphery. Each worker is thus considered equally likely to find employment at any point in the central area.

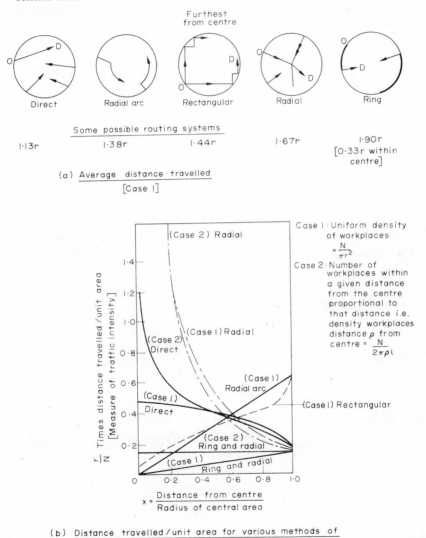

(a) Average distance travelled
[Case 1]

(b) Distance travelled/unit area for various methods of routing

FIG. 1.8. Average distance travelled and distance travelled per unit area in central areas radius *r*. (Source: R. J. Smeed, *Jn. Instn. Highway Engrs.*, 1965, **10** (1).)

Let Kr be the average distance travelled by workers in the central area; values for different route systems are shown in Fig. 1.8(b). The work journey, into and out of the central area, of radius r, will occupy travel space during the peak hours of travel equal to Kr times the average width of travel required per person, λ. It has been found that as city size increases the peak travel period lengthens and is up to about 4 h in London. The value of λ depends on the nature of the transport facility, vehicle occupancy and direction of the peak travel period:

$$\lambda = \frac{w}{cpT}$$

where T = peak travel period in which the travelled width, w, is used to capacity, h/day.

Therefore, the total space required for travel by N central area workers to and from work is $NKr\lambda$, but if different parts of the carriageway are needed for the IN and OUT directions of travel, then twice this space is needed, i.e. $2NKr\lambda$. Each worker will require working space, which can be determined as an equivalent ground space, G, and parking space, P, when travelling by car. Given that the radius of the central area is r, then the total space for both working and travel by N workers is:

$$\pi r^2 = 2NKr\lambda + N(G + P)$$

and solving the equation for r:

$$r = \frac{NK\lambda}{\pi} \left[1 + \left\{ 1 + \frac{\pi(G + P)}{NK^2 \lambda^2} \right\}^{\frac{1}{2}} \right]$$

and the total ground area needed for travel to and from work in the peak period is $2NK\lambda$ times the above. The effect on the proportion of the central area occupied by transport for values of, A, is shown in Fig. 1.9.

If the fraction of travel space is fixed at a value f of the total area, then

$$2NKr\lambda + NP < f\pi r^2$$

and

$$N < \frac{\pi\{fG - P(1 - f)\}^2}{4K^2 \lambda^2\, G(1 - f)}$$

providing

$$P < \frac{fG}{1 - f},$$

i.e.

$$f > \frac{P}{P + G}$$

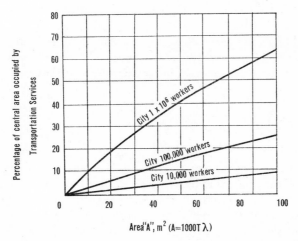

Area "A", m² (A=1000T λ)

FIG. 1.9. Central area occupied by transport facilities by size of working population and area required for travel.

If the proportion of ground space for roads, at different distances from the centre, when the maximum numbers are travelling by car is R, at distance rX from the centre, then:

$$R = \frac{\pi X}{K}\left[f - (1-f)\frac{P}{G}\right]$$

where X = distance travelled per unit area, by method of routeing, at distance rX from the centre.

Comparisons have been made with real towns, and on the basis of peak hour travel traffic, the average distance travelled, in Imperial units, lay between $0.70A^{\frac{1}{2}}$ and $1.07A^{\frac{1}{2}}$ (mean $0.87A^{\frac{1}{2}}$) where A = area of town centre. The road width λ needed for a peak period of $1\,h = \dfrac{1}{68 - 0.13V^2}$ where V is measured in mph.

If Q vehicles travel in this period, the total carriageway space required = $Q[0.87A^{\frac{1}{2}}/(68 - 0.13V^2)]$ and if the fraction of carriageway available for this type of movement in the period is J, given that f is the fraction of space allocated to roads, then the total available area for movement = JfA and $Q = (78 - 0.15V^2)JfA^{\frac{1}{2}}$.

Smeed found values of J ranging from 0·22 at Maidenhead to 0·46 at Leicester, and values of $Q/fA^{\frac{1}{2}}$ of 12, 24, 30·5 and 32 for Edinburgh, Birmingham, London and Glasgow, respectively. With an average speed between 6 – 14 mph, the expected upper and lower values of Q are $34\,fA^{\frac{1}{2}}$ and $11\,fA^{\frac{1}{2}}$ respectively, in car equivalents per hour.

Planning for Central Areas

Large cities are greatly affected by the mode of transport used for work iourneys because of concentrated central development and high-density land use. If the centre is to be served by transport forms requiring a large area for individual movement, then both the radius of the centre and the percentage of space devoted to transport facilities increases rapidly with population size. These provisions will in turn affect the city environment. If insufficient transport facilities, or unacceptable modes of travel, result from present planning, then the existing central areas may well decay and be replaced in importance by isolated suburban developments. This situation may be preceded, where there is an extensive demand for road space, by rationing either in price or by other restrictions.

The planner, determining the needs of urban central areas, may well set the city pattern well into the next century. The broad alternatives are as follows:

(a) High-density central development with individual shops, offices and warehouses grouped into high blocks and sharing common service arrangements. Terminal transport facilities would be provided at different levels for passenger and goods delivery. Personal travel by car would be restricted to a multi-level peripheral ring road, with direct access to parking facilities. In general, building and terminal costs would be high, but access between buildings and within blocks could be served horizontally by moving pavements (travellators), and vertically by escalators and lifts because of the short distances involved. The long-term plan can be arrived at by stage development.

(b) Low-density central development demands the penetration of the motor vehicle throughout the area. The greatly increased space required for transport necessitates the overspill of the existing centre into surrounding residential areas. The final layout would include individual zones for shops, offices and public buildings, grouped in precincts, each containing individual parking. Mass transit facilities cannot generally be operated economically for the intra-central area movement demands between the individual precincts. This form of development is expensive in terms of land, and requires the displacement of inner zone residential inhabitants either to the suburbs, resulting in a spread of the city, or their accommodation elsewhere. The already heavy pressure from overspill population displaced from obsolescent housing areas would seem to prevent this type of solution in Great Britain.

(c) The dispersion of the existing centre to surburban areas in a fully motorised city, bringing inevitable problems of declining land values, increased travel and loss of civic amenity.

Solutions mid-way between the types are possible, such as grouping high-density activities around mass transit terminals, but all the long-term effects must be carefully evaluated. It should also be borne in mind that major changes in the methods of selling goods and shopping may occur in the next few decades and that deliveries might be made to the customer's door, with products selected from a dialled close circuit television display. Some major offices are already moving away from centres of population and the development of new computer and communication systems could lead to smaller staffs more diversely located. Central areas can only be successful if they are attractive, clean and served by good transport accessibility.

Conclusion

The traffic engineer has a substantial contribution to make to tackling the complex problem facing a motorised society. Whatever plans are propounded and carried into practice, they must be as a result of intensive study and co-operation between the planner, sociologist, architect and engineer and, not least, the general and local public. Planning is a continuous process, evolving over a number of years, and subject to monitoring in order to gauge the success of current policies and, where necessary, to revise the objectives.

The principal stages in the plan are as follows:

1. An evaluation of the current situation, with an inventory of

facilities for all travel modes and its use and capabilities in relation to the perceived travel desires and demands of the users in the overall land-use context.

2.   The estimation of future needs, based on future land-use and population characteristics in conjunction with priorities and budgets.

3.   An engineering plan, applied to all modes of movement, setting out the type of improvement, new forms of mass transit, new and improved roads and traffic engineering measures to be developed on the existing network. The plans and priorities are tested and based on assignments and an evaluation of costs and benefits. The effects on the community and the environment must be taken into account at all stages.

4.   Each level of plan must fit into a hierarchy of policies and implementation phases, interlocking with plans both above and below the considered level.

Forecasting

Planning work invariably involves prediction and, as there are no means of foretelling the future, forecasts are based on projections extrapolated from current and historical events. Many assumptions have to be made in forecasting, and the forecasts themselves will be influenced by both the set goals and their implementation. All possible influences in forecasts should be taken into account, and sensitivity tests undertaken to ascertain which factors are most likely to be dominant. Processes can also be modelled and simulations developed to consider the many interactions and complexities of urban analysis. In any estimate of the future, the bands of uncertainty widen with time and the margin of error for particular events will, at some date in the forecast period, become so great as to preclude its use on any satisfactory basis. The value of long-range forecasting is of diminishing significance, and to overcome this disadvantage plans must be flexible enough to accommodate major changes resulting from the policy revisions in the monitoring process. It is convenient for many projections to use high, medium and low-level estimates corresponding to optimistic, average and pessimistic values, and to derive the evaluations on the basis of trend characteristics in terms of variability, rate and the shape of change.

The following chapters briefly describe the essential factors which are of direct concern to the traffic engineer, but it is, more than ever, important to view engineering within an overall context. The influential factors outside engineering, which have been discussed earlier, are economic, technological, social, educational, and town planning. These impinge to a greater or lesser extent on both traffic generation and control.

FURTHER READING

ASHWORTH, R. (1966) *Highway Engineering*. Heinemann.
BRUTON, M. J. (1970) *Introduction to Transportation Planning*. Hutchinson Technical Education, London.
BUCHANAN, C. D. (1958) *Mixed Blessing*. Leonard Hill (Books) Ltd., London.
BUCHANAN, C. D. (1963) *Traffic in Towns*. Ministry of Transport, H.M.S.O.
BURKE, J. *Encyclopedia of Road Traffic, Law and Practice*. The Local Government Library, Sweet & Maxwell (updated).
CHADWICK, G. (1971) *A Systems View of Planning: Towards a Theory of the Urban and Regional Planning Process*. Pergamon Press.
DANFORTH, P. (1970) *Transport Control*. Science & Technology Series, Aldus Books, London.
DAVIES, E. (Ed.) (1960) *Roads and Their Traffic*. Blackie, London.
DAVIES, E. (Ed.) (1968) *Traffic Engineering Practice* (2nd ed). E. & F. N. Spon, London.
GWILLIAM, K. M. (1964) *Transport and Public Policy*. George Allen & Unwin, London.
HAGGETT, P. AND CHORLEY, R. J. (1967) *Models in Geography*. London.
HAY, W. W. (1961) *An Introduction to Transportation Engineering*. John Wiley & Sons, London.
H.M.S.O. (1963) *Traffic in Towns*. Reports of the Steering Group and Working Group appointed by the Ministry of Transport. H.M.S.O., London.
MATSON, T. M., SMITH, W. S. and HURD, F. W. (1955) *Traffic Engineering*. McGraw-Hill, London.
MCLOUGHLIN, J. B. (1969) *Urban and Regional Planning*. Faber, London.
MINISTRY OF TRANSPORT (1967) *Cars for Cities*. H.M.S.O., London.
MINISTRY OF TRANSPORT (1967) *Better Use of Town Roads*. H.M.S.O., London.
MINISTRY OF TRANSPORT (1969) *Planning and Transport, The Leeds Approach*. H.M.S.O., London.
MUNBY, D. (Ed.) (1968) *Transport*. Penguin Modern Economics, Penguin Education, London.

O'FLAHERTY, C. A. (1966) *Highway Engineering*. Arnold.

REES JEFFREYS, W. (1949) *The King's Highway*. Batchworth Press, London.

RITTER, P. (1964) *Planning for Man and Motor*. Pergamon Press, London.

ROYAL COMMISSION ON LOCAL GOVERNMENT IN ENGLAND 1966–1969 (1969) Cmnd. 4040, H.M.S.O.

SMEED, R. J. (1961) *The Traffic Problem in Towns*. Manchester Statistical Society.

SMEED, R. J. (1968) Traffic studies and urban congestion. *J. Transport Econ. & Policy*, Jan.

TEC PUBLICATIONS: *Vocabulary of Traffic Engineering Terms* (Rev. Ed. 1973); *Bibliography of Traffic Engineering* (Rev. Ed. 1973); *Elements of Traffic Engineering* (Rev. Ed. 1970). Traff. Engng. and Control, London.

URBAN MOTORWAYS COMMITTEE (1972) *New Roads in Towns*. Dept. of the Environment, H.M.S.O., London.

WEBB, S. and B. (1920) *English Local Government: The Story of the King's Highway* Longmans, Green & Co., London.

WILLIAMS, T. H. (Ed.) (1962) *Urban Survival and Traffic*, E. & F. N. Spon, London.

CHAPTER 2

Traffic Studies

TRAFFIC studies form a major part of the traffic engineer's work, as most control and design problems demand a detailed knowledge of the operating characteristics of the traffic concerned. The results of data collection are used in traffic planning, traffic management, economic studies, traffic and environmental control, and monitoring trends, both for the establishment and updating of design standards. The studies discussed in this chapter relate principally to volume, speed, delay and environmental factors and in the main are those concerned with the characteristics of traffic in transit. Later chapters deal separately with studies necessary to determine characteristics related to land use movements (Chapter 3), parking (Chapter 4) and accidents (Chapter 10). The automatic collection of information reduces the expense of manual fieldwork, but attention to data handling and processing is also necessary as the further stages of analysis can be both expensive and time consuming.

VOLUME

Volume is a variable of the greatest importance to the traffic engineer and is essentially a counting process referring to the quantity of movement per unit of time at a specified location. The quantity of movement may refer specifically to single types of traffic unit—pedestrians, cars, buses, or goods vehicles—or to composite groups. Selected time periods will depend on the purpose of the study and, in turn, the required level of accuracy will determine the frequency, duration and subdivision of the particular flow. Volume studies basically establish: (i) the relative importance of any route; (ii) the fluctuation in flows; (iii) the distribution of traffic on a road system; and (iv) the trends in road use, but are also used for many other purposes as shown in Table 2.1.

TABLE 2.1. PURPOSE OF TRAFFIC VOLUME STUDIES

General	Traffic design	Traffic studies
Highway classification and budget programmes	Capacity requirements Geometric design	Volume distribution on road network by day, week and month
Trends in highway use	Accident rates	Classified volumes for design of roads and terminals
Scaling surveys and checking synthesised traffic calculations	Economic computations Traffic and environmental management	Structural design Noise and pollution
Planning	Traffic control	Parking

COUNTING PERIODS

Counting periods will vary from short counts at spot points to continuous counts at permanent stations. Hourly counts are generally significant in all engineering design while daily and annual traffic is important in economic calculations, road system classifications and investment programmes. Continuous counts are made to establish national and local highway use, trends of use and behaviour, and for estimating purposes.

For statistical analysis the basic counting periods are usually the hour, the 24 h day (12 midnight to 12 midnight), the 16 h day (6 a.m. to 10 p.m.), the 12 h day (8 a.m. to 8 p.m.), and the year. Some 200 to 1000 h of counting will be normally required to deduce the annual flow, the average daily traffic, the average hourly volume and a design peak hour within about 10% of the true total, at a reasonable level of confidence. The volumes may be averaged or may be particular maxima or minima and may related to a road as a whole, to a particular direction, a specified turning movement, or a selected lane. With such a wide range of divisions, it is essential that a precise definition should be given for any quoted volume.

MEASUREMENT OF VOLUME

Manual Count

Usually, a proportion of all counting must be made manually, either for checking instrument operation or for extending the range and type of observations collected automatically. In its simplest form an observer records, on a census sheet, the passage of each vehicle according to its classification and uses a separate form for each counting period. Sheets are totalled later to reveal the number of units of each class of vehicle passing the observer during the period. The observer's task can be eased by the use of mechanical or electrical tally counters, often clipped to a board so that totals, for each time period and vehicle category, can be conveniently abstracted before the counter is reset to zero. Electrical counters usually have simple push-button switches that can be operated remotely from the supply.

Detectors

The essential element in automatically counting traffic is a detector (sensor) which signals a response to a counter on the passage of vehicles past a selected point. Many practical vehicle detectors have been produced based on a number of principles. The principal groups can be referred to as contact types, of which the pneumatic tube is most commonly used. Air pulses, actuated by vehicle wheels, pass along the tube activating a metal diaphragm, which causes contacts to close and energise a circuit. Other forms have electrical contact between conducting surfaces or changes in capacitance between electrodes, but the most widely used, particularly for traffic control, is the inductive loop detector. A loop of wire, with a configuration dependent on required operating characteristics, is normally installed in a narrow slot cut into the road surface. The presence of a vehicle's metallic mass alters the inductance of the conducting loop and this change can be detected in various ways. Another group of detectors operate through the distortion of the earth's magnetic field, or an artificially produced field, by the passage of a vehicle. All the above types are surface or within-surface installations.

Vehicle detectors, mounted adjacent to the lanes or overhead, are not often solely used for periodic traffic counting because of their relatively high cost, but are frequently installed at permanent counting stations and in traffic control schemes. The main types are photo-electric and infrared, which depend on the interruption of a beam, or reflected beam, and ultrasonic or radar types, which transmit pulses of energy or direct a continuous beam towards the approaching vehicles. The former, known as pulsed types, reflect energy from the road surface until a vehicle impinges on the beam and causes a reduction in transit time of the reflected pulse. This is detected by the receiver. Vehicle occupancy can be measured by recording the time over which the vehicle's presence changes the signal. Continuous beam types operate by detecting the frequency shift of energy reflected from approaching vehicles.

Most traffic counting instruments operate with pneumatic or coaxial capacitance detectors installed temporarily to the running surface, providing good mobility but at the expense of reliability if not frequently maintained. For more permanent siting, inductive-loop detectors are more accurate and consistent in their zonal discrimination than most magnetic, ultrasonic and radar detectors. Their initial cost and installation, by sawing a slot in the surface, is both cheap and rapid.

Detectors can be selected for various modes of operation dependent on their function requirement. Passage detectors respond on the movement of a vehicle and may or may not be directionally actuated or sensitive above or below certain speeds. Presence detectors are of two types, limited-presence which reset after responding to a stationary vehicle for a limited period, and continuous-presence which respond indefinitely while moving or stationary vehicles occupy their sensing area. Large loop types can also be made to vary their output with the total number of vehicles present, for instance in a queue.

Automatic Counters.   Generally, portable volume counters make use of a basically similar transducer unit actuated by air pulses from a thick-walled rubber tube set at right angles to the traffic flow and fixed to the road with straps, nailed or plugged to the surface. Each axle passing over the tube causes a pressure pulse to operate a diaphragm switch. Electro-magnets, triggered by the switch and energised by batteries, actuate a counter which is usually set to register one unit for every two axles. The simplest type is purely an integrator and has to be read at selected times. More elaborate counters use a clock where the mechanism can be set to register volumes for pre-selected periods of the day or days of the week. For complete volumetric analysis there are counters with a mechanism for recording the information, at regular intervals from 5 to 60 minutes, continuously over at least a week.

In recent years many developments have taken place in volume counters and a far wider choice of instruments is available than hitherto. They differ principally in their method of recording information and the suitability of each type must be considered in relation to its proposed siting and use, availability of labour to check and adjust instruments, and the purpose for which the data is to be used. Graphical recording counters may be more appropriate if the records are needed to obtain a general pattern, with only occasional figures abstracted for more than a subjective comparison. However, if large amounts of detailed statistical analysis are needed, the handling of data by a computer is very time-saving, and consideration of computer compatibility and data preparation is necessary. This has led to the use of punched tape as the recording medium, but more recently the advantages of magnetic tape recording have been recognised and such instruments are now available. They are both reliable with low power consumption and, because information can be closely "packed", can be left unattended for long periods of time.

Refined counters of the radar type can also sense the size of passing vehicles and, by making use of the Doppler effect, measure speeds as well as recording vehicle counts.

Counter Installation. Careful siting of the detector and instrument are necessary, ensuring that the individual vehicles to be counted will be intercepted correctly by the detector. Normally intersections, accesses, bus stops, parking areas, pedestrian crossing points, sharp curves, queue points and speed change areas must be avoided with rubber tubes. Counters will be chained to street furniture, avoiding obstruction of the footpath, or attached to an angle iron stake driven into the verge, avoiding buried cables. Kerbs should be marked where the tube crosses the channel to indicate to drivers of street cleansing vehicles the position of the rubber tube. A minimum of a weekly check is required on the operation of the counter and, for other than minor adjustments, all repairs should be made in the workshop. Regular overhauls are also needed to ensure accurate recording and to preserve the life of the mechanism. Spare counters, about one for every four operated, should be held in stock.

Moving Car Observer. Volume counting, whether manual or automatic, has usually to be carried out on a sampling basis. In the first instance, unless a counter is in operation continuously, it is a sample in time and in the second instance it is a sample in space, i.e. it is the volume at a particular point and will not necessarily be the same as the volume at another point on the road. A method which widens the sample from a space point of view is the moving car observer technique which determines a mean volume along a length of road. This system, developed by Wardrop and Charlesworth at the Road Research Laboratory, also provides other useful information, in particular speed.

It is carried out by observers travelling in a car, and if the method is made part of a routine programme it provides first-hand experience of the road situation at all times of the year, and gives the traffic engineer a qualitative as well as quantitative picture of traffic conditions.

The vehicle makes a series of runs over the selected route, which is split into carefully determined sections. Each section should have consistent conditions prevailing throughout and will generally start and finish at such points as major intersections. The number of runs necessary will normally be about six rising to a maximum of sixteen, depending on the stability of the flow under measurement. It is advantageous to use two or more cars, particularly at times when volumes are rapidly changing (e.g. peak hour) and as many runs as possible should be made under the most constant conditions.

A full crew for a moving car observer run consists of a journey observer, an "opposing" counter, a "tally" counter and a driver. The journey observer records, on a prepared log sheet, the times of stopping and starting along the route, the times of passing control points, and, at the end of each section, the details passed to him by the counters. His task is greatly simplified by the use of a "split second" stop-watch, preferably graduated in hundredths of a minute. The split second hand can be stopped momentarily to show the time of an event and then returned to coincide with the progressing main second hand. The "opposing" counter records the number of vehicles, in required classifications, moving past the test car in the opposite direction giving the totals to the journey observer at the end of each section. These totals are referred to as the "x counts". The "tally" counter separately counts the numbers of vehicles which overtake the test car and those which the test vehicle itself overtakes. The excess of vehicles overtaking the test car to those overtaken is called the "y count". It may be positive or negative and is recorded by the journey observer.

Simple hand tally counters may be used by the "opposing" and "tally" counters, both men recording the cumulative totals at the end of each section. In heavy traffic, however, the tasks of the counters and of the observer are made easier by the use of remote reading electrical counters. These are operated by the "opposing" and "tally" counters with push buttons, but record on a bank in front of the observer. More expensive apparatus using punched or magnetic tape to record times and counts enables subsequent analysis to be done rapidly by computer. Another method which enables all counting and recording to be done by one observer is to use a portable wire recorder into which the observer dictates the various items of information using a suitable code.

The traffic volume in one direction for each section of the route and for each class of vehicle is obtained from the formula:

$$q = \frac{x + y}{t_a + t_w}$$

where $q =$ vehicles (of the appropriate class) per minute in the direction of the stream being considered,

$x \quad =$ number of vehicles (of the same class) met travelling against the stream,

$y \quad =$ number of vehicles (of the same class) overtaking the test vehicle minus the number overtaken whilst the vehicle travelled with the stream,

$t_a \quad =$ journey time, in minutes, of the test vehicle travelling against the stream,

$t_w \quad =$ journey time, in minutes, of the test vehicle travelling with the stream.

The average journey in minutes of the particular class of vehicle in the stream is given by

$$\bar{t} = t_w - \frac{y}{q}$$

and this information is of use in speed and delay studies considered later. A typical analysis of runs along an urban road is shown in Fig. 2.1.

VOLUME CHARACTERISTICS

If continuous volume counts are taken, the resulting time pattern shows three main cyclical trends illustrated in Fig. 2.2. First there is the variation throughout the hours of the day, secondly a variation for the days of the week and finally a seasonal variation.

Daily Variation

A typical daily flow pattern is shown in Fig. 2.2(a). The flow in each hour has been expressed as a percentage of the daily flow since this is the most convenient way of studying such patterns and permits easy comparison. Weekdays, Saturdays and Sundays usually have distinctive patterns but, comparing day with day, patterns for routes of a similar nature often show a marked similarity, which is useful in enabling predictions to be made.

Especially significant in the design of roads and control of traffic is the peak hour volume, which is usually 8 – 10% of total daily flow or 2 – 2½ times the average hourly volume. Very pronounced in urban areas, and to a lesser extent in rural areas, there are two dominant peaks in the weekday patterns. These are a morning and an evening peak with the latter generally predominant. These include many work trips which are relatively stable in time and fairly insensitive to change from day to day and to weather and other travel conditions.

FIG. 2.1. Calculation sheet for "moving car observer" studies.

Run No.	CARS	TRUCKS	PSV		TOTAL	CARS	TRUCKS	PSV		TOTAL	t_a	t_w
1	77	3	8		88						1·73	2·50
2	82	4	10		96		2				3·38	3·45
3	60	6	6		72	3					2·30	2·42
4	56	6	3		65			2			2·40	2·71
Σt	27·5	19	27		321	0·25		2			10·01	11·58
$\frac{\Sigma t}{n}$	68·8	4·75	6·75		80·3						2·50	2·89

$$q = \frac{x_1 + y_1}{t_a + t_w} = \frac{68 \cdot 8 + 0 \cdot 25}{2 \cdot 50 + 2 \cdot 89} = \frac{69 \cdot 05}{5 \cdot 39} = 12 \cdot 8 \text{ Cars per min}$$

$$q_2 = \frac{4 \cdot 75 + 0}{5 \cdot 39} = \frac{4 \cdot 75}{5 \cdot 39} = 0 \cdot 88 \text{ trucks per min}$$

$$q_3 = \frac{6 \cdot 75 + 0}{5 \cdot 39} = \frac{6 \cdot 75}{5 \cdot 39} = 1 \cdot 25 \text{ PSV per min}$$

$$q_4 = \frac{80 \cdot 3 + 0 \cdot 25}{5 \cdot 39} = \frac{80 \cdot 55}{5 \cdot 39} = 14 \cdot 9 \text{ vehicles per min}$$

$$t_1 = t_{w_1} - \frac{y_1}{q_1} = 2 \cdot 89 - \frac{0 \cdot 25}{12 \cdot 8} = 2 \cdot 89 - 0 \cdot 02 = 2 \cdot 87 \text{ mins}$$

$$t_2 = 2 \cdot 89 - 0 = 2 \cdot 89 - 0 \cdot 88 = 2 \cdot 89 \text{ mins}$$

$$t_3 = 2 \cdot 89 - 0 = 1 \cdot 25 = 2 \cdot 89 \text{ mins}$$

$$t_5 = 2 \cdot 89 - \frac{0 \cdot 25}{14 \cdot 9} = 2 \cdot 89 - 0 \cdot 02 = 2 \cdot 87 \text{ mins}$$

Moving Car Observer Results Sheet

Route A 38 Direction NORTH

PRIORY RD. — BELGRAVE RD.

Ref. Sheet No. 4

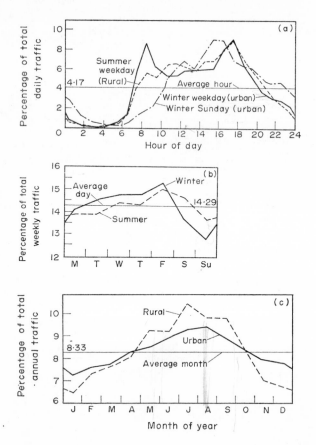

Fig. 2.2.   Daily, weekly and seasonal flow patterns.

Weekly Variation

Figure 2.2(b) gives a typical weekly flow pattern with volumes expressed as a percentage of the total flow for the week. Traffic flows for the weekdays, Monday to Friday, remain fairly constant, but weekend flows are more variable and depend to a large extent on season and weather. On the average weekend, flows in the centre of a large city will be considerably lower than for weekdays, but main routes out of the city, although lower in the winter months, may be higher in the summer when there is more attraction for recreational travelling.

Seasonal Variation

Figure 2.2(c). Volumes, in general, are above average in the more pleasant motoring months of summer, but this is more pronounced in rural than urban areas.

The monthly average flow is usually at a maximum for most rural roads in August and at its lowest in January. A number of central urban areas show a dip in midsummer flows but remain fairly consistent during the remainder of the year. Seasonal patterns for a given type of route are the most consistent of all the variation patterns and represent the economic and social condition of the area served. It is only as these conditions change, usually by a gradual process, that the patterns change.

Journey Purpose Variation

As mentioned above, work trips are least variable daily whereas shopping trips differ more, both in time and number on a daily, weekly and seasonal basis.

Type of Route

The type and use made of the road on which volumes are being considered affects the patterns of flow to be expected. The two general categories of road are rural and urban. The former sub-classify into through and local routes. Urban roads consist of through routes, radial roads leading to the city centre, circumferential roads circling the city centre, city centre streets and residential roads. The main influences prevailing in the use of these are recreational, commercial, commuting and general purpose. The possible combinations of the various classifications according

c

to type and use preclude a full discussion of the effect of these variants, but Table 2.2 gives an indication of the likely effects.

TABLE 2.2.   EFFECT ON VOLUME PATTERNS OF ROAD TYPE AND
ROAD USE

Classification	General effect on volume patterns
Type of road	
Rural — through route	Higher in summer particularly at weekends
— local route	Slightly higher in summer
Urban — through route	Higher in summer but less pronounced with increase in city size
— radial road	Slightly higher in summer
	Distinctive directional peaks
— circumferential roads	Slightly higher in summer
— city centre roads	Different pattern on Saturday; very low flow on Sunday
— residential roads	Slight increase in summer
Type of use	
Recreational	Large increase in summer, particularly at weekends
Commercial	Slightly higher in summer
	Low at weekends
Commuting	Slightly higher in summer
	Directional peaks
General purpose	Higher in summer

Composition of the Traffic Stream

The use being made of a road is partly reflected by the proportions of the different classes of vehicles in the traffic stream and for a full study, classified counts of volume are necessary.

It is clear that for the greater precision in classification more labour is required in counting and analysis and it is as well to restrict classifications to those which are significant to the purpose and location of a specific volume count. For instance, in the central streets of many large British cities, pedal and autocycles are so rare as not to warrant consideration whereas in similar cities in Holland they are so numerous that a volume count would lose its significance if they were excluded. A limited classification, which has been of great use on a wide variety of roads in the United Kingdom, is given in Table 2.3.

TABLE 2.3.   GENERAL PURPOSE CLASSIFICATION OF VEHICLES

Classification	Includes
Passenger cars	Motor cycle combinations
	Motor cars
	Light goods vehicles
	($<$30 cwt unladen)
Trucks	Goods vehicles
	($>$30 cwt unladen)
Buses	All passenger service vehicles

In this general purpose classification vehicles with similar operating characteristics have been grouped together. Where solo motor cyclists or other vehicles are significant an extra class or classes must be added.

Passenger Car Units

The Ministry of Transport in Circular No. 727 introduced the idea of passenger car units (pcu) whereby the relative effects of different classes of vehicles are allowed for by the use of appropriate multiplying factors as shown in Table 2.4.

TABLE 2.4.   PASSENGER CAR UNITS

Class of vehicle	Equivalent value in passenger car units (pcu)			
	Urban standards	Rural standards	Round-about design	Traffic signal design
Private car, taxi, motor cycle combination, light goods vehicle (up to 30 cwt unladen)	1·00	1·00	1·00	1·00
Motor cycle (solo), motor scooter, moped	0·75	1·00	0·75	0·33
Medium or heavy goods vehicle (over 30 cwt unladen), horse-drawn vehicle	2·00	3·00	2·80	1·75
Bus, coach, trolley bus, tram	3·00	3·00	2·80	2·25
Pedal cycle	0·33	0·50	0·50	0·20

Consider a volume of 500 veh/h on a rural road composed as follows:

	veh/h
Pedal cyclists	30
Motor cycles, cars and light goods vehicles	345
Heavy goods, buses and coaches	125
Total	500

Converted to passenger car units the volume becomes:

Pedal cyclists	$30 \times 0.5 =$	15
Motor cyclists, etc.	$345 \times 1.0 =$	345
Heavy goods, etc.	$125 \times 3.0 =$	$\underline{375}$
Total		$\overline{735}$ pcu/h

By this it is seen that a volume of 500 veh/h with this composition is said to have the same effect as a volume of 735 passenger cars per hour. This, however, must be treated with considerable reserve. The effect of a heavy vehicle in a stream in equivalent car units may vary between 1.0 to 7.0, or more on heavy gradients, so that the arbitrary selection of a figure like 3 will not apply in all cases. Further, in using such an equivalent volume for design purposes it must be expanded to anticipate future requirements. If it is expanded by, say 150%, over-design may well result when it is seen that the rate of growth of heavy vehicles is very much lower than that for cars and motor cycles. The use of equivalent passenger car units can prove helpful for a broad comparison of the importance of different routes, but it must be used warily and preferably not used for design purposes.

Peak Flow

Because the peak flow is indicative of a design requirement it is of vital concern. As used in design procedures in the United Kingdom it is usually the maximum hour's flow during a 7-day August traffic census. Since traffic is very near the year's peak in August, this maximum hour's flow is likely to approach the busiest hour of the year. However, factors such as weather, temporary congestion, location, etc., are likely to influence the value and although useful in certain circumstances it is not as precise as often required.

An alternative method suggested by the Road Research Laboratory overcomes these defects by averaging the flows in a selected peak hour of each day during the highest 13-week period which, in the United Kingdom, is usually June, July and August. This average is taken as the peak-flow hour and may be used for design purposes after suitable allowance is made for future growth.

Typical American practice is to select one of the most highly used hours of the year, often the 30th highest, and to use the volume in this hour, after expansion, for design. By definition, the 30th highest hour is that flow which is exceeded in only 29 h of the year and if the correct expansion has been made for, say, a 20-year design period, 29 h of overloading would occur a year at the end of that period. Figure 2.3 gives examples of highest hour curves for different types of roads. The examples show the effect of selecting different ranking highest hours on the size of road required. Choosing the highest hour for design on curve A the road calls for a four-lane highway, whereas at the other extreme, using the 80th highest hour and accepting a measure of congestion for 79 h in the year, only two lanes are needed.

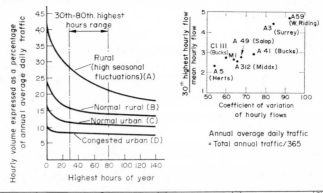

Annual average daily traffic
= Total annual traffic/365

Annual traffic design volume	Annual average daily traffic	Highest hour (v.p.h)	Lanes	30th. highest hour (v.p.h)	Lanes	80th. highest hour (v.p.h)	Lanes	Curve
1,575,000	4320	1950	4	1250	3	900	2	A
1,750,000	4800	1150	3	770	2	670	2	B
13,150,000	36,000	6100	6	4100	4	3800	4	C

Numbers of lanes shown are approximate and for two-way operation

Fig. 2.3.   Highest hour curves.

Periodic Volume Counts

The true and exact determination of the annual volume, and hence average daily and hourly volumes, can only be made by continuous counting throughout the year. Because of the cost of doing this, various methods involving counting for much shorter periods have been developed based on the cyclical variation in volume previously discussed.

The counting periods must, of course, sample the variability of traffic in the right proportions of daily, weekly and seasonal fluctuations. The smaller and more erratic the traffic characteristics the larger the required sample size or, conversely, for a given number of counting hours the poorer the confidence that the counts will be near to the true values. In North America the use of factors to determine peak design flow have been obtained from observations of the distributions of hourly flows throughout the year for many types of routes. When composite volume units are used (passenger car units) care must be taken in identifying the peak hour. While 5.00 to 6.00 p.m. is the normal peak hour, in terms of vehicle numbers, the period 4.00 to 5.00 p.m. may, for instance, exceed this value in pcu.

In using short-period counts, the best method is one which samples the volumes prevailing at different times throughout the year in such a way as to reveal the maximum amount of data with the counting time and resources available. This is done, in general, by spreading the counts over the hours of the day, days of the week and months of the year. Assuming that 52 h of counting are available for one location, a more exact estimate of the annual flow will be obtained by counting for a different hour each week throughout the year than by counting for 52 consecutive hours. Similarly, a better estimate of a day's flow will be made if the total count is spread so that a few minutes are counted each hour rather than if the counting is taken as a single sample. As with all sampling procedures, more accurate predictions may be made the greater the size of the sample; and by spreading the sample widely during the year, chance fluctuations due to such things as weather are evened out.

Estimated volumes based on sample counts will be more reliable if the counts are taken at times when the volume patterns show the most consistency. From examination of continuous counts taken at 50 points in England, Scotland and Wales, Garwood has shown (The sampling and use of traffic flow statistics, *J. Appl. Statist.* **11**(1), 1962) that:

(i) For the prediction of the day's volume from an hour's volume, the maximum consistency occurs between 9 a.m. and 7 p.m.

(ii) For transition from the day's to the week's volume, any day of the week except Sunday is reasonably consistent, with Monday showing the minimum variation.

(iii) For an estimate of annual volume, expansion based on counts in April and September give the best results.

It can be seen that the most reliable prediction of the annual traffic based on an hour's count is made if the count is taken between 9 a.m. and 7 p.m. on a Monday in April or September.

The expansion of a sample count to the daily, monthly or annual volume is based on volume patterns established for the route or for a like route serving an area of similar economic and social content. Providing the patterns are reliable, a 1 h count could be used, as in the following example based on Fig. 2.2.

Suppose 600 vehicles were counted between 12.30 and 1.30 p.m. on a Monday in April for a similar urban route.

From Fig. 2.2(a) the volume in this hour represents 6% of the 24-h total.

$$\text{Therefore 24-h total} = 600 \times \frac{100}{6} = 10,000 \text{ vehicles.}$$

From Fig. 2.2(b) Monday's volume is 14% of the weekly total.

$$\text{Therefore weekly total} = 10,000 \times \frac{100}{14} = 71,430 \text{ vehicles or}$$

$$71,430 \times \frac{30}{7} = 306,130 \text{ vehicles for the month.}$$

From Fig. 2.2(c), the volume for April is 8·33% of the total traffic for the year.

$$\text{Therefore annual total} = 306,130 \times \frac{100}{8·33} = 3,675,000 \text{ vehicles.}$$

This example is extreme and obviously patterns must be used with discretion and must be established for a particular set of conditions. Accuracy of any prediction made on a sample count is dependent on the consistency and accuracy of the patterns.

Volume Trends

The upper curve of Fig. 2.4 shows the yearly increase of travel in Great Britain, which has nearly doubled since 1961. However, the rate is by no means uniform with inner city areas showing an increasing trend but at a considerably decreased rate. There, the lower rate of increase is due largely to the frustration of inadequate roads but elsewhere it may be brought about by the relatively slower rate of economic

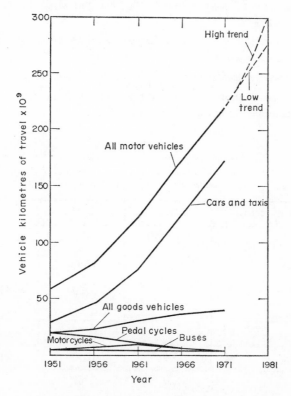

FIG. 2.4.   Vehicle kilometres of travel by vehicle categories.

development of an area compared to the country as a whole. Whatever the cause, the traffic engineer will need to determine the traffic trends for a particular area and accordingly will sample representative locations to obtain the required information. From the data, and with development information, it will enable more reliable predictions to be made as to the future traffic loads that can be expected on the present and future roads system.

Traffic volumes, in general, rise to follow the increasing numbers of licensed vehicles and a method of predicting this latter increase has been made by J. C. Tanner (Forecasts of future numbers of vehicles in Great Britain, *Roads and Road Construction* **40,** 1962, and **43,** 1965). The predictions are based on:

(a) The assumption that the increase in vehicle ownership per head follows a logistic curve,

(b) Separately predicted growth of the population, and

(c) The assumption that the average annual kilometres per vehicle remains constant (trends are shown in Table 2.5).

TABLE 2.5.   TRENDS IN KILOMETRES TRAVELLED BY VEHICLE TYPE IN GREAT BRITAIN (T.R.R.L. REPORT LR 543, *Forecasts of Vehicles and Traffic in Great Britain*, by A. H. Tolpule)

Class of vehicle	1951	1961	1971
Motor cycles	6,800	5,400	3,700
Cars and taxis	11,700	12,600	14,200
Buses	49,100	50,200	45,300
Goods vehicles	19,600	20,700	23,600
All vehicles	13,400	12,900	14,700

The formula of a suitable logistic curve to predict vehicle ownership is

$$Y_n = \frac{Y_s Y_o}{Y_o + (Y_s - Y_o)\, e^{-\beta}}$$

where y_n = vehicles per head in the nth year,

y_o = vehicles per head in the base year,

y_s = saturation or maximum vehicles per head likely to be reached,

and $\beta = \dfrac{y_s x n}{(y_s - y_o)}$, where $100x$ = annual percentage growth during base year.

This curve varies from $y = 0$ at $n = -\infty$ to $y = y_s$ at $n = +\infty$ and, in its entirety, is S-shaped. A portion from 1965 to 2020 for car ownership is illustrated in Fig. 2.5 based on the indicated values. The inset diagram shows a method for determining the saturation level. Values for the rate of growth of towns and sub-areas are plotted against the appropriate cars per head level and the curve is extended to intercept the zero growth line, i.e. saturation level.

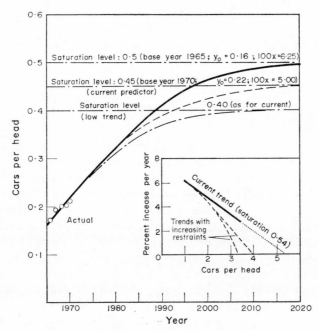

FIG. 2.5. Logistic growth curve for car ownership.

Volume Distribution

Examples of the statistical distributions of volume, both by amount of traffic passed and by length of time prevailing, are shown in Fig. 2.6. These frequency distribution and cumulative frequency curves are prepared using standard statistical methods and each is characteristic of the type of road concerned.

The upper curves of section (a) of the figure show along the abscissa the hourly volume (as a proportion of the Average Annual Hourly Volume) in increasing increments. The ordinate height of each increment represents the proportion of the annual traffic that passes at that volume. For example, 53% of the traffic along the urban road passes at the rate of 100 – 150% of the average annual hourly volume. This contrasts with the seasonal rural route which only passes 20% of the annual traffic at this volume.

The abscissa of the curves in section (b) are also hourly volumes, but the ordinates represent the proportions of the total time in the year for which the various volumes prevail. The urban road carries a volume of 100 – 150% of the average for 47% of the time. On the other hand, the seasonal rural road passes this flow for only 11% of the year.

Flow Maps

The distribution of volumes by location may be represented using a flow map. Such maps show the width of the route in proportion to the volume for a specified period. In rural areas the most useful volume is likely to be the annual average daily volume, whereas in urban areas, particularly where congestion occurs, average peak hour volumes may be more informative. The volumes may be separated in direction and relate to different classes of vehicles, and can also show pedestrians' movements. An example of a flow is shown in Fig. 3.26 (p. 151).

Volumes at intersections, where the numbers of turning vehicles are particularly important, may be displayed in a similar fashion, the width of the band again indicating the volume, or may be represented by simple lines with figures showing the numbers or percentages of vehicles undertaking the various manoeuvres. Figure 2.7 gives an example.

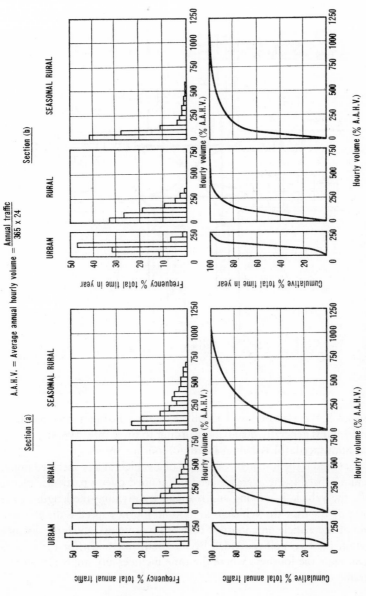

Fig. 2.6. Volume distribution by flow rate and by time.

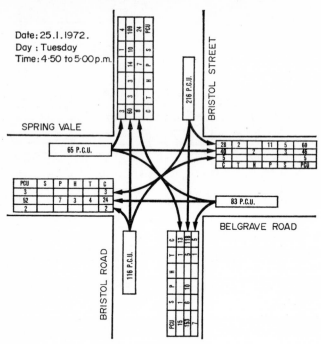

Fig. 2.7.   Intersection flow diagram.

SPEED

Speed is the rate of travel usually expressed in kilometres per hour (km/h) and is generally qualified according to three main types:

(a) Spot speed, (b) Running speed, (c) Journey speed.

Spot speed is the instantaneous speed of a vehicle at any specified point. Running speed is the average speed maintained over a particular course while the vehicle is moving and is found by dividing the length of the course by the time the vehicle is in motion. Journey speed is the effective speed of the vehicle on a journey between two points, and is the distance between the two points divided by the total time taken for the vehicle to complete the journey, where the time includes any stopped time due to traffic delays.

In a typical journey, where stopped delays are incurred, it follows that journey speed must be slower than the running speed, and that spot speeds will vary from zero to some maximum in excess of the running speed.

High running speeds with low journey speeds are undesirable and represent stop–go conditions with enforced decelerations and accelerations. Uniformity between the two speed measures denotes comfortable travel conditions. On long trips, high journey speeds mean substantial time savings, but on short runs, particularly in urban areas, the necessity of high journey speeds is less significant in terms of time savings. For example, with a journey of 500 km, raising the speed from 50 km/h to 100 km/h results in a saving of 5 h. For a short journey of 5 km the saving would be only 3 min, but, on the other hand, raising the speed from 15 to 30 km/h would save 10 min.

MEASUREMENT OF SPOT SPEED

Enoscope

The apparatus consists of a simple open housing containing a mirror mounted on a tripod at the side of the road in such a way that an observer's line of sight is turned through 90°. The observer stands at one end of a section with the enoscope at the other and times the passage of a vehicle through the section using a $\frac{1}{10}$ s stop-watch. It can be seen that the speed measured is actually the mean speed over the length of the section, but for most practical purposes the results can be used as the relevant spot speeds. Due to the difficulty of associating the observed shadow flash in the mirror box with the passage of a particular vehicle it is only possible to use this system on roads carrying low traffic volumes and if speeds are high correspondingly longer timing distances are required.

Electronic Timing Apparatus

The use of eletronic timing instruments enables speeds to be measured over very short distances. The method of operation is to total on decade counters the number of pulses received from a crystal oscillator during the passage of a vehicle's front wheels across two pneumatic road tubes. The passage of the vehicle over the first tube transmits a pressure pulse to a diaphragm switch which starts the timing operation and a matching diaphragm switch terminates the timing when the wheels pass over the second tube. The apparatus is fully portable and battery operated. Again, the speed measured is a mean speed over the length between tubes, but only in exceptional cases will this be significantly different from the true spot speeds.

It is possible to connect the speed meter to data-logging equipment to give a digital print-out of speeds measured. Alternatively, the output can be made on punched or magnetic tape which can be used directly for computer analysis.

Radar Speed Meters and Optical Instruments

The apparatus transmits high-frequency electro-magnetic waves in a narrow beam towards a selected vehicle, and the reflected waves, altered in length depending on the vehicle's speed, are returned to a receiving unit calibrated to directly record the spot speed.

Another type developed more recently uses a system of narrow reflecting strips producing an image of the vehicle as a succession of separated vertical events focused on a photodiode. The output voltage from the cell varies as a frequency directly related to the speed of the target vehicle. Measurements are made at right-angles to the flow and the meter is passive in operation, not transmitting light or radio energy.

Recently developed optical meters enable the speed of other vehicles to be measured directly from a moving vehicle by timing its passage for a length of travel. The target vehicle can be moving in any direction relative to the observer provided that it remains visible during the timing operation.

Time-lapse photography

This method employs a camera to record the distance moved by a vehicle in a selected short period of time. Exposures are made at a constant time interval and the interval and the distance travelled between exposures is measured by projecting the film. The distance divided by the time interval between exposures gives a speed measurement. Cameras are usually 16 mm triggered to take single shots at pre-selected frequencies or use suitable repeat-cycle timers called intervalometers. The projectors are operated to advance the film frame by frame and are equipped with resettable frame counters. Films are either front projected on to prepared grid screens or back projected through a mirror box into a plastic or frosted screen. Photographic methods are also frequently used to make measurements of parking, concentration, saturation flow, turning movements, vehicle spacing and lane use, congestion and delay, and may also be used to study a wide range of vehicle characteristics and pedestrian behaviour.

Pen Recorders

Impulses received from detectors are fed to multi-pen apparatus which event-mark a moving chart. By suitably arranged detectors lane volumes, lane speeds and headways can be evaluated or push-button switches used to record events. Chart speed is usually variable.

Headways

The time interval in seconds between successive vehicles in the traffic streams is an important measurement of use in the determination of capacity and other values. Measurements can be made with stop watches, pen recorders or special purpose headway meters. An example of the latter is a single detector tube which operates a timing circuit from the passage of the first axle. The elapse of time is recorded on a meter and a suitable built-in variable time delay can be set to mask the effect of subsequent axles of the vehicle. The count is stopped on one meter and started simultaneously on another with the passage of the front axle of the next vehicle over the detector. By feeding the start–stop pulses to the two meters in alternation, the headways of successive vehicles in the traffic stream may be measured and recorded. More elaborate instruments record the information directly onto punched or magnetic tape and often additionally measure spot speeds and lane densities in separate lanes.

ANALYSIS OF SPOT SPEED MEASUREMENTS

A series of spot speed measurements at a given location may be represented simply by the arithmetic mean of the speeds, but the information so revealed is confined to the central tendency. The traffic engineer is concerned with the distribution, the range and the dispersion of the speeds in addition to the mean and, for full benefit to be gained from the measurements, standard statistical methods of analysis must be adopted. These are briefly alluded to below.

Distribution

Table 2.6 shows a frequency distribution table for spot speed of cars measured on a three-lane rural trunk road. Speeds are grouped in class intervals, i.e. the frequency, recorded in column 3. For example, out of the 187 cars, 47 were travelling at speeds between 70·0 and 79·9 km/h.

Arithmetic Mean

The arithmetic mean or average speed is a measure of central tendency. It is computed from grouped data by multiplying each mid-class point (column 2) by the frequency (f) for that class (column 3) and summing (column 6) and dividing by the total number of measured speeds:

$$\bar{x} = \frac{\Sigma fx}{\Sigma f}$$

where $\bar{x}$ = mean spot speed, km/h,

   x = mid-class spot speed, km/h,

   f = frequency in each class.

The average spot speed for this example is 72·1 km/h.

TABLE 2.6.   SPOT SPEED DISTRIBUTION

1	2	3	4	5	6	7	8	9
Class intervals km/h	Mid-class km/h x	Frequency f	Frequency %	Cumulative frequency %	fx	Deviation from assumed mean d_1	fd_1	$fd_1{}^2$
30·0– 39·9	35·0	3	1·6	1·6	105·0	−4	−12	48
40·0– 49·9	45·0	6	3·2	4·8	270·0	−3	−18	54
50·0– 59·9	55·0	24	12·8	17·6	1320·0	−2	−48	96
60·0– 69·9	65·0	60	32·1	49·7	3900·0	−1	−60	60
70·0– 79·9	75·0	47	25·2	74·9	3525·0	0	0	0
80·0– 89·9	85·0	25	13·4	88·3	2125·0	1	25	25
90·0– 99·9	95·0	12	6·4	94·7	1140·0	2	24	48
100·0–109·9	105·0	6	3·2	97·9	630·0	3	18	54
110·0–119·9	115·0	3	1·6	99·5	345·0	4	12	48
120·0–129·9	125·0	1	0·5	100·0	125·0	5	5	25
Totals	—	187	100·0	—	13485	—	−54	458

Arithmetic mean, $\bar{x} = \dfrac{13485}{187} = 72 \cdot 1$ km/h.

Standard deviation, $s = \sqrt{\dfrac{458}{187} - \left(\dfrac{-54}{187}\right)^2} \times 10 = 15 \cdot 4$ km/h.

Coefficient of variation, $V = \dfrac{100 \times 15 \cdot 4}{72 \cdot 1} = 21 \cdot 3\%$.

Histogram and Frequency Curve

The information revealed.by the frequency distribution table is best presented graphically by histograms and frequency curves as in Fig. 2.8. The histogram is plotted directly from columns 1 and 4 of the table and the frequency curve is found by rounding off the histogram in such a way that the area under the curve is equal to the area of the histogram. The modal speed is the speed occurring most frequently and is the peak of the

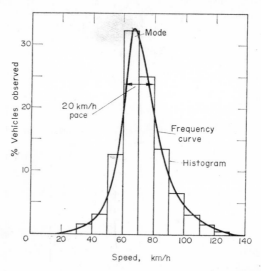

Fig. 2.8.   Histogram and frequency curve spot speeds on three-lane rural trunk road.

frequency curve. The curve is also useful for determining the pace of the vehicles where the pace is the speed range, for some nominal increment of speed (usually 20 km/h) which contains the most vehicles. In the example the mode is approximately 68 km/h and the 20 km/h pace is 60 – 80 km/h.

Cumulative Frequency

The cumulative frequency curve or ogive is used for determining the number of vehicles travelling above or below a given speed. It is plotted from columns 5 and 1 of the table and the shape of the curve is seen in Fig. 2.9. The median speed, another measure of central tendency, is that speed below which 50% of the vehicles are moving, in this case, 70 km/h. Percentile speeds (i.e. that speed below which a specified percentage of vehicles are travelling) are also readily indicated. The percentile speeds of particular interest are the 98th percentile which is often used as a design speed in geometric layout, the 85th percentile which can be used in the consideration of speed limit imposition or overtaking distances, and the 15th percentile shows the slower vehicles whose speed may be causing interference within the traffic stream. These percentile speeds are respectively 112 km/h, 90 km/h and 58 km/h for this road.

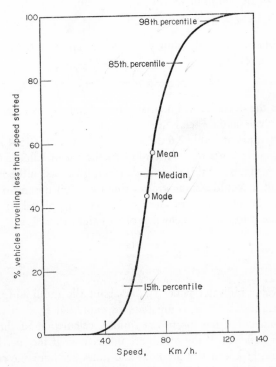

Fig. 2.9. Cumulative frequency curve spot speeds on three-lane trunk road.

Measurement of Dispersion

Two important measurements of dispersion used in speed and other analyses are the standard deviation and coefficient of variation. The standard deviation of a grouped frequency distribution is given by

$$s = \sqrt{\frac{\text{sum of frequencies multiplied by deviations squared}}{\text{sum of frequencies}}},$$

i.e. $s = \sqrt{\dfrac{\Sigma\,(fd^2)}{\Sigma f}}$

where s = standard deviation,
f = frequency in each class,
d = deviation of mid-class point from arithmetic mean,
i.e. d = $x - \bar{x}$.

For computation it is often convenient to use an assumed mean as in the following expression

$$s = \sqrt{\frac{\Sigma f d_1{}^2}{\Sigma f} - \left\{\frac{(\Sigma f d_1)}{\Sigma f}\right\}^2}$$

where d_1 is the deviation from an assumed mean expressed as a multiple of class intervals, and i = class interval.

In the example of Table 2.6 the standard deviation is 15·4 km/h. This value, however, bears no relationship to the mean value and whereas a standard deviation of this magnitude is not great when the mean speed is 72·1 km/h it would assume greater significance if the mean speed was 20·0 km/h. To provide a measure of dispersion, related to the mean, it is convenient to use the coefficient of variation, V, where

$$V = \frac{100s}{\bar{x}}$$

A higher value indicates wider scatter about the mean and vice versa. If the distributions to be compared are expressed in similar units of measurement and if the means are similar, calculation of the standard deviation is sufficient. If the means are different or if the speed distributions are, say, in kilometres per hour and miles per hour the coefficients of variation will show relative and comparable dispersions.

Sample Accuracy

The determination of spot speeds of vehicles on a road must be made on a sample basis. The standard deviation of the distribution of sample means is known as the standard error and is given approximately by

$$\text{S.E.} = \frac{s}{\sqrt{n}}$$

where   S.E. = standard error,
   s = standard deviation calculated for the sample,
   n = number of observations in the sample.

Hence, the standard error of the example quoted is

$$\text{S.E.} = \frac{15\cdot4}{\sqrt{187}} = 1\cdot12\,\text{km/h}.$$

The distribution of sample means lies on a normal curve and using the properties of this curve it can be shown that approximately 95% of the sample means will lie within two standard deviations of the true mean. Accordingly there is 95% chance that the true mean of spot speeds of vehicles on the road lies within the range

$$(72\cdot1 \pm 2 \times 1\cdot12), \text{ i.e. between } 69\cdot86 \text{ and } 74\cdot34.$$

If it was required to narrow this range to say $\pm 1\cdot20$ km/h it would be necessary to increase the sample size so that

$$\frac{1\cdot20}{2} = 0\cdot60 = \frac{15\cdot4}{\sqrt{x}}$$

where x = sample size required, i.e. number of observations required, x, is 659.

Similar techniques can be used to estimate volume. If p is the proportion of a day's traffic passing in 1 h and $\bar{p}$ the mean of the distribution, standard deviation s, then an estimate of the day's traffic from a 1 h count is $T = t/\bar{p}$ and will lie within the range (95% confidence) given by $T/1 + 2V < \chi < T/1 + 2V$ where χ is the unknown traffic and $V = s/\bar{p}$. Similar methods can be applied to a month's flow substituting a day's count (d) and $\bar{q}$, the mean proportion of a month's traffic in a day, i.e. $T_m = d/\bar{q}$ ($V_m = s/\bar{q}$).

SPOT SPEED CHARACTERISTICS

Measurements of spot speeds show a wide distribution and many interacting circumstances serve to determine the particular speed which individual drivers adopt. These circumstances will include those peculiar to the driver himself (such as his psychological and physiological traits), those concerned with his immediate environment and those affected by the more remote consideration of law enforcement, type of district, public opinion, etc.

The main elements of the immediate environment are type of vehicle, road alignment, cross section and surface, weather, speed limits and volume. The effects of some of these are shown in Table 2.7 and Figs. 2.10a–d.

TABLE 2.7.   MEAN JOURNEY SPEEDS ON RURAL MAIN ROADS
(consistent geometry, sections generally level and from 1·5 to 8 km)

Route category	Carriage-way layout	Vehicle types: Speeds km/h						No. of observa-tions
		Car	Van	Truck	Bus*	Motor cycle*	All	
Motorway	Dual 2–1	94·1	83·3	72·6	85·4	69·2	87·3	980
Motorway (heavy rain)	Dual 2–1	78·7	74·8	64·5	83·7	78·1	75·3	215
Trunk Road (limited access)	Dual 2–1	85·0	71·8	68·6	–	84·5	79·8	250
Trunk road	Dual 2–1	78·4	73·0	64·2	73·2	68·4	75·5	525
Class 1 road	3–1, 2-way	69·6	67·5	57·7	51·1	59·3	66·9	540
Class 1 road	2–1, 2-way	69·8	65·1	62·1	63·7	64·0	67·2	425
Class 1 road (narrow width)	2–1, 2-way	64·6	61·7	55·9	54·7	67·4	63·0	680
Class 1 road (narrow uphill 8% grade)	2–1, 2-way	40·1	38·9	34·6	–	36·4	39·7	225

*Small samples

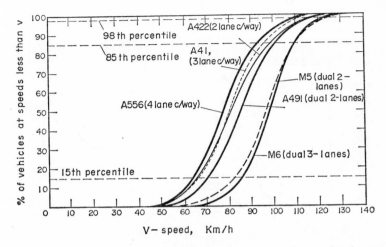

FIG. 2.10a. Cumulative frequency curves for speeds of cars on various types of carriageway. (Source: Ackroyd, L. W. and Bettison, M. (1970), Effect of maximum motorway gradients on the speeds of goods vehicles, *Traff. Engng. and Control,* **12**(10).)

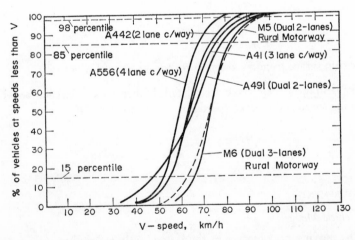

FIG. 2.10b. Cumulative frequency curves for speeds of heavy vehicles on various types of carriageway. (Source: Ackroyd, L. W. and Bettison, M. (1970), Effect of maximum motorway gradients on the speeds of goods vehicles, *Traff. Engng. and Control,* **12**(10).)

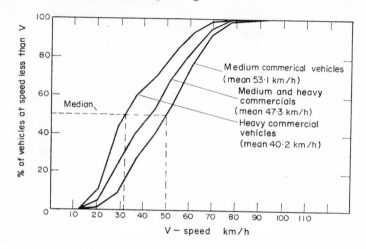

Fig. 2.10c. Goods vehicle speeds after ascending 1·2 km of straight 3·8% gradient. (Source: Ackroyd, L. W. and Bettison, M. (1970), Effect of maximum motorway gradients on the speeds of goods vehicles, *Traff. Engng. and Control*, **12**(10).)

RUNNING SPEED, JOURNEY SPEED AND STOPPED DELAY

By definition these three are related. If there is a difference between running speed and journey speed it is due to stopped traffic delays.

MEASUREMENT

In-Vehicle Methods

The moving car observer method, previously referred to on page 50, enables both speeds and delays to be determined. By using the following formula the mean journey time can be calculated from $t = t_w - y/q$. If the length of the section is l, the mean speed of all vehicles along the section

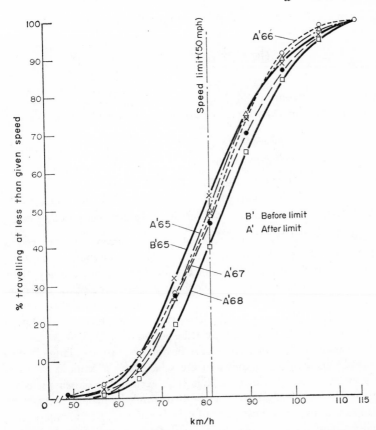

FIG. 2.10d. Cumulative frequency curves for speeds before and after the introduction of a 50 mph (80·5 km/h) speed limit on 25 August 1965, showing immediate effect and subsequent trend. (Source: Jarvis, J. R., Department of Transportation and Environmental Planning, University of Birmingham, Report Number 37: 50 mph Speed Limit.)

is l/t. As this is based on the mean journey time it is the space–mean speed as opposed to a time–mean speed which would result if the journey speeds of separate vehicles were averaged. To explain this point, consider three vehicles travelling a kilometre-long section in 1 min, 2 min and 3 min respectively. The average journey time is 2 min and this gives a space–mean speed of 30 km/h. Alternatively, the average of the individual journey speeds, V, for n observations is

$$\frac{60 + 30 + 20}{3} \text{ or } 36 \cdot 7 \text{ km/h.}$$

which is the time–mean speed and has a different value.

The relationship between these two speeds has been shown by Wardrop to be

$$\bar{V}_t = \bar{V}_s + \frac{S_s{}^2}{V_s}$$

where $\bar{V}_t$ = time–mean speed   = $\Sigma\ V/n$,

$\bar{V}_s$ = space–mean speed = $1/\Sigma\ t/n = 1/\bar{t}$,

S_s = standard deviation of the space distribution of speeds.

The stopped delay times recorded by the journey observer can be deducted from the mean journey time to give an estimate of the mean running time and hence the mean running speed. The accuracy of the estimate will depend upon how close the stopped time of the observing vehicle approaches the average stopped time for the traffic stream as a whole and this will be closer the more runs that are made and the more consistent the traffic situation is over the period of observation.

Similar data, for selected routes, can be obtained by the trailing observer method. Vehicles to be followed are selected by a random sampling procedure, i.e. every vehicle has to have an even chance of being selected, although it is customary to use a stratified sample by making separate sets of observations for each category of vehicle required. Because there exists well-established relationships for the difference in speeds between classes of vehicles over all speed ranges, as shown in Fig. 2.11, it is often only necessary to select, say, cars in the base sample. The normal procedure is to select the first vehicle randomly and follow it part way along the route taking care to terminate at the same distance from the vehicle as the starting distance taken (allowing for the observer's vehicle to have accelerated to the running speed of the trailed vehicle). Another vehicle is now randomly selected and followed over a further length of route until the whole route is completed. The procedure is repeated; the number of times (usually 3–5) is dependent on the traffic variability and the required reliability of the results.

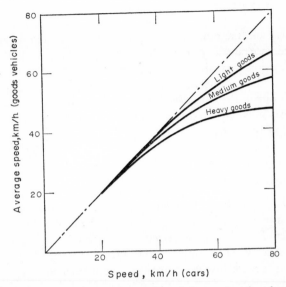

Fig. 2.11. Relationship between average speed of cars to that of goods vehicles.

Registration Number Method

This system requires observers to be stationed along the route, one at each section point. Using synchronised watches the observers record the time and registration number for each passing vehicle. Subsequent matching of numbers, carried out either manually or by computer, identifies the journey times of through vehicles and allows non-stop and stopping vehicles to be estimated. The method does not reveal the cause, location or duration of stopped delays and so gives only journey speeds and fails to provide running speeds which are often needed.

Vantage Point Method

Where the length of the route or section under consideration is short, such as a street in the central area of a city, it is often possible to station an observer where there is a reasonably unobstructed view of the entire length. Vehicles are selected at random and their course traced along the road by noting the time of entering the section, the duration and nature of any delay and the time of leaving. In this way, all the necessary data is obtained to evaluate journey and running speeds and delays. Closed circuit television may also be used for this purpose over a network of streets covered by cameras. Alternatively, time lapse photography can be used to obtain the data. Very extensive information on traffic flows, congestion points, speeds, delays and parking can be derived from aerial photography over extensive areas.

CONGESTION DELAY

Stopped delay is simple to define and measure. In contrast, congestion delay is less precise. It is the delay caused by the constricting or slowing down effect of overloading intersections, inadequate carriageway widths, parked cars, crowded pavements and similar factors. Its effect is to reduce the running speed below what might be considered an acceptable speed and it is the absence of a universally acceptable definition of what is a reasonable, for different types of road, running speed that makes it difficult to measure.

There are two main approaches to this problem. The first is appropriate to main routes and is to determine the average running speed when the traffic conditions are free-moving and vehicles are not impeded, and to call this a reasonable running speed with the possible proviso that if it exceeds any imposed speed limit the limit is taken as the reasonable speed. The second approach, applicable to city centre streets, is to use the average of spot speeds measured at points where there is no immediate interference to traffic flow, i.e. at points as far removed from intersections, pedestrian crossings, etc., as possible and where, by observation, there appears to be the minimum restriction to travel.

To see how the two methods compare consider the following measurements taken in city centre conditions:

Length of route	335 m
Average running speed	21 km/h
Average journey time	75 s
Average running time	57 s

Reasonable speed

1st method – speed limit	50 km/h
2nd method – average spot speed at point of minimum interference as measured	26·9 km/h

Running time at reasonable speed (50 km/h) by 1st method

$$= \frac{335}{50} \times \frac{3600}{1000} = 24 \text{ s}$$

Running time at reasonable speed (26·9 km/h) by 2nd method

$$= \frac{335}{26·9} \times \frac{3600}{1000} = 44·8 \text{ s}$$

Congestion delay by 1st method

$$= 57–24 \qquad = 33 \text{ s}$$

or

$$= \frac{33}{75} \times 100 = 44\% \text{ of journey time}$$

Congestion delay by 2nd method

$$= 57–44·8 \qquad = 12·2 \text{ s}$$

or

$$= \frac{12·2}{75} \times 100 = 16·3\% \text{ of journey time}$$

The road on which these measurements were taken is a city centre shopping street. With the activity that might reasonably be expected in such conditions the slower of the two "reasonable" running speeds should be taken and congestion delay accepted as 12 s. If the road had been a main route, say a radial road leading to the centre or a ring road circling the centre, 50 km/h would, in general, be a reasonable running speed. The congestion delay would then be 33 s and this value used in any assessment of running conditions.

PRESENTATION OF RESULTS

Journey speeds and running speeds may be presented in tabular form or graphically as shown in Fig. 2.12. This shows a route divided into 0·16 km sections and illustrates the comparison between the speeds in all

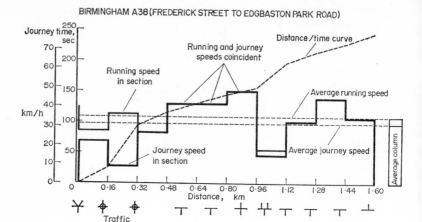

Fig. 2.12. Running and journey speeds—city radial route.

sections which can be related to the diagrammatic route presentation shown underneath, and indicating possible reasons for the fluctuations. The figure also shows a comparison of the running and journey speeds in each individual section and where these are widely divergent suggests considerable stopped delay time.

The main features of delay which need to be presented are frequency, nature and magnitude. The last two may be shown graphically as in Fig. 2.13, while the frequency may be expressed in delays per unit length or delays per unit of time as in Table 2.8.

An isochronal map, as shown in Fig. 2.14, although showing no detailed analysis is a useful method of presentation of composite speed/delay information for routes having a common origin or destination. Contours are drawn at suitable intervals connecting all points having the same journey time from the common terminal. If prepared periodically over a number of years, the map shows any deterioration or improvement in the road systems and provides a convenient indication of the sections to which improvement funds should be allocated. They are also used in conjunction with road accident maps.

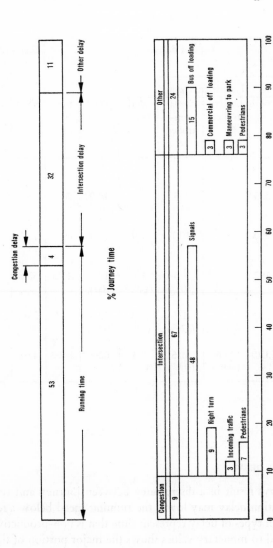

Fig. 2.13. Graphical presentation of delay studies.

TABLE 2.8.   DELAYS ON CENTRAL ONE-WAY STREETS, BIRMINGHAM

Name of street	Length (m)	Type of delay (s)					Rates of total delay	
		Pedestrian crossing			Total	Journey time (s)	s/km	s/100 s of journey time
		Uncontrolled	Signal controlled	Mid block				
New street	335	7·7 (43%)	7·5 (42%)	2·7 (15%)	17·9 (100%)	76·5	53·4	23·4
Corporation street	290	8·4 (40%)	10·7 (51%)	1·9 (9%)	21·0 (100%)	69·5	72·5	30·2
Bull street	192	0·6 (6%)	8·6 (80%)	1·5 (14%)	10·7 (100%)	45·3	55·8	23·6
Colmore row	510	6·9 (54%)	4·7 (37%)	1·2 (9%)	12·8 (100%)	77·0	25·2	16·6
Whole circuit	1320	23·6 (38%)	31·5 (50%)	7·3 (12%)	62·4 (100%)	268·3	47·1	23·3

SIGNIFICANCE OF DELAY

Stopped delays result in a discrepancy between journey and running speeds. Congestion delay may lower the running speed below a reasonable value. Both types of delay represent time that is non-productive and when converted to monetary values shows the major portion of the cost to the community of an inadequate road. They also show part of the economic return to be expected if the route is improved to reduce delays and this permits priorities for road-improvement works to be established.

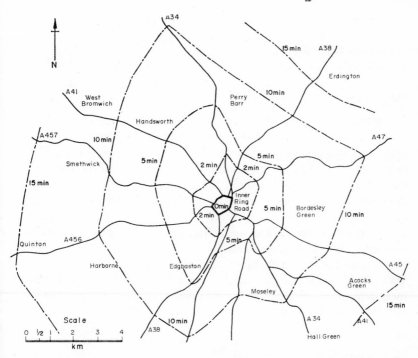

Fig. 2,14. Off-peak mean journey time by car, outwards from Birmingham inner ring road (1969).

MISCELLANEOUS MEASUREMENTS

Accelerometers

There are a number of accelerometers suitable for traffic engineering use, allowing simultaneous measurement of both lateral and longitudinal acceleration. Corrections normally have to be applied to allow for body tilt and roll. Acceleration and deceleration measurements are used in studying traffic flow; when aggregated they are referred to as acceleration "noise" and indicate a performance measure for a route. Besides their use in studying the behaviour of traffic flows they are also required for the accurate measurement of braking conditions, driver behaviour, horizontal and vertical curve performance and for the siting of control devices and road signs.

Fuel Meters

The traffic engineer is often concerned in the economic assessment of new facilities and control schemes and, in addition to journey speed and delay measurement, requires data on the changes in running and vehicle operating costs. While acceleration noise is a measure of the wear and tear costs in operating a vehicle, the consumption of fuel is another important consideration. Instruments developed for commercial use are quite suitable for most traffic engineering purposes. Readings are made at control points along the test run and can be considered in relation to distance travelled, the use of brake, clutch and accelerator and also the height gained or lost on the journey. Multi-channel recording apparatus, with suitable computer compatible output, has been developed for the measurement of all these traffic parameters required in cost benefit calculations and road traffic performance characteristics.

FURTHER READING

ACKROYD, L. W. and ABISS, J. C. (1970) Traffic flow patterns at a rural motorway location. *Traff. Engng. and Control*, **12**(7).

ACKROYD, L. W. and BETTISON, M. (1970) Effect of maximum motorway gradients on the speeds of goods vehicles. *Traff. Engng. and Control*, **12**(10).

ASHWORTH, R. (1969) Effect of lane closure on traffic delays. *Traff. Engng. and Control*, **11**(8).

ASHWORTH, R. (1971) Delays to pedestrians crossing a road. *Traff. Engng. and Control*, **13**(3).

BAERWALD, J. E. (Ed.) (1965) *Traffic Engineering Handbook* (3rd ed.). Inst. of Traff. Engrs., Washington.

BELLIS, W. R. and JONES, J. E. (1963) *30th Peak Hour Factor Trend*, H.R. Record 27.

CONSTANTINE, T. (1964) Time-lapse kinematography for traffic studies. *Traff. Engng. and Control*, **5**.

DEPARTMENT SCIENTIFIC AND INDUSTRIAL RESEARCH (1965) *Research on Road Traffic*. Road Research Laboratory, H.M.S.O.

DUNN, J. B., Traffic census results for 1971. TRRL Report LR 548.

EMMERSON, J. (1961) Speeds of cars on sharp horizontal curves. *Traff. Engng. and Control*, **11**(3).

GARWOOD, F. (1962) The sampling and use of traffic flow statistics. *J. Appl. Statist.*, **11**(1).

GYENES, L. (1973) The distribution of hourly volumes of traffic at fifty sites in 1970, TRRL Report LR 549. The Transport and Road Research Laboratory.

HIGHWAY RESEARCH BOARD. *Characteristics of Traffic Flow*, H.R. Record 230; *Economic Factors influencing Engineering Decisions*, H.R. Record 245; *Highway Design Practices*, H.R. Record 371; *Visibility*, H.R. Record 377.

HOBBS, F. D. and RICHARDSON, B. D. (1967) Instrumentation in traffic engineering. *Traff. Engng. and Control*, **8**(12), **9**(1), (2), (3), (4), and (5).

LEEMING, J. J. (1963) *Statistical Methods for Engineers*. Blackie, London.

LYNAM, D. A. and EVERALL, P. F. (1971) Car journey times in London 1970, RRL Report LR 416; and Public transport journey times in London 1970, RRL Report LR 413. The Road Research Laboratory.

MARLOW, M. (1971) Repeat traffic studies in 1967 in eight towns previously surveyed in 1963/64. RRL Report LR 390. The Road Research Laboratory.

MINISTRY OF TRANSPORT (1965) *Urban Traffic Engineering Techniques*. H.M.S.O.

MINISTRY OF TRANSPORT (1968) *Traffic Prediction for Rural Roads*. H.M.S.O.

O'FLAHERTY, C. A. and COOMBE, R. D. (1971) Speeds on level roads. *Traff. Engng. and Control*, **13**(1), (2) and (3).

PATERSON, I. M. (1970) Some RRL apparatus for automatic data collecting. *Traff. Engng. and Control*, **11**(9).

RUHM, K. (1971) Traffic data collection and analysis by photogrammetric method. *Traff. Engng. and Control*, **13**(8).

TANNER, J. C. (1962) Forecasts of future numbers of vehicles in Great Britain. *Rds. and Rd. Constr.*, **40**(477).

TANNER, J. C. (1965) Forecasts of vehicle ownership in Great Britain. *Rds. and Rd. Constr.*, **43**(515) and (516).

TOLPULE, A. H. (1969) Forecasts of vehicles and traffic in Great Britain 1969, RRL Report LR 288; and 1972 Revision, TRRL Report LR 543. The Road Research Laboratory.

WARDROP, J. G. and CHARLESWORTH, G. (1954) A method of estimating speed and flow of traffic from a moving vehicle. *J. Instn. Av. Engns.*, Part 11, **3**(1).

WARDROP, J. G. (1968) Journey speed and flow in central urban areas. *Traff. Engng. and Control*, **9**(11).

WILLIAMS, T. E. H. and EMMERSON, J. (1961) Traffic volumes, journey times and speeds by moving-observer method. *Traff. Engng. and Control*, **3**(3).

CHAPTER 3

Traffic Surveys and Analysis

THE scope and nature of traffic engineering has changed in recent years. Information is required not only for the planning of road systems but on the social and environmental consequences to the community of such plans. Nor can road planning be considered in isolation; the scope of the work has widened and travel requirements must be seen in a context of the interaction between all modes. Policy decisions affect the facilities available, changing and creating new opportunities in urban life, which lead to new habits. Adequate monitoring of these changes is essential if greater flexibility is to be maintained in planning and new trends incorporated in the previous long-term forecasts on which a plan has been based.

Surveys are needed for many purposes and if these are to be efficiently conducted it is essential that their objectives are clearly defined. The types of survey range from the determination and characteristics of a large-scale movement pattern, for use in a structure plan, to small surveys to ascertain the local plan needs, or the response of a small group of citizens. These may vary from the study of a potential pedestrian precinct to the special problems of access to a public road from industrial or commercial premises, involving the movements of a work force and visitors, or the location of passenger traffic and freight terminals. There are also the problems of preservation and conservation of areas, the growth of urban and rural traffic and the development of tourism.

TRANSPORTATION SURVEYS

The fundamental interaction between land use planning and the nature of the travel pattern has been brought together in a unified process which includes public policy decisions and the evaluation of alternative strategies.

The first phase of a study is the formulation of goals for the defined area and the setting of objectives based on available resources, time spans and public aims. The next stage is the planning of relevant surveys, determining the level of detail required to obtain a specified accuracy, based on current information, and completing surveys, analysis and model building. Finally, forecasts are made for predetermined periods; usually, long-term alternatives are tested at an interim stage, each being evaluated against sets of economic, operational and social criteria laid down in the goal formulation phase. The transportation planning process is shown diagrammatically in Fig. 3.1.

Land Use

A distribution of residential, educational, commercial, manufacturing and service industry is tabulated by intensity of use and by age and condition of property. Similarly information is collected on recreational land and vacant space and on the potential of underdeveloped or derelict land. The environmental state and quality of both the natural and built environment is assessed.

Socio-economic Activity

Population characteristics are reviewed for the major activities of work, education, shopping and recreation. The associated economic base information is also collected and budgetary constraints examined.

Transportation Facilities

An inventory of all existing travel facilities is prepared by mode and examined in relation to current use. Where considerable base material is available within the area, or available from a similar place, it is possible to synthesise travel movements and reduce the need for full-scale travel surveys. The size and scope of the studies is influenced by the objectives, degree of likely change, particularly of land use in the forecast period,

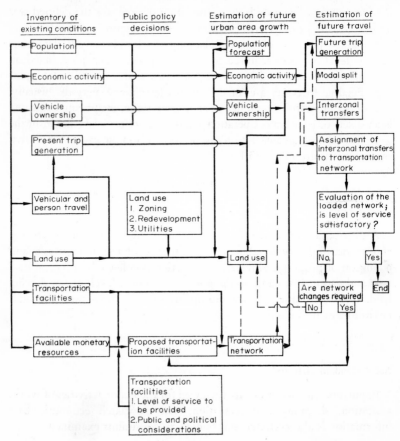

FIG. 3.1. The transportation planning process. (Source: Memmott, Martin and Bone, Predicting future demand for urban area transportation, *H.R.B. Bull.* 326.)

diversification of the population and complexity of the detailed projections required in the plan testing and evaluation stage.

Definition of Study Area

Surveys can range from the national level through regional, county, district or local levels down to a single land-use generator. In ascending size order each level overlaps and includes the preceding group, and it is often necessary to use outputs from one survey level as inputs to another, although the nature and type of detail will vary with each survey purpose.

The outer edges of the study area are bounded by an external cordon whose delineation may create difficulties but in all cases would include land capable of development in the project period. Criteria used to distinguish areas include population density. Usually a minimum of 400 persons/km^2 is taken to define the limit of an urban area, but would, in any case, include all settlements within 2·5 km of the main urban area boundary. The proportion of the working population who commute from outlying areas to the main centre is often important and where the proportion exceeds 15% of the active residents of an outlying area it is generally included in the study. Information on these commuting proportions is obtained from the Registrar-General's Work Place Tables. Shopping and recreational movements may also be considered in defining the total area under review, but the finally selected cordon should be compatible with other survey boundaries.

TRAVEL SURVEYS

The activities, resulting from land use and economic characteristics of an area, generate travel, and the type and extent of these movements are studied by travel surveys. Survey techniques include the external observation of journeys or the direct interview of travellers. Interviews can be undertaken either during the course of the journey or at terminals (homes, offices, factories, schools, etc.) and interchanges (stations, bus stops, airports, depots, etc.). Travellers entering an area from external zones are intercepted by cordons placed around the survey area or, where comparisons are required of the use of alternative routes, by screen lines drawn across the axis of movement. Within cities, screen lines and cordons are often used to compare and check travel between areas with the information derived from home interviews and counts of vehicles at each point. Screen lines should be sited to avoid central areas and localities where vehicles are cruising around to find parking or points where the line may be crossed several times on the same journey. Natural and man-made barriers, like rivers and railways, where crossing points are limited, make good boundaries.

It is necessary to know the basic volumetric characteristics of the system being studied in order to plan the proposed survey; later extensions may be both difficult and expensive to carry out. Sampling techniques are widely used to reduce the overall field-work and subsequent analysis. The choice of an adequate sample is important in establishing an accuracy for the expanded results.

SURVEY METHODS

There are five basic methods which can be used singly or in combination, depending on the nature of the problem and the information required.

Registration Number Surveys

This is a simple method not needing police or elaborate site equipment, but it has the major disadvantage that neither primary origins nor final destinations are obtained. Observers need good vantage points and, for large flows, the registration numbers and passing times of vehicles may be tape recorded. Recording stations must be simultaneously manned with starting and finishing times offset by the time required to travel between stations. Sampling methods are difficult to apply, but one method is to record only registrations ending in selected digits. If the journey time between two stations is of the order of a few minutes, little error is introduced by recording only the digits of a registration. The probability of any one number appearing on x vehicles in a group of v vehicles passing in the selected time period can be determined from the Poisson distribution.

The method can be readily applied to a variety of routes without causing delay or influencing the habits of road users and is not badly affected by weather conditions as observers can be stationed under cover, although night conditions cause obvious difficulties. Bias will result from the false recording of a registration number as a vehicle will have been noted as entering the area and not leaving it and another as leaving the area only. Mistakes are difficult to avoid under intensive recording conditions and legibility also suffers, making transcription difficult. A large number of observers are required, as all the stations of a cordon must be manned at the same time, but different hours of the day can be sampled on different days. Two observers must be used, one calling and the other recording (unless tape recordings are made), for unidirectional flows in excess of about 250 veh/h. A skilled observer can call out up to 1000 registration numbers for periods less than an hour.

For manual analysis, the station lists are called out in turn and matches of registration numbers appearing at other stations, in the correct time order, are booked separately from those that enter and terminate in the area or are generated and sighted leaving the cordon. In a second method, a card index system is used and the information for the IN direction is worked through for all posts and placed on a card from a series, which is numbered 1 to 999, representing the three digits of a vehicle's registration. The OUT direction sheets are then recorded on the cards in a similar manner and vehicles are matched, times abstracted and movements through posts summarised. Similar listing and matching can be carried out using punched card machinery or by computer program but transcription costs are relatively high and manual methods can directly eliminate the more obvious recording and transcription errors. Evans has given a method to reduce the probable errors due to inaccurate recording—The estimation of road traffic flow by registration number observation, A.W. Evans, *Jn. Royal Stats. Soc.*, **22,** 1, 1973.

Tag and Disc Surveys

In this method, survey stations are set up and precoded tags or discs, showing such items as vehicle classification, post number and the time of entry, can be stamped with a time clock before they are fixed to the vehicle or given to the driver for collection at exit points from the system. The tags are again time stamped and the exit post number is also recorded. Vehicle delay is kept to a minimum, but a similar disadvantage to that of registration number surveys applies so that full origin and destination information is not available. While there is also less likelihood of bias, some drivers may lose the tags or object to their being fixed to their vehicles. Coloured tags or separate stickers, according to station of issue, may also be used in conjunction with additional observers sited at intermediate points, noting the numbers of the various colours present on their sections of route. Analysis work is similar to the techniques employed for registration number surveys, although simpler, and can be carried out manually or by machine methods. Mark-sense cards are particularly suitable as no subsequent office coding is needed.

Postcard Surveys

This method is useful for preplanning purposes in a major transportation survey to obtain general information on the movement pattern. It is also used where interview methods may cause extensive queuing and delay and is also often used in surveys of public transport passengers. Survey stations can be sited on cordons or screen lines, with police control to stop vehicles, or they may be located at traffic signals, bus stops, stations, parking sites or on board a vehicle in transit. Cards are usually prepaid for subsequent posting but, alternatively, they can be collected at another cordon point or left in a collection box at a station or car park.

Detailed information on passengers, journeys and purposes, vehicle types and garaging and routes used can be obtained with little delay. While few enumerators and minimum site organisation is required, it is important that ample prepublicity is given in the local press and on radio if worthwhile results are to be obtained. Bias is almost certain to be present due to the vagaries of human nature and response rates are usually low, ranging from 25 to 50%. It has been found that lower returns are recorded for truck drivers, visiting traffic and night drivers and that the response rate is likely to fall off through the day. Drivers who make a number of journeys across a cordon in the course of a day are often reluctant to complete more than one of the several cards they receive. Numbered cards have been used in a lottery to encourage a higher response rate, but cards may be collected and falsely completed.

Route Interviews

This method is generally adopted for rural and external city cordon surveys. The traveller is stopped by a police officer and an interviewer records journey details from a predetermined set of questions. Information collected on journeys includes starting and finishing points, last purpose and next purpose stops (i.e. excluding casual stops for petrol and refreshment), journey purpose, vehicle classification, numbers of passengers, goods carried, reasons for routeing or mode choice, income and travel costs. Sampling methods employ time and volume clusters or random sampling techniques.

(1) *Time cluster sampling*. During each hour of the survey a period of time t is selected when all vehicle drivers are interviewed and a further time period T when no interviews are carried out. The size of the sample, expressed as a percentage, is then $100t/(t+T)$. A convenient time interval for a 50% sample is 15 min for both t and T and the interviewers can then alternate interview directions to cover both IN and OUT flows. It is important that accurate time intervals are maintained and that all vehicles arriving within the selected periods are interviewed. If both directions are being covered, this will normally require centre of the road stations and the switching of half the interviewers to the other direction on or about 2 min before the end of the selected period. The remaining interviewers will switch direction on completion of their 15-min interviews. The main disadvantage is that small queues may begin to form during each period, and without the aid of the station supervisor for the additional interviewing, the back-log may not be readily overcome. Alternatively, if the change over of direction is difficult to arrange, a $33\frac{1}{3}$% sample can be taken using a 10-min interview period and a 5-min break to change interview direction.

(2) *Volume cluster sampling*. A predetermined number of vehicles x to be interviewed is selected, the number adopted per cluster is generally dependent on the availability of interviewers. To avoid confusion, interviewers should ideally carry out only one interview in each cluster.

Also, depending on the sample size, a cluster of vehicles X is allowed to pass without interviewing. The size of the sample expressed as a percentage is then $100x/(x+X)$. While interviews in both directions can be conducted at the same time, more interviewers than method 1 will be required.

(3) *Variable rate sampling.* In this method of random sampling developed by the Road Research Laboratory, interviewers are employed at a constant rate, the sampling size fluctuating according to the volume flow. Depending on the characteristics of the stream, sample rates are calculated for either $\frac{1}{2}$ h or 1 h periods, and usually, to reduce the possibility of bias, for individual classes of vehicle. This is likely to occur where vehicles are bunched and groups are led by slow vehicles. The operation is controlled by the supervisor who is in a position to see both the interviewers and the police controller responsible for drawing the required vehicles from the stream. Vehicles not being interviewed are allowed to pass the station continuously at reduced speed. When all interviews in one group have been completed at the station, the supervisor signals the police controller to let in a further group, by drawing out the NEXT vehicles in the stream, equal in number to the interviewers. Combinations of methods 1, 2 and 3 can be used and examples of station layout are shown in Fig. 3.2.

Organisation

Route interview surveys require the most elaborate organisation and are susceptible to interference from the weather. Careful framing of questions is needed to avoid bias and ambiguity together with a strict site organisation for interview procedure and handling the recorded data. Duties of interviewers must be clearly outlined and some previous training at a low volume survey station is desirable. It is particularly important that interviewers rigidly adhere to the standard questions and that care is taken to avoid recording false answers, either deliberate or unintentional, on the part of the drivers, e.g. giving next major town as destination, omitting intermediate stops or including a casual stop.

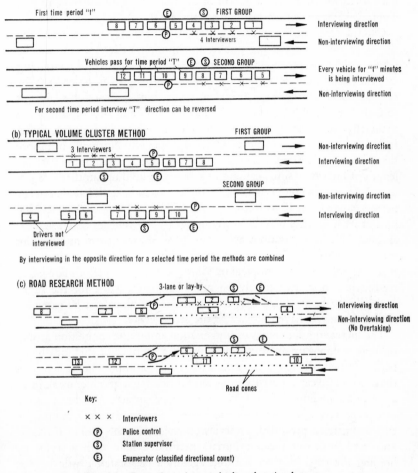

Fig. 3.2. Route interview methods and station layouts.

However, the method when properly conducted is most satisfactory, and gives little delay to the motorist (30 s interviews for simple by-pass studies to 90 s for full interviews including journey purpose, but this does not include the total time spent from leaving the traffic stream to rejoining it). Where travel characteristics are fairly uniform, the interviews may be carried out over a period of days or weeks on different routes. Typical examples of forms, and questions, are shown in Fig. 3.3.

Careful siting of the interview stations is necessary to safeguard the site crew and the travelling public. In choosing a site, account will be taken of sight distances on the approaches, vehicle speeds and overtaking and these will help determine the positition of signs and letter sizes for warnings and instructions. Interview points must be carefully laid out so that drivers move quickly to their interviewer and safely out into the main stream. A station supervisor allocates shifts and duties, issues forms and checks and collates recorded information. Normally not more than about four interviewers are used at a station because of the variable length of interview time, causing one driver to hold up another's departure. Each site also requires a continuous census to be undertaken. Survey periods range from 12 to 16 h (typically 0700 to 1900 h and 0600 to 2200 h), but 24-h surveys may be warranted (e.g. 500 vehicles between 2200 and 0600 h). While stations are normally sited away from intersections it is possible to conduct surveys at traffic lights during the red phase, but it is advisable to only complete one interview in each period. For safety reasons it is best, particularly on multi-lane approaches, for the signal controller to be operated manually and the red phase can be extended if all interviewers have not vacated the carriageway.

The increasing difficulties of organisation and traffic congestion arising on high volume urban routes have led to a number of methods being tried to reduce the interview time and/or analysis time. One system uses the mark-sense card specially prepared for making a graphite mark in an appropriate coding area usually on an upper surface. Another method uses preperforated cards with up to a dozen commonly occurring origins and destinations precoded. Interviewers memorise the coding for these areas and push out the appropriate perforated hole with a stylus by holding the card in a set position against a perforated plastic holder. Destinations or origins, other than those which have been precoded, must be written in by hand for subsequent office coding.

With all types of survey it is helpful to have self-coding items recorded at the time of interview for such items as station number, time period, vehicle type, direction, journey purpose, number of passengers, type of

"Xville" Travel Survey

Sheet No.	
Time	
Day	
Date	

Station No. ------------ Direction ------------------------ Interviewer ------------------- Weather -------------------

		1	2	3	4	5
1	Vehicle type					
2	No. of passengers					
3	Where did you start this journey today					
4	Where was your last stop (excluding casual stops)					
5	Where are you travelling to today					
6	What stops will you be making before you get there (excluding casual stops)					
	ONLY ASK THE FOLLOWING QUESTIONS IF "XVILLE" INCLUDED IN ANSWER TO QUESTION 5 OR 6					
7	Where in "Xville" are you going to stop (All addresses)					
8	What is the purpose of this journey					
9	Is this vehicle normally kept in "Xville"					
10	If so give full address					

"XVILLE" TRAFFIC SURVEY - INTERVIEW SHEET Sheet No.

STATION NUMBER ------- DATE ------- HOUR BEGINNING ----------- INITIALS -------------

Interview No.	Car	Light van	2 axle goods	Over 2 axle	M/cycle	Coach	Occupants	ORIGIN	LAST PURPOSE STOP	NEXT PURPOSE STOP	DESTINATION	To/from work	Business	Commercial	Shopping	Recreational
	1	2	3	4	5	6						1	2	3	4	5
1																
2																
3																

FIG. 3.3. Examples of route interview forms.

goods carried, etc. Direct gang punching of the general station information is a further aid and interview cards with coloured time strips marked on them for each hourly period, or individually coloured cards according to direction or vehicle type, improve site control and subsequent office procedures. Weather protection is necessary for the interview forms in the event of rain. This can be provided by using plastic overlays to the recorder's clipboard.

Updating and Monitoring Surveys

Trends in the movement pattern and changes due to road improvements are essential factors in traffic planning. The New York Port Authority has used a continuous survey procedure which enables full-time trained interviewers to be employed. This overcomes, to some extent, the possibility of error due to haste and inexperience which may occur on the more usual route interviews. It dispenses with the need to employ a large labour force during the survey period, both for interviews and subsequent coding, and eliminates the errors associated with data expansion to suit seasonal influences. The effects of route improvements and the monitoring of traffic trends can be made within the survey area. Each stage of the sample is selected randomly for a time period, site direction and lane and the required sample size is precalculated. Rotation from lane to lane and by direction is prearranged after the first position has been selected at random. In this way little inconvenience is experienced and the majority of lanes and ramps are free from interview congestion. The interview team also code the work which allows a change in task and avoids monotony. This familiarity with the whole procedure both improves speed and the accuracy of the work.

Sample Size

The selection of a sample size consistent with the required accuracy of the estimate and causing minimum delay to the motorist is most important. If all journeys on a road are the same, obviously one interview and a volume count could supply all the information needed. Conversely the greater the variation in journeys the larger is the required sample size.

Wide variation will occur where there are small flows in a traffic stream for a variety of origins and destinations but, in general, it can be stated that there are diminishing returns for increasingly large samples of highly consistent high volume flows.

It is important in a sample to be able to estimate within a range of values where the true value is likely to lie. Such a range is called a confidence interval, u, and can be measured in units of standard deviation, e.g. $0.95u = 1.96$, $0.90u = 1.65$, i.e. 90% confidence that the population mean lies within 1.65 s.d.'s either side. The sample can be tested for statistical adequacy by considering a sample n, out of total flow T, to have a number of trips n' with a required journey attribute and for which a confidence interval $I_{N'}$ can be determined from

$$I_{N'} = \frac{n'}{n} \pm u \sqrt{K\left[\left(\frac{n'}{n}\right)\left(\frac{n-n'}{n}\right)\right]} \Big/ n$$

where $K = (1 - n/T)$ and approaches 1 as T becomes increasingly larger than n.

A 10% sample of households yielded 1010 trips in zone i of which 90 went to zone j. The estimate of total flow for a 10% sample of T is 10100, trips of attribute $N' = 900$, as n' was 90. Then for $u = 1.65$, $I_{N'} = 0.0891 \pm 0.014$, i.e. $10100 (0.0891 \pm 0.014) = 758 < N' < 1041$ trips, defining the upper and lower limits of the confidence interval and the suitability of the sample size for that particular attribute.

Table 3.1 shows the relationship between sample size and the probable accuracy for a given volume of trips for a confidence interval of 0.95.

TABLE 3.1. ESTIMATED VARIATIONS DUE TO SAMPLE RATE

Estimated number of journeys	Percentage variation $\pm$ for given sample rates of							
	1	2	3	4	5	10	20	30
100	200	145	115	100	90	65	44	36
500	90	65	52	44	40	28	20	16
1000	65	44	36	32	28	20	14	12
10000	20	14	12	10	9	6·5	4·4	3·6

HOME SURVEYS

In many places, particularly urban areas, route interviews and similar surveys are difficult to carry out due to the multiplicity of routes and the high flows at peak hours. Furthermore, they do not adequately sample the distribution of travel in time nor yield suitable and sufficient socio-economic information for use in model building.

The home survey methods, usually by direct interview or question-naire, enable the maximum amount of information to be collected on travel habits which are subsequently used for predicting traffic flows and travel choices. The increasing use of mathematical models, based on land use, make it necessary to distinguish journeys between all types of ter-minals and activities, for instance commercial, industrial, shopping, educational and recreational purposes.

SAMPLING

The normal method of conducting the survey is for a random sample to be drawn from the whole population using, as a sample frame, either the Register of Electors or the Valuation List. The former lists addresses of qualified electors (i.e. those over 18 years) and is compiled annually, whereas Valuation Lists are only up-dated by the Inland Revenue every five years, although they include commercial and industrial premises, besides residential property, and the data is often held on punched cards. Careful checks must be made to ensure that the sampling list, usually households, is up to date and representative. Other sampling methods may be appropriate for different types of survey, including random sampling of land uses from grid coordinates on maps and stratified quota sampling of sectors of the population with the required attributes.

Sample size is affected by the type, density and distribution of land uses, population characteristics and travel facilities but primarily by the required accuracy of the estimates and the likelihood of their variability. Table 3.2 indicates typical sample sizes for home interview surveys in general transportation studies, but where local information is only re-quired to calibrate established base data, much smaller samples are needed. Samples of residences will omit a number of essential travellers who are temporarily or permanently residing away from a home and living in institutions, hotels, educational establishments and military camps. It is often necessary for data completeness to obtain information on these institutional residents by sampling from room lists.

TABLE 3.2. HOME INTERVIEW SAMPLE RATES

Total population (1000's)	Sample size (%)
<20	>25
20–100	25–10
100–250	10–5
250–1000	$5-1\frac{1}{2}$
>1000	$1\frac{1}{2}-\frac{1}{2}$

COMMERCIAL VEHICLE AND TAXI CAB SURVEYS

The travel movements of commercial vehicles and taxis is usually obtained directly from vehicle operators selected from rating lists or a land-use survey. Local authority vehicle registers will exclude firms with vehicles registered elsewhere and may include vehicles operated in other areas.

Log sheets are designed for a record to be kept for each vehicle of journey purpose (picking-up or delivering goods and service calls) for all destinations stratified by land use, time of day and vehicle type. Because of the variety of commercial vehicle trips, and a tendency to under report, it is necessary to adopt intensive survey methods and correspondingly larger samples. These range from 10–20% in large cities, 20–30% in medium-sized towns, to 50% in smaller urban areas. Similar problems arise in taxi surveys where these form a significant proportion of travel within an area. The usual procedure is for a substantial proportion of drivers to be requested to complete trip record cards. Because of journey variability, surveys of commercial vehicles and taxis are usually based on a week's trip pattern.

HOME INTERVIEW AND QUESTIONNAIRE SURVEY PROCEDURES

Usually, after an explanatory letter about the objectives of the survey has been sent to the selected address, an interviewer calls and collects pretabulated information about the household and the trip making of the occupants for a selected time period. A cheaper alternative to interviewing is to distribute a questionnaire for self-completion by the occupants. Forms are delivered with a covering letter explaining the purpose of the survey, the date the forms will be collected when any assistance can also be given. In either method the required information is similar. Items are collected on the distribution of household ages, sexes, occupations, incomes, type and age of vehicles owned or used, as well as a detailed record in time of the purpose and mode of all journeys made by the household. Minor journeys may be forgotten if more than a day old and trip record cards should be issued for completion as a diary where information is needed over an extended time period. The intensive interview method overcomes the disadvantage of one person answering for others by requiring all members of a household (usually those over the age of 16) to be contacted directly.

Misleading information may result if interviewers prompt respondents or the questions are not clearly stated without ambiguity. The preferred method is to undertake a presurvey to check procedures and the validity of questions to extract the required information. Both weekday and weekend travel characteristics are generally investigated, and account taken of seasonal influences in sample design. If interviews are confined to a short period, then bias may result due to weather conditions, school holidays or unusual events.

Because questions and answers can be presented and recorded unhurriedly by these methods, good travel estimates are possible provided that the sample frame is both up-dated and accurate and that correct sampling procedures are employed. The questionnaire method poses the questions in a standard form and it may also be easier for a family to collectively recall journeys. Simplicity of coding and checking procedures is essential for minimising the data edit costs. Call backs (usually two or three) are needed to complete the sample, but alternatively with questionnaire methods a stamped envelope can be left for the return of the forms. Typical survey forms are shown in Figs. 3.4a, b.

UCTIONS
answer all questions with an "X" unless otherwise stated.
ps made by every person aged 3 years and over should be entered below.
group one person's trips together.

11 AGE GROUP			19–20 OCCUPATION OR PROFESSION	26–33 WHERE DID YOU GO ?	34–35 36–37 WHAT TIME DID YOU		38–39 WHAT WAS THE PURPOSE OF YOUR TRIP ?								40–42 HOW DID YOU TRAVEL ?							43 WHERE DID YOU PARK THE VEHICLE?							
0	1	2			Leave ?	Arrive ?	0	1	2	3	4	5	6	7	0	1	2	3	4	5	6	0	1	2	3	4	5		
3–14 years.	15–20 years.	Over 20 years.	Please be as explicit as possible. e.g. Engineer(Professional), Chargehand toolmaker	Give address if in SOLIHULL or BIRMINGHAM otherwise give name of town only. If to or from Home state "Home".			Home.	Work.	School.	On Firm's Business.	Lunch.	Social and Recreational.	Other reasons.		Bus.	Train.	Drove Car or Van.	Passenger in Car or Van.	Motor Cycle	Walking or Cycling.	Other means.	Car Park at Work.	Multi-storey Car Park.	Open Car Park.	Roadside.	Drive or garage at home.	Other.	For Office Use Only.
				FROM																									
				To																									
				FROM																									
				To																									

ZONE

REF NO.

All Information on this Form is for

Mark Your Answers with an "X" unless otherwise stat'

PLEASE ANSWER THE FIRST FOUR QUESTIONS AND QUESTION 7.
ALSO ANSWER QUESTIONS 5, 6 AND 8 IF THEY APPLY TO YOU.
ONE OF THESE FORMS SHOULD BE FILLED IN FOR EACH MEMBER OF THE HOUSHOLD AGED 3 YEARS AND OVER.

(There are some explanatory notes on the back of this form which may help you.)

PART I **1 Age Group**   **2 Sex**   **3 Occupation**

3 – 14 years	15 – 20 years	21 yrs & over

Male	Female

PART II For the **TRIP TO WORK OR SCHOOL** (Excluding trips back to work or school after lunch etc.)

4 DID YOU GO TO WORK OR SCHOOL ON   Work ☐   School ☐   Neither ☐
(Mark the square which applies to you).

5 IF YOU DID GO TO WORK OR SCHOOL, PLEASE FILL IN THE FOLLOWING:

Give Name and Address of Firm, School, etc., or Street Name and No.	WHAT TIME DID YOU		HOW DID YOU TRAVEL?	To WORK ETC.	FROM WORK ETC.	IF YOU DROVE A CAR OR VAN ON ALL, OR PART OF YOUR JOURNEY TO WORK –	
	Leave Home?	Arrive Home?				Where did you park it during the day? (Write where.)	Why did you take it?
			1. Drove Truck				
			2. Drove Car, Van				
			3. Taxi Passenger			Personal Transport only ☐	
			4. Bus Passenger				
			5. Car, Van , etc. Passenger				
			6. Motor or Power Cycle	drive passenger		Business Use as well as Personal Transport ☐	
			7. Pedal Cycle				
			8. Train				
			9. Walk				

6 If you did not go to work or school because you were on holiday give name of normal place of work or name of school you attended last term.

PART III For **ALL OTHER TRIPS** on

TO BE FILLED IN whether or not you go to Work or School but do not include the trip to and from Work or School which you fill in on the opposite page.

NOT TO BE FILLED IN for trips by persons driving TRUCKS, VANS, BUSES or TAXIS on business or DELIVERIES. This information is being obtained in other ways.

7 DID YOU MAKE ANY TRIPS OTHER THAN THOSE TO AND FROM WORK OR SCHOOL?   ☐ YES   ☐ NO
(Mark only the square which applies to you.)

8 IF ANSWER TO QUESTION 7 WAS "YES" PLEASE GIVE THE FOLLOWING DETAILS:

	Where did you go? Give Street Name and No. if in Stevenage, otherwise name of place only. If to home, put "Home"	APPROX. TIME ARRIVED AT PLACE VISITED	APPROX. TIME DEPARTED FROM PLACE VISITED	How did you travel?									If you drove a car or van where did you park at each place visited?	Why did you go?					OFFICE USE
				1. Drove Truck	2. Drove Car, Van	3. Taxi Passenger	4. Bus Passenger	5. Car, Van , etc. Passenger	6. Motor or Power Cycle	7. Train	8. Walk		On Work or Firm's Business	Personal Business	Shopping	Breakfast, lunch, dinner	Social, Recreational	Picking up or putting down a passenger	
1st.																			
2nd.																			
3rd.																			
4th.																			
5th.																			
6th.																			
7th.																			
8th.																			

FIG. 3.4a. Home questionnaire form.

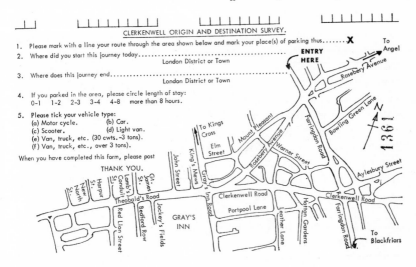

1. Please mark with a line your route through the area shown below and mark your place(s) of parking thus.......**X**

2. Where did you start this journey today..
London District or Town

3. Where does this journey end..
London District or Town

4. If you parked in the area, please circle length of stay:
0-1   1-2   2-3   3-4   4-8   more than 8 hours.

5. Please tick your vehicle type:
(a) Motor cycle.   (b) Car.
(c) Scooter.   (d) Light van.
(e) Van, truck, etc. (30 cwts.-3 tons).
(f) Van, truck, etc., over 3 tons).

When you have completed this form, please post

THANK YOU.

FIG. 3.4b.   Pre-paid postcard.

Survey errors are those associated with sampling from the frequency distribution of daily trips from a dwelling, at one point in time, and the non-response bias caused by some householders not being contacted even after call backs, and refusals.

When calls are made, the small sized and low income group households are least likely to have anyone at home and those households containing the most prolific travellers are also most likely to be vacant. Supervisory sample checks should also be made at the interview stage to detect the rate and type of reporting and recording errors of interviews.

Alternative methods to the above have been tried and these include telephone interviews, where a large proportion of the intended respondents are telephone subscribers, interview forms set out in newspapers and in special radio or television programmes. In the latter case the question-naires have been delivered to households prior to the programme, or are cut out from weekly programme guides, and are completed during the course of the programme after explanatory films and talks.

CHECKING TRAVEL DATA

Besides providing the basic data on external to internal traffic, the cordon and screen counts and surveys are used to adjust the home interview surveys. Where discrepancies occur between the origin and destination trip pattern, deduced from the route interview surveys and vehicle counts, and an assignment of the expanded home interview data to the existing network (i.e. the reproduction of the current flow map on the base year network), it is customary to adjust the trip rates from the home interviews accordingly. If the total number of movements is correct, but distortions have arisen between particular areas or sectors, then screenline data may be used to adjust the trip attraction or generation equations or the distribution functions.

It is important that a large proportion of the total traffic crossing a cordon or line must be at risk for sampling, and only minor roads, carrying less than 5% of the total crossing traffic, are excluded. Normally, volume counting programmes are instituted at key locations to monitor weekly and seasonal patterns and identify special cases for additional interview surveys.

Generally, the decision to adjust data depends on a number of factors, particularly the degree of disparity between the observed and expanded totals and other population and social data comparisons. If these are too great then non-response or additional surveys may be required.

ZONING

The collected data will consist of a multitude of journeys with different specific origins, destinations, purposes and modes which must be related to other traffic, sociological and economic factors. Without aggregation the amount of data will only serve to confuse and obscure underlying relationships, but the degree of aggregation varies with the particular requirements, and it is useful to have methods which permit this to be variable at different stages for different purposes. With external traffic generators a whole country or state is zoned and as areas further away from the study centre tend to have decreasing influence, this is represented by a coarsening of the scale of zoning. In these outer areas, population centres, ports, intercommunication centres, topographical features, particularly mountain regions and rivers, must all be taken into account and influence the drawing up of the zonal boundaries.

For internal traffic within the city, the aim is to obtain zones of a similar generating size and also of a uniform traffic nature. Topographical features often form the main boundaries, with a further breakdown by land use, e.g. residential, shopping, recreational, industrial and communications centres, determining the size of individual zones. A compromise has often to be made on zonal homogeneity by selecting a predominant land-use activity. One criterion which determines a zone's size is the capacity of its road network. At a saturation level of 0·5 veh/person this limits the zonal population to about 5000 persons and for industrial zones to about 2500 persons. It should also be small enough to reduce any major errors in assuming that the zonal centroid is the centre of the road network which limits the area to about 1 km². The centroid is determined from either the trip generation or population density. However, the smaller the zones the more extensive will be the survey work to obtain statistically reliable data and correspondingly greater computing requirements in the subsequent model building phase. Study costs are also usually proportional to the square of the number of zones.

Zonal boundaries are determined by the transport network and act as a "watershed" of traffic generation enclosing the main public transport stops and corridor movements with the principal roads bisecting the zone. For some general planning purposes zones may require clustering into sectors and districts and conversely for detailed traffic analysis a breakdown of zones into a number of sub-zones which can include groups of shops, factories, hospitals, schools and stations. A further boundary consideration is the need for compatibility with the Registrar-General's census districts and other local authority areas. External areas often have a three-stage breakdown into regions, compatible with economic planning or standard regions, areas which include single or groups of counties and also zones to match the smaller local authority and district boundaries. The use of a grid system, based on the standard Ordnance Survey, permits the later reformulation of zones into any size and boundary configuration (8 figure references allow 100 m squares) and give complete interchangeability of data between different surveys and areas. An example of zoning and a numbering system are shown in Fig. 3.5.

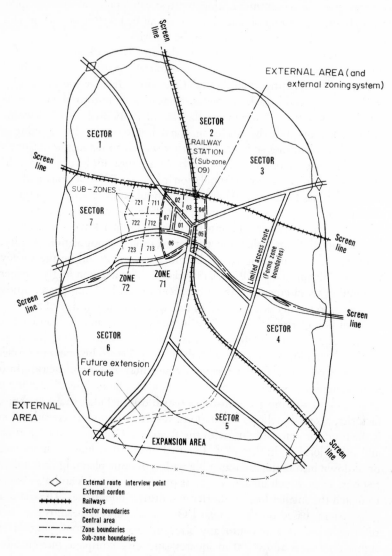

Fig. 3.5. Zoning.

TRAVEL CHARACTERISTICS

The first stage of the analysis is to form a matrix of the zone-to-zone flows, for the principal journey purposes and time periods as shown in Fig. 3.6. An aid to understanding the information is the diagrammatic

TABULATION CHART : MATRIX OF ZONE TO ZONE FLOWS

TIME PERIOD ------------ MODE ------------ PURPOSE ------------

To Zone \ From Zone	INTERNAL ZONES	Sub total	EXTERNAL CORDON POINTS	Sub total	Grand total
I N T E R N A L Z O N E S	TABULATION PROCEDURE 1. Sum sub zones - sub total of zone 2. Sum zones - sub total of sectors 3. Sum external cordon - sub total External - External, External - Internal, Internal - External. 4. Sum sectors and External cordon - Grand total of exchanges. 5. Sum totals across screen line and compare to count.				
Sub total					
E X T E R N A L C O R D O N P O I N T S					
Sub total					
Grand total					

FIG. 3.6. Tabulation of zone-to-zone flows by time period, mode and purpose.

representation of the movement pattern, for comparison with the base planning data, as shown in Fig. 3.7. Desire line charts, which show to scale by line thickness the numbers of journeys between zones, indicate by selected time periods the area's movement pattern. Other distinctive divisions can be made between major and minor flows, between zones and sub-zones and between central and other sectors. Traffic is assumed to be generated at zone centroids and sometimes cordon points, and movements are traced between origin and destination pairs. Other methods

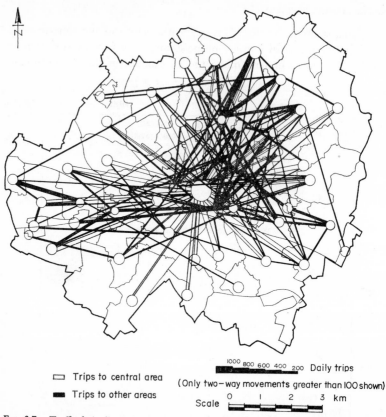

Trips to central area
Trips to other areas

1000 800 600 400 200 Daily trips

(Only two—way movements greater than 100 shown)

Scale   0   1   2   3   km

Fig. 3.7.   Traffic desire lines are shown by time (e.g. peak hour, 24 h by mode and purpose).
(Source: Coventry Transportation Study, Phase 1, 1968, City of Coventry.)

of illustrating traffic statistics and base social and economic information
is by the use of single and multiple dimensional pie and bar charts.
If the individual journeys between zones are summed as they cross each
side of a grid square, values of equal magnitude throughout the survey area
can be traced out by a contour line of equal desire line intensity. Various
measures including modes and journey time waitings can be similarly
traced out. Automatic methods of plotting trip data can be used with
computer graphical plotting equipment or oscilloscopes directly from the

input cards or tapes. On an oscilloscope a light trace is programmed to move between coordinates of the grid at a speed inversely proportional to the number of journeys between each pair of points and thus expose a photographic film to a greater or lesser extent. The result is a map plate of varying light intensities proportional to the traffic desire lines and flows.

From the build-up of information from many surveys certain general characteristics emerge, particularly for towns and cities of similar nature and size, which are of particular use to planning authorities and for the conducting of other local surveys. The principal factors which influence city travel are (i) population size, (ii) land use, (iii) type of city development, employment and growth, (iv) available transport systems, (v) population/vehicle ownership ratios and incomes, (vi) climate, (vii) journey length and (viii) purpose of journey. Some typical relationships are shown in Tables 3.3 and 3.4 and Figs. 3.8 to 3.10a, b.

TABLE 3.3.   DISTRIBUTION OF TRIPS BY PURPOSE (%)
(*London Traffic Survey*, Vol. 1, 1964, L.C.C.)

Purpose	Car-owning households	Non-car households
Work	38·7	60·6
Employer's business	2·6	1·1
Personal business	15·9	6·6
Entertainment	5·3	5·4
Sport	0·9	0·9
Social	7·3	7·0
Shopping (convenience)	5·4	6·5
Shopping (hard goods)	2·2	2·8
School	5·9	3·3
Miscellaneous (non-home based)	15·8	5·8

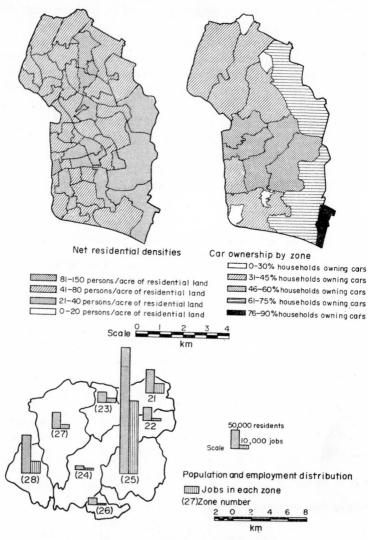

Net residential densities

Car ownership by zone

81–150 persons/acre of residential land
41–80 persons/acre of residential land
21–40 persons/acre of residential land
0–20 persons/acre of residential land

0–30% households owning cars
31–45% households owning cars
46–60% households owning cars
61–75% households owning cars
76–90% households owning cars

Scale 0 1 2 3 4
            km

(23)   21
(27)   22
(28)   (24)   (25)
        (26)

50,000 residents
10,000 jobs
Scale

Population and employment distribution
Jobs in each zone
(27) Zone number

2 0 2 4 6 8
        km

Fig. 3.8. Inventory of planning data.

Total internal city traffic is proportional to the urban population with work journeys forming the largest category and usually linearly related to total population. The proportion of work journeys by car mainly depends on car ownership levels, type of employment, availability of mass transit, parking policy and relative accessibility for different trans-

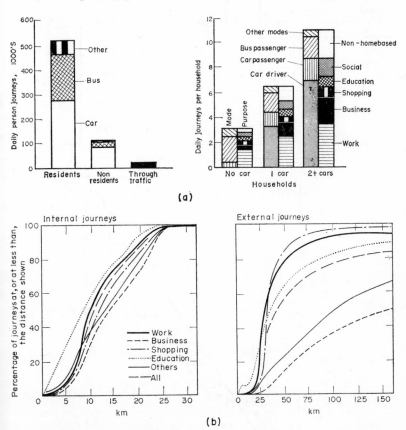

FIG. 3.9. (a) Daily trip characteristics of Coventry (Source: Coventry Transportation Study, Phase 1, 1968, City of Coventry).
(b) Journey lengths for internal and external journeys, West Midlands (West Midlands Transportation Study, Vol. 1. Freeman Fox Wilburn Smith and Associates, 1968).

Destination/Purpose	Year	Work	Shopping	Social	Home & other	Proportion of total trips
Solihull	1963	3·8	6·3	6·0	83·8	56·6
	1968	6·1	10·6	12·2	71·1	78·5
Birmingham	1963	60·0	5·9	6·8	27·4	20·6
	1968	55·4	7·6	7·6	29·4	16·1
Other areas	1963	14·1	14·3	20·0	51·6	22·8
	1968	28·1	3·1	15·6	53·2	5·5

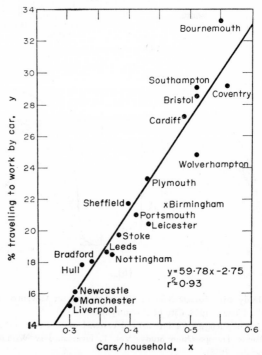

FIG. 3.10a. Travel to work by car, 1966. National sample census, 1966.

118

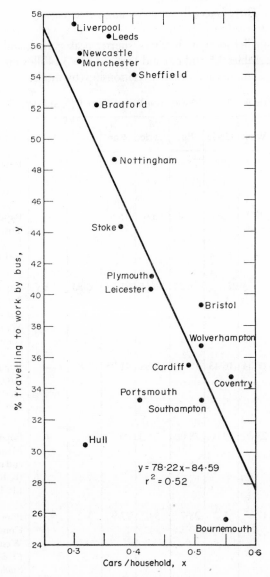

FIG. 3.10b. Travel to work by bus, 1966. National sample census, 1966.

E

port modes. There is usually an increasing percentage of walking and car trips with decreasing population size due to less well-developed public transport, smaller journey distances, shorter peak periods and less overall congestion. Tables 3.5 and 3.6 and Figs. 3.11 to 3.14 illustrate characteristics of travel modes and distance relationships by mode.

TABLE 3.5.   TRAVEL MODE FOR WORK TRIPS (%). SURVEYS 1962–66

All work trips in	Walk	Cycle	Bus	M/ cycle	Car	Train	Others	Town characteristics
Doncaster	16·7	19·9	38·6	6·4	18·4	–	–	Popn. 86,402. Yorkshire manufacturing town.
West Bromwich	22·9	13·4	42·2	5·6	15·9	–	–	Popn. 95,909. Town within W. Midland conurbation.
Solihull (high income zones only)	4·97		6·26	0·55	81·57	3·83	2·8	Popn. 96,010. Town on southern fringe of W. Midland conurbation.
Stevenage	11·34	16·43	19·78	8·88	41·75	–	–	Popn. 42,964 (100,000 future). Hertfordshire new town.
Northampton	23·00	19·00	28·00	30·00		–	–	Popn. 123,530. Manufacturing and market town. (R.R.L. Report LR 141.)
West Midlands	17·1	5·7	38·7	3·0	27·9	1·2	6·4	Popn. 2,400,000. Conurbation. West Midlands. (*Transportation Study*, Vol. 1, 1966.)

The proportion of centrally oriented trips is not only determined by size but by function and historical development. Some conurbations, which in the past existed as free standing towns have coalesced, retaining competitive centres with their own surrounding catchment areas. Generally the proportion of central area journeys to the total internal journeys decreases slowly with increasing city size. Travel to the centre is greatest from the innermost residential zones but diminishes with distance. Whereas bus travellers predominate near the centre, the proportion travelling by car for each distance band outwards increases as the level of public transport falls. This pattern is changed where high capacity rail systems serve outlying "dormitory" towns often developed around stations which serve as a focal point for local bus services. Car ownership reflects this pattern with fewer owners in the older and poorer inner areas where even garaging costs may be prohibitive. The high income

TABLE 3.6. MODES OF TRAVEL TO WORK AND JOURNEY TIME

| | Work journey catchment areas | | | | | |
| | Dagenham (Essex) | | | Bilston (Staffordshire) | | |
Travel mode to work	Num-bers (%)	Total time (minutes)	Mean time (minutes)	Num-bers (%)	Total time (minutes)	Mean time (minutes)
Walk	1322 (3·8%)	27,070	20·5	2554 (20·8%)	42,660	16·7
Ferry	506 (1·5%)	26,780	52·9	—	—	—
Cycle	2802 (7·9%)	77,650	27·7	1940 (15·8%)	33,760	17·4
Public transport	11,057 (31·3%)	469,375	42·5	3838 (31·3%)	128,200	33·4
Private motorised	19,579 (55·5%)	715,576	36·6	3940 (32·1%)	81·960	20·8
Totals and overall means	35,266	1,316,720	37·3	12,272	286,580	23·4

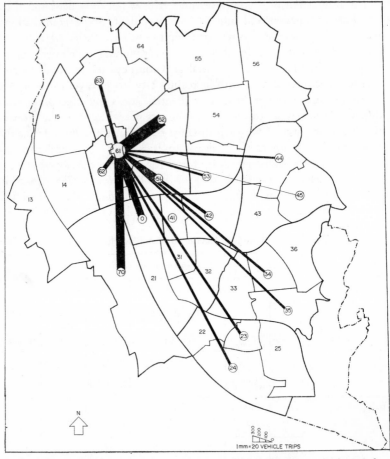

Fig. 3.11. Stevenage: internal commercial vehicle trips from High Street, 24-hr period.

populations may use taxis for internal journeys retaining their own cars for out-of-town journeys. Journeys by rail usually show an increase with distance from the centre.

By-passes serve the function of removing extraneous traffic from a town or a part of it, e.g. a central area. The percentage of rural to rural traffic which is by-passable falls as a proportion of the total internal journeys from

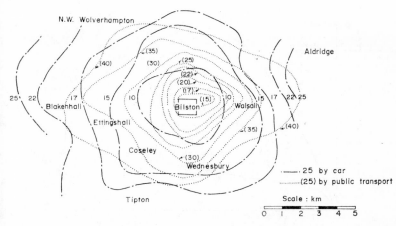

FIG. 3.12. Journey time isochrones to factory area Bilston, West Midlands conurbation (minutes).

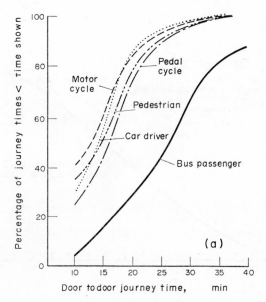

FIG. 3.13. (a) Journey time to work by different modes. (Source: F. R. Wilson, *Journey to Work.*)

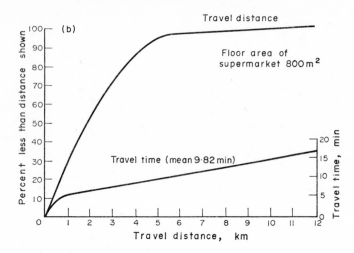

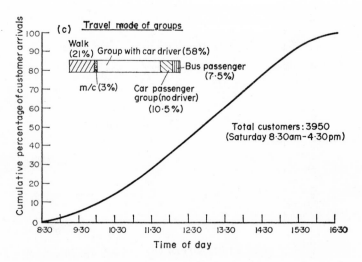

FIG. 3.13. (b) Journey distance and time distribution by shoppers to supermarket.
(c) Cumulative frequency curve of customer arrivals at supermarket.

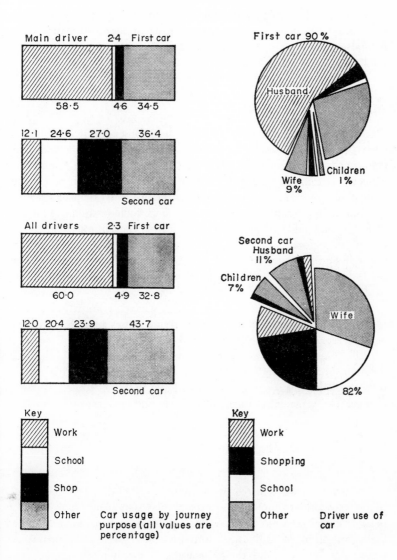

Fig. 3.14. First and second car use. (Source: L. W. Ackroyd and S. J. W. Druitt, A comparison of first and second car usage patterns, *Traffic Engineering and Control*, **9**, 1969.)

about 50% with a town population of 5000 to a few per cent in the largest cities. Similar principles apply to parts of towns in the creation of environmental and pedestrian areas and leads to the creation of a hierarchical road network serving definitive traffic functions.

ANALYSIS OF TRAVEL SURVEYS

Surveys are carried out for a variety of purposes and it is essential, if pertinent and useful results are to ensue, to avoid unnecessary and costly field work by settting down clear aims for the study with assumptions explicitly stated. Thereafter the process is one of identifying problems, evaluating constraints and setting down the principles of plan selection. The more important types of survey work include studies for traffic management, public transport, route selection, development and structure plans, regional and conurbation transportation, land-use surveys and research. Forecasting and strategic planning nearly always forms an essential feature of the work. The required accuracies and form of modelling used varies with the type of work and forecast period. As the forecast period lengthens so the band of uncertainty widens. Tomorrow's forecast is likely to be correct because the underlying causes and effects will not have changed measurably, whereas those for 20 years will certainly contain different socio-economic factors and attitudes may be very different. It is advisable for long forecast periods to provide interim reviews so that plans can be monitored and modified to accommodate change. The principal elements of a transportation survey are shown in Fig. 3.1.

TRAFFIC MODELS

The analyst seeks to develop, usually in a mathematical form, a model of the real world, i.e. in the case of travel models by identifying wherever possible causal relationships describing population behaviour, albeit by the aggregation of individuals into groups. Travel determinants are principally land use and the propensity of the individual to expend "effort" and resources to overcome spatial separation. Early nineteenth-century developments in social science first studied human interaction and location in a form analogous to Newton's law of gravitational attraction which equates the force (F) between masses m_1 and m_2 inversely to their distance apart (d) squared: $F = m_1 m_2 / d^2$. Early models took the form $M_{ij} = P_i P_j (d_{ij})^{-2}$ where M_{ij} is the market attraction of two towns with populations P_i and P_j sited at distances d_{ij} apart. Markets and trips are part of the same phenomenon and as a general proposition they can be studied in terms of their interactance, i.e. the product of attributes describing population, vehicle numbers, floor areas or retail trade, etc., and their separation in distance, time, effort or cost, etc.:

Thus $t_{ij} = K a_j g_i f(d_{ij})$

where $t_{ij} =$ the number of trips attracted between centroids of an attracting zone a_j and a generating zone g_i,

$f(d_{ij}) =$ is a function of the zonal separation and can be of a number of forms, e.g. $(d_{ij})^{-\alpha}$ where α ranges from 1 to 3 or as an exponential function $e^{-\alpha d_{ij}}$,

K is a constant for dimensional adjustment of the measures used in a_j and g_i; α is an empirically derived exponent.

TRIP GENERATION

(A trip is defined as a single journey made by an individual between two points by a specified mode of travel and for a defined purpose.) Differences in definition and the disaggregation of complex trip types creates difficulties of comparison of trip attributes between surveys. Usually multimode and purpose journeys are simplified into trips identified by a principal mode and purpose, ignoring intermediate stages and stops for secondary purposes. (Trips are often considered as generated by a particular land use and attracted to other specific land uses.) About three-quarters of all trips are home based, i.e. they arise or terminate at a residence. Non-home-based trips are mainly those between attracting land uses, e.g. from work to a restaurant.

(The number of trips arising in unit time, usually for a specified zonal land use, is called the trip generation rate.) It can also be estimated for a zone by aggregating the trip production rate of individual cars or households for the total numbers in each selected category. Both methods make use of the correlation between trips made and particular characteristics of an area. Typical independent variables applicable to zonal generation methods are the number of residents, employees, vehicles garaged or distance of zone from the central area. Trip production estimators are mean household income, residential density, numbers of persons and cars per household and rateable value. The general form of these models is a multiple regression equation as follows:

$$Y = a_0 + a_1 x_1 + a_2 x_2 + a_n x_n$$

where Y represents the number of trips specified in time and by purpose for a zone, or by car and household types in trip production methods,

$x_1, x_2 \ldots x_n$ are independent explanatory variables,

$a_0, a_1, \ldots a_n$ are constants generally derived by the method of least squares.

By selecting appropriate explanatory variables the dependent variable Y can be used as an estimator of trip rates for specific journey purposes such as work, personal business, social, shopping and education. Similar regression techniques can also be used to estimate the number of trips attracted to a zone with independent variables based on employment, density and output. Examples of trip characteristics are shown in Table 3.7 and Figs. 3.15 and 3.16.

TABLE 3.7.   CHANGES IN CAR OWNERSHIP AND ALL TRIP CATEGORIES FOR
HIGH INCOME HOUSEHOLDS IN SOLIHULL

House-hold size	Cars per household		Cars per person		Trips per household		Trips per person	
	1963	1968	1963	1968	1963	1968	1963	1968
1	0·25	0·33	0·25	0·33	2·25	2·33	2·25	2·33
2	1·02	1·30	0·51	0·65	6·21	5·63	3·11	2·88
3	1·22	1·66	0·41	0.56	8·92	9·17	2·97	3·06
4	1·55	1·75	0·39	0·44	10·49	13·08	2·62	3·27
5	1·77	1·67	0·35	0·23	14·91	19·67	2·98	3·93
6	1·60	2·00	0·27	0.33	16·20	13·67	2·70	2·28
	1·26	1·43	0·40	0·48	8·99	9·44	2·88	3·10

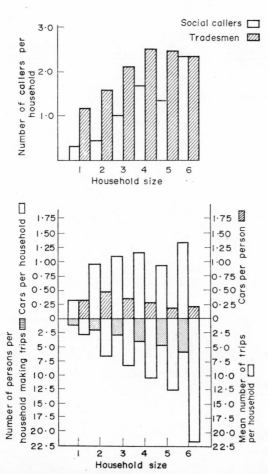

Fig. 3.15. Trip generation by persons and households for medium/high income residential estate borders of conurbation.

In the analysis, points of generation are usually considered as the home end (origins or destinations) of a home-based trip or the origin of a non-based trip. Attraction points are identified by trips made to work, and other purpose visits. By assigning suitable values to the independent

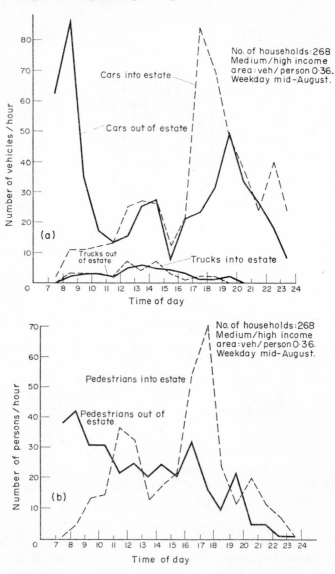

FIG. 3.16. Total movements into and out of estate by Cordon Survey: (a) by vehicular traffic, (b) by pedestrians.

variables of the regression equations forecasts can be made of the future trip ends for zones by either method.

An alternative method of deriving zonal trip generations, which partly overcomes the disadvantage of models derived from data whose relationships are assumed to be invariate in time, is Category Analysis. This method, developed by Wooton and Pick, is based on the well-established influence of car ownership, household structure and income on trip-making by households. They define six categories of household, three categories of car ownership and six income categories giving, in all, a possible total of 108 categories (6 x 3 x 6). Thus by assuming a trip rate for a limited number of households and incomes a forecast can be made for any future aggregation of household types.

The stages in the calculation of a future trip rate for a zone require an assumption about rates of income growth (g) and car purchasing growth (g_c) for the forecast period of (x) years. At present the relative cost of car purchase to income is growing more rapidly than total income growth but its stability as a predictor is open to doubt. A compound interest relationship is used to find the income growth factor from $f = (1 + g)^x$ where x is the forecast period in years. A car purchasing factor is similarly determined and hence current mean zone incomes and car purchasing income can be projected to their future values. A further questionable assumption is made in that the ratio of mean incomes to the standard deviation of incomes remains constant in time and to estimate the number of households in each income category an income distribution must be accepted, usually the gamma distribution.

Similar methods are used to distribute households by car purchasing incomes. The likelihood of car ownership by households is determined from a set of conditional probability functions, usually stratified by residential densities, into none, one and multi-car households. Binomial probability tables can be used to distribute the households of various sizes into categories based on the number of employed persons. Computer packages have been developed, such as the Synthetic Trip End Production (STEP) by Freeman Fox, Wilbur Smith & Associates, to apply the category analysis method to households and derive trip rates for the 108 categories for the forecast year. As a computational simplification it is usual to form two matrices, car ownership groups with household structure group and then with income group. Each contains row and column totals and initial cell values which are iteratively balanced to agree with row and column totals. Every separate household category is associated with a trip rate, derived from surveys of similar areas or obtained directly, but the method is based on the weak assumption that these trip rates remain stable in time with changes only arising from differences in employment, cars/household or income, i.e. households moving in status or composition from one category to another during the forecast period.

Trip production rates are usually categorised by purpose (e.g. work, business, education, shopping, social and non-home based) and by mode (e.g. drivers of cars and motor cycles, public transport passengers and other, mainly car, passengers). Thus, using these examples there are 18 purpose and mode combinations to be associated with each household category. There are many possible ways of estimating car owning households, either directly or indirectly, as in the case of category analysis, and of the future trip movements by both non-car owning and car owning households. However, the method of category analysis is widely used in the U.K.

TRIP ATTRACTION

Trip attractions are derived directly from zonal data or are calculated by applying attraction rates to categories of land use based, for instance, on the Standard Industrial Classification, floor area and employment densities. More refined methods can be developed by using sets of explanatory variables in a multiple regression equation. Typical classifications include primary industry, manufacturing, construction, utilities, retail, commerce, wholesale, professional, transport and employment centres in residential areas with a further breakdown into five or six categories of employees per hectare, e.g. 0–2.50, 2.50–5.00, 5.00–7.50, 7.50–10.00, 10.00–12.50 and over 12.50. Thus, using the above stratifications of land use and density, 60 categories result with each of which there will be 18 purpose and mode associated trip rates. The final stage of the trip generation phase is to derive the trip production and attraction vectors based on the trip ends. If data from other survey areas is being used to synthesise the trip movements they are calculated by multiplying each household in each category by the appropriate trip production rate from the data bank. It is usual in these cases to calibrate the model by conducting a small sample survey by home interviews of representative households in the survey area and then applying an adjustment factor of observed trips/synthesised trips to the model results. A further balancing factor has to be produced to ensure that the sums of productions and attractions are equal by adjusting the attractions strata to fit that of the productions strata, i.e. total productions/total attractions. The use of calibrations and adjustment factors, particularly where the differences are considerable, is a weakness of the process and a justification should be sought to check and explain differences. All the methods described are founded on the assumption that the desirability, necessity and social status of trip making will continue unchanged, relatively, for the forecast period.

TRIP DISTRIBUTION

Trip generation estimates the number and types of trips originating and terminating in zones. Trip distribution is the process of computing the number of trips between one zone and all others. A trip matrix is drawn up as shown in Fig. 3.17, with the sums of rows indicating the total number of trips g_i originating in zone i and the sums of columns the total number of destinations a_j attracted to zone j. The purpose of the procedure is to complete each cell entry t_{ij} so that the sums of rows and columns are as nearly equal as possible to the total future trip ends at origins and destinations. Generally trips should be distributed over the area proportionally to the attractiveness of activities and inversely proportional to the travel resistances between areas. A distribution is shown in Fig. 3.18. The choice of growth factor or synthetic distribution methods depends on such factors as the likely degree of change in land use and mobility over the projection period.

Originally a single growth factor was obtained for the whole survey area from the ratio Projected trips/Existing trips and all interzonal flows were multiplied by this value. The method of successive iterations was first introduced by Fratar to the problem of trip distributions, but other models which have been widely adopted are the Average Factor and Detroit Methods. However, the most frequently used in Britain is that of Furness, and an example of the iterative procedure is shown in Fig. 3.19.

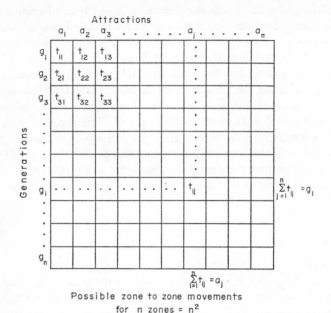

FIG. 3.17. Trip matrix of n zones.

Growth factor methods are generally simple and by using a combination of zonal expansion factors to multiply the existing trip pattern tend to maintain a *status quo* on land use and the travel networks. Iterative procedures are used to successively reduce the divergence of the growth factors from their initial values. After calculating each new cell entry t_{ij} in the distribution matrix it is unlikely that the row and column totals will agree with the desired totals of future trip ends and a balancing process will have to be introduced.

Trip distribution models have been extensively investigated by Evans who has shown that the Furness method is to be preferred as convergence is proved to a unique limit and it has simple computational qualities. Instead of averaging, the method employs multiplication, alternatively balancing rows and columns. The first step is to compute the growth-factor (F_i), thus $F_i = T_i'/T_i$, where T_i and T_i' are respectively the existing and future trips originating in zone i. The iterative stages are as follows:

$$t_{ij}' = t_{ij}F_i.$$

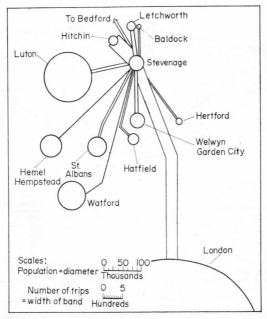

FIG. 3.18. Total daily trips from Stevenage to external destinations.

The balancing factor for the column multiplication is obtained such that $F_j = T_j'/T_j$ and $t_{ij}'' = t_{ij}'F_j$; T_j' is the column total after one iteration. Thus $T_{ij}' = r_i s_i T_{ij}$ and the process is to find r_i and s_j, the row and column multipliers to balance the totals.

Basically, the method consists of

$$T_{ij}^{r+1} = T_{ij}^r x_i, \text{ where } x_i = \frac{T_i'}{\sum_j t_{ij}^r} \text{ (row values)}$$

and $T_{ij}^{r+2} = T_{ij}^{r+1} y_i$, where $y_i = \dfrac{T_j'}{\sum_i t_{ij}^{r+1}}$ (column values).

The major disadvantages of growth methods are that zones which are to be developed by the design year contain no existing trips to be balanced against future trip totals and they do not take into account any changes in accessibility during the forecast period. Synthetic models have been developed to overcome some of these deficiencies.

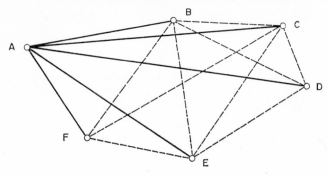

		A	B	Destinations C	D	E	F	Present origins	Future origins	Growth factors
	A	15	27	27	19	17	19	30	157	315	2·00
Origins	B		28	61	24	14	20	34	181	430	2·38
	C		18	22	33	11	19	25	128	366	2·86
	D		16	13	11	13	5	7	65	239	3·68
	E		12	19	18	6	2	4	61	98	1·60
	F		28	34	23	7	4	3	99	256	2·59
Existing destinations		157	176	128	68	59	103	691	—	2·52
Future destinations		309	418	367	246	96	268	—	1704	—
Growth factors		1·97	2·37	2·87	3·62	1·63	2·60	2·51	—	—

	1st iteration destinations A	B	C	D	E	F	2nd iteration destinations A	B	C	D	E	F	Total origins	Future origins	Growth factors
A	110	54	38	34	18	60	90	53	44	48	12	64	311	315	1·01
B	67	145	57	33	48	81	55	142	66	47	31	86	427	430	1·01
C	51	63	94	31	54	71	42	62	108	44	35	75	366	366	1·00
D	59	48	40	48	18	26	48	47	68	12	28	249	239	0·96
E	19	30	29	10	3	6	16	29	33	14	2	6	100	98	0·98
F	73	88	60	18	10	8	60	86	69	25	6	8	254	256	1·01

Mean Growth Factor: 0·995

Total
destinations 379 428 318 174 151 252
Future
destinations 309 418 367 246 96 268
Growth
factors   0·82 0·98 1·15 1·41 0·64 1·06
Mean Growth Factor: 1·01

All growth factors fall within the prescribed
limits: 0·95 ⩽ G.F. ⩽ 1·05

Fig. 3.19. Furness distribution method.

The Time Function Iteration (TFI) model was an extension of the Furness Growth Factor Method in which interzonal journey time was selected to represent accessibility in the distribution of trips. The distribution function is an index of zonal separations measured in journey time,

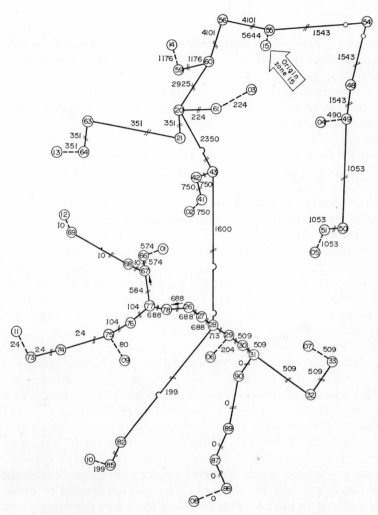

Fig. 3.20. Design year minimum path and assigned flows, Zone 15.

distance or generalised cost drawn up for the travel network. The journey time matrix for the base year is obtained from values, measured in a travel time study, inserted against each link (with or without junction penalties) of the network. The network consists of a series of links and nodes representing streets and intersections. Traffic from a zone originates at the zone centroid, and dummy links may have to be inserted from the centroid to the network with a value to represent the intrazonal travel time.

It is assumed that the trips between zones will be by the most direct or cheapest routes and, taking each zone in turn, a minimum path is traced out to all other zones to form a minimum path tree (example in Fig. 3.20). Several algorithms are available for finding minimum path trees for the design year network by adding new routes and zones as links and centroids and assuming travel times on them on an estimated speed/flow basis.

The Time Function Iteration makes use of the base year trip matrix and that of the interzonal journey times to produce a time function curve as a calibration device. For each cell of the matrix, a value is inserted from the curve appropriate to the interzonal travel time, and the Furness iterative procedure is applied to obtain the specified trip totals. However, a more suitable synthetic distribution model has been derived by applying the explanatory logic of the gravity model in fitting the travel interchange between spatially separated areas as a distribution model. Sample data are used to calibrate the resistance function used. Calibration reduces the differences between a local and generalised behaviour by balancing a synthetic matrix with that of an observed one in an iterative procedure. The basic equation $T_{ij} = KT_j\ T_i\ F(C_{ij})$ contains the resistance function $F(C_{ij})$ which is preferably measured as a generalised cost instead of a simple distance or time function. Generalised cost infers an inclusion of time, distance and some measure of comfort. The value of $F(C_{ij})$ is determined by plotting T_{ij}/T_iT_j for each trip length of (C_{ij}) and then forming a synthetic distribution matrix for comparison with the observed. A trip length frequency distribution is derived from the synthetic matrix for comparison with the observed. The values are brought to within acceptable limits by an iterative procedure, applied by calculating a new $F(C_{ij})$, as shown in Fig. 3.21.

Many alternative forms of the gravity model have been developed, the general form recommended by the Bureau of Public Roads, and widely used is a singly constrained model as follows:

$$T_{ij} = \frac{P_i \, A_j \, F(d_{ij}) \, K_{ij}}{\sum\limits_{j=1}^{J} A_j \, F(d_{ij}) \, K_{ij}}$$

where T_{ij} = number of trips generated in zone i and attracted by zone j,

P_i = total trips generated in zone i,

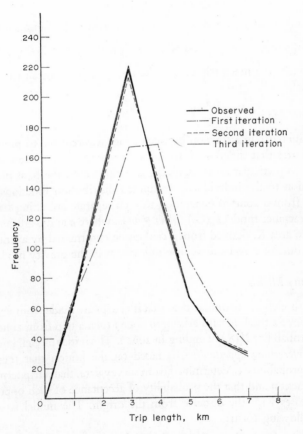

FIG. 3.21. Gravity model trip frequencies by journey time for successive iterations

A_j = total trips attracted by zone j,

$F(d_{ij})$ = an expression of the spatial separation between zones i and j,

K_{ij} = an adjustment factor accounting for any special zonal characteristics of i and j.

An equation of proportionality $T_{ij} \propto P_i A_j F(C_{ij})$ has been developed as an exponential model with $F(C_{ij}) = e^{-\alpha C_{ij}}$ and introducing balancing factors r_i and s_j such that T_{ij} is doubly constrained as follows:

$$T_{ij} = r_i\, s_j\, P_i\, A_j\, e^{-\alpha C_{ij}}$$

The r_i and s_j values are chosen so that the row and column totals are equal to the proportion of observations in each (i.e. $a_i = \sum_{j=1}^{J} T_{ij}$; $b_j = \sum_{i=1}^{I} T_{ij}$) and α so that the mean trip cost of the data equals the mean trip cost of the model.

Interactance Models

The difference in attraction between zones was referred to previously, and indicates that different distribution functions might better describe the trips to particular areas. A model is calibrated on the basis of fitting an equation to the individually computed distribution functions found for trips from a zone of generation to each separate attracting land use. The interactance model $F_k(C_{ij}) = ae^{-\beta C_{ij}} C_{ij}$, where a and β are constants, specific to area K, derived from a calibration constrained by average trip length, hours of travel and vehicle mileage, as in the gravity model.

Opportunity Models

These models are formulated so that if t_{ij} trips are made from zone i to zone j out of a total T_i trips arising in zone i then a trip from zone i will have a probability $P_r(S_j)$ of ending in zone j. The initial model, known as that of *intervening opportunities*, is based on the notion that there is a constant probability L, determined from survey data, that a trip terminates at an attraction and that the probability of acceptance of such opportunities decreases with the distance from the origin. The model is written in the following form:

$$T_{ij} = P_i \left\{ e^{-LA_o} - e^{-L(A_o + A_j)} \right\}$$

where L is the probability of the trip terminating at the zone under consideration, A_o is the number of attractions nearer in time to zone i than zone j, and A_j is the total of attractions in zone j. Trips are usually stratified by purpose types and the synthetic matrix is adjusted to fit the observed distribution in a calibration process similar to that of the constrained gravity model for the given trip length distribution and aggregate network travel time.

In the *competing opportunities model* the probability that any trip, randomly selected from zone i, will terminate in zone j is based on the number of attractions, spaced in time bands round zone i, which minimise travel time. However, the selection of time bands influences the results, and calibrating the future trip distribution matrix is difficult.

TRAFFIC ASSIGNMENT

The process of determining the route choice of travellers to a whole or part of a network is described as traffic assignment. The attractiveness of new facilities varies between those which divert traffic from adjacent streets to those which divert travel from other modes, or generate new traffic entirely (primary generation). Changes also occur in time because improvements in accessibility promote land-use changes, creating new development and future traffic (secondary generation). Furthermore, resulting from socio-economic changes, there is a growing vehicle ownership which leads to more vehicle travel (growth traffic).

Comprehensive surveys and projections seek to identify land use and traffic generation changes related to the proposed transport network. In practice, the assignment network used is only notionally representative of the principal features of the street and transport system. A link may represent a single route or a collection of parallel streets, with a homogeneity of traffic, and separated from adjoining links by a node, indicating a traffic interchange. Traffic is loaded from zones either at an interchange or at inserted dummy nodes. These sometimes have dummy links to represent the mean centre of generation and the mean travel time within the zone to the loading node. The turning movements at complex interchanges may also be represented by insertions in this way. Assignments are often further simplified to eliminate directional and intra-zonal movements and only include 24-h flows. Even where peak hour assignments are used they ignore the build-up of traffic within the network. Because of the nature of these limiting assumptions, the reality of the results must be subjected to close scrutiny and careful interpretation.

Diversion Curve Assignments

Diversion curves are constructed either from an analysis of "before and after" surveys of the use of alternative routes or logically developed from a consideration of driver behaviour. Explanatory variables used include travel distance, travel time and travel cost in the form of ratios, e.g. Distance (or Time) on New Route/Distance (or Time) on Old Routes, or time and distance differentials between new and old routes, e.g. Distance (or Time) on Old Route/Distance (or Time) on New Route. Only those parts of a route which are not common need be measured in the point of choice method. However, the values obtained for ratios by this method will differ from those obtained by using the full journey distances or times.

In applying diversion curves care must be taken to ensure that the basis of measurements is the same and that the locality and route conditions are similar. General refinements have sometimes included such factors as the length and proportion of the journey available by a new route. More elaborate curves have been developed to express the proportion of traffic expected to use a new route in terms of both distance and time (or speed) variables. These have the characteristics of assigning proportionately more traffic for greater distance and time saved, but also of assigning a proportion of the traffic where the saving is only made in either time or distance. Some drivers will always select the quickest route in time, irrespective of distances, while others will take the shortest distance notwithstanding increased journey time. Figure 3.22 illustrates the various types of diversion curve referred to above.

Several parallel routes can also be compared using diversion curves by nominating the shortest of them as a reference base to estimate the relative time and distance differences between them. The next stage is to determine from the values the proportion of diverted traffic from a diversion curve and then to weight each route according to the traffic assigned to it expressed as a fraction of that not assigned to it (multiple

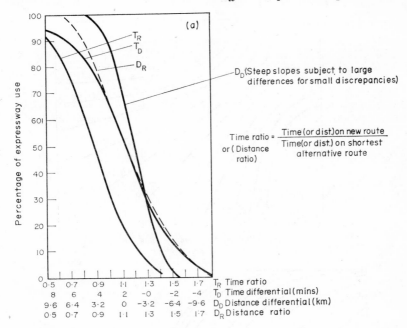

Time ratio = $\dfrac{\text{Time (or dist.) on new route}}{\text{Time (or dist.) on shortest}}$
or (Distance ratio) alternative route

0·5	0·7	0·9	1·1	1·3	1·5	1·7	T_R Time ratio
8	6	4	2	-0	-2	-4	T_D Time differential (mins)
9·6	6·4	3·2	0	-3·2	-6·4	-9·6	D_D Distance differential (km)
0·5	0·7	0·9	1·1	1·3	1·5	1·7	D_R Distance ratio

Percentage traffic diverted from other roads to motorways distance x away

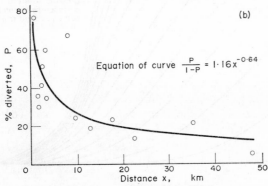

Equation of curve $\dfrac{P}{1-P} = 1\cdot16x^{-0.64}$

Fig. 3.22. Diversion curves: (a) mean curves of six U.S.A. expressways, (b) diversion to motorways (U.K.).

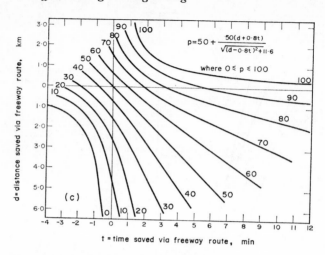

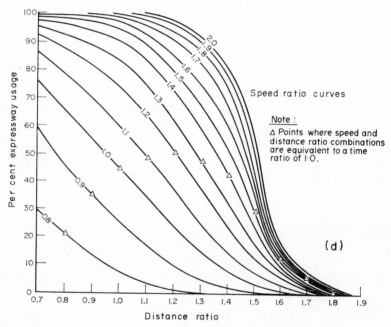

Fig. 3.22 (*cont.*). Diversion curves: (c) and (d), speed and distance ratios.

route assignment). Another model randomly selects a link time, for an origin and destination pair, from a journey time distribution which has the link time as its mean, and its mean deviation, derived from field measurements, increasing in value with decreasing link length. However, for simplicity it is accepted that once a link time has been selected from

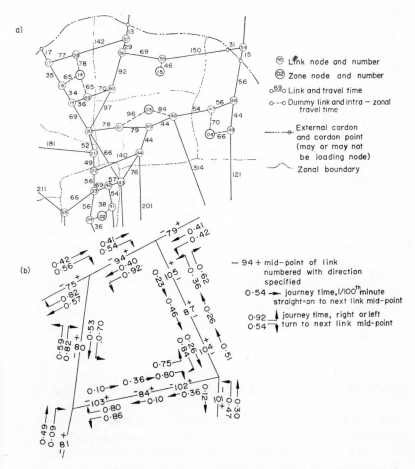

Fig. 3.23. Network descriptions: (a) traffic loaded at nodes from dummy links (additional nodes may be added at link nodes for this purpose), (b) nodes located between intersections for traffic loading and turning movements and times represented directly.

an origin its time remains constant thereafter, and all traffic is assigned on that basis. Where all the traffic from one zone to another is assigned to the shortest path (distance, time or cost), it is known as an *all-or-nothing assignment*.

Junction delays can be allowed for directly in the link time, or can be separately included by introducing weighted turning penalties for all movements which incur delay. Because of the coarseness of most assignment procedures such refinements do not necessarily discriminate sufficiently to be worth while.

Network Assignment

Major changes in the network or in future trip patterns are most suitably studied comprehensively in a network assignment as shown in Fig. 3.23 which converts all interzonal movements into traffic flows on the existing or future private and public transport networks. An origin and destination table, which is usually derived as passenger movements, is converted to vehicles or, often, pcus. If productions and attractions have been used they also have to be transformed into an origin and destination tabulation. Also included in the road traffic assignment will be the commercial vehicle movements and traffic having an external origin or destination, or both.

All interzonal movements are loaded onto minimum path trees, starting at the destinations and working back to the origins. The volumes on each tree are finally combined to give the network loading of every link for annual average 24 h and peak hour flows, thus representing the desired travel paths between all zones (desire assignment), but no account has been taken of the relationship between speed and flow. This fundamental disadvantage of the "all or nothing" assignments is partly overcome by capacity restraint methods, although overloaded links, when compared to initially ascribed capacities, can be relieved by reassigning some traffic to underloaded links by judgement. Alternatively additional facilities or improved public transport can be provided. However, in some instances it may be necessary to review the attractions or generations of zones contributing to the overloading by restructuring the basic land-use plan.

Most capacity restraint methods are iterative and allow street or system capacities to influence the distribution, at various stages, of link flows. This procedure is effected by adjusting the speed on a link and hence changing the travel time in relation to the assigned flow at that point in time. The less loaded a link is at a particular stage, then the more the speed is raised to attract traffic away from all the overloaded links. These are, conversely, made less attractive by speed reductions. Some capacity restraint methods use incremental loading, recalculating speeds and shortest routes until the whole of the traffic has been allocated. Another method, suggested by Smock in H.R.B. Bulletin 347, initially assigns all the traffic to the quickest routes between origin and destination pairs and is based on preset speed values for all the network elements. In the next stage the ratio of assigned flow to practical capacity of a link is calculated; this value is then used to compute a new travel time for each link. Hence, a new set of shortest routes can be found for all trips between zonal pairs. The relationship used to adjust link travel times is as follows:

$$t(i) = e^{\{R(i)-1\}} . t(o)$$

where $t(i)$ = travel time on link after the ith iteration,

$R(i)$ = the ratio of average assigned volume to capacity for all iterations; e.g. $q(i)/C$; where $q(i)$ is the link flow after the ith iteration and C is the design capacity of the link.

$t(o)$ = original travel time on link (tabulated values for standard route types).

At each iteration the flows are divided between all the shortest routes generated and a new travel time is computed for the average assigned link flow at each pass. The iteration continues until changes in the link flows and travel times have converged to a preset value.

Network checks are made in assignments to ensure that longer journeys are being made on the primary roads, and network efficiencies are investigated by comparing total passenger hours and the average journey times by different modes. Because of the many simplifying assumptions behavioural distortions occur and the results, even from the more costly capacity restraint methods, must be treated with reservation.

Public Transport Assignments

Travellers are usually assigned to the quickest or least cost route between origin and destination pairs, but in this instance routes and services are scheduled. Additionally, a distribution of waiting times is required, besides walking and transfer times. The earliest public transport assignments were largely developed from highway programmes for private

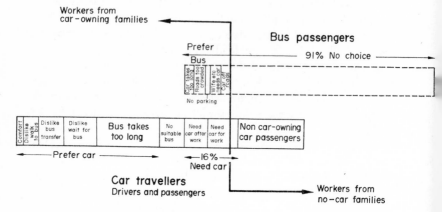

Fig. 3.24. Car ownership and journey to work. (Source: 1964 journey-to-work survey; sample size 11,680 workers. City of Coventry.)

car travellers by substituting waiting times for turning penalties. However, purpose built routines are now available, such as in the *Public Transport Network Development Manual* (Alan M. Voorhees and Associates) and *An Explanation of the Transient Algorithm* (Research Memorandum No. 198, G.L.C.).

MODAL CHOICE

While the determination of mode use is an essential requirement of transportation planning, it is not yet adequately handled in the process. If the factors perceived by a traveller are seen to be equal between modes (i.e. perceived "costs" are equal), then it is equally likely that either mode will be chosen. However, irrespective of costs, some travellers must use a particular mode and are considered to be "captive" to that mode, as shown in Fig. 3.24. In a single-car owning household the vehicle must be still available if a different trip is to be made by a car.

It has been difficult to effectively incorporate modal choice in the transport models because its influence overlays the whole process, from the generation of journeys to assignment. However, for simplicity, it has often been considered at the trip generation stage of the drawing up of two separate strata based on public and private travellers allocated on journey purpose and mode availability at the origin. No account is effectively taken of the supply of facilities or their operating conditions, i.e. network and congestion effects. Choice can also be made during generation as on the category analysis. If the split is made after distribution, their cost, levels of service and journey time can be considered in the model, and distortions eliminated by iteration.

Many models have been developed, usually based on empirical studies, leading to diversion curves, multiple regression and discriminant analysis using probability or least squares techniques to fit the observed data. The London Traffic Survey extended the 108 household categories by adding accessibility groups (low, medium and high) for bus and train levels of service indices for a zone. The procedure, adopted by T.R.C. in the Washington Study, compiled 80 categories of trips and trip makers (4

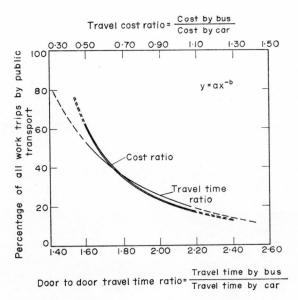

Fig. 3.25a. Diversion curves of work trips to Coventry employment centres (F. R. Wilson, *Journey to Work*, Maclaren).

categories of car ownership, 5 of income and 4 for service ratios) separating work and non-work journeys. Diversion curves were constructed to assign the public transport users as a function of travel time, cost and service ratios, stratified by the traveller's economic status. The relative convenience of modes was assessed by the service ratio, including excess time; the ratio of excess time spent on a public transport journey to that of the car was taken as the relative convenience factor in the service ratios. Public transport excess time included walking, waiting and transfer time while that for the car was the time spent walking to and from parking areas and parking time. Examples of modal choice diversion curves, journey time regressions and bus flows are shown in Figs. 3.25 and 3.26.

The Local Government Operational Research Unit (LGORU) model determines the probability of using a car from the following expression:

$$P(i) = \frac{e^z + b_o}{1 + e^z + b_o}$$

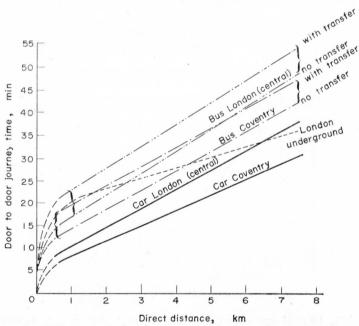

FIG. 3.25b. Regression lines for journey times by distance for selected modes.

where z is determined from three time differences, walking (x_1), waiting (x_2) and in vehicle time (x_3), and a cost difference (x_4) calibrated for a number of towns. Similarly, b_o is a general constant for the town, e.g.

$$Z_L = 0 \cdot 07x_1 + 0 \cdot 037x_2 + 0 \cdot 023x_3 + 0 \cdot 026x_4 \quad \text{and} \quad b_o = -1 \cdot 436.$$

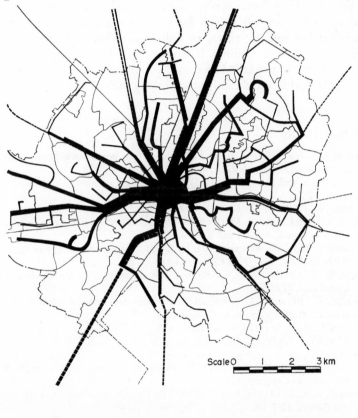

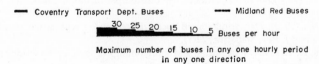

Fig. 3.26. Coventry: morning peak period bus flow, 1967. (Source: Coventry Transportation Study, Phase 1, 1968, City of Coventry.)

Kain developed an economic model primarily based on residential location and the trip-making behaviour of the household, or the individual, after observing that there is a direct relationship between accessibility and land values. Families were distributed in accordance with the location of house types and the time and costs of transportation. The mode of transport chosen for the work journey also influences residential location. However, an individual's choice of space needed varies as do tastes in facilities. Regression techniques are again used in this econometric model. Models used for modal split must take into account both choice and captive trip-making individuals.

FURTHER READING

ALLISON, J. R. *et al.* (1970) A method of analysis of the pedestrian system of a town centre. *Town Planning Institute*, **56**(8).

BEESLEY, M. E. and KAIN, J. F. (1965) Forecasting car ownership and use. *Urban Studies*, **2**(2).

BLUNDEN, W. R. (1971) *The Land-Use Transport System*. Pergamon Press.

BRIDLE, R. J. and CLEAVY, S. M. (1969, 1970) Accessibility and traffic synthesis. *Instn. Highway Engnrs.*, **xvi**(10) and **xvii**(6).

BROADBENT, T. A. and MACKINDER, I. H. (1973) Transport planning and structure planning. *Traff. Engng. and Control*, **14**(11).

BURNS, W. (Chairman) (1972) *New Roads in Towns*. Report of the Urban Motorways Committee, H.M.S.O.

CLARK, C. and PETERS, G. H. (1965) The 'intervening opportunities' method of traffic analysis. *Traffic Quarterly*, **xix**, January.

COBURN, T. M., BEESLEY, M. E. and REYNOLDS, D. J. (1960) *The London–Birmingham Motorway: Traffic and Economics*. Road Research Technical Paper No. 46. H.M.S.O.

DAVIES, E. W. and JACOMB, A. W. (1971) *Transportation Aspects of Structure Planning*, Pub. Works Congress, 8.

DOUGLAS, A. A. and LEWIS, R. J. (1970/1) Trip generation techniques. *Traff. Engng. and Control*, **12**(7–10).

EVANS, A. W. (1970) Some properties of trip distribution methods. *Trans. Research*, **4**(1).

EVANS, A. W. (1973) The estimation of road traffic flow by registration number observation. *J. Roy. Stats. Soc.*, **22**(1).

FAIRTHORNE, D. B. (1964) Description and shortcomings of some urban road traffic models. *Operational Research Quarterly*, **xv**(1).

FRATAR, T. J. (1954) Vehicular trip distribution by successive approximation. *Traffic Quarterly*.

FURNESS, K. P. (1965) Time function iteration. *Traff. Engng. and Control*, **7**(7).

GOOD, G. E. (1972) A gravity distribution model. *Traff. Engng. and Control*, **13**(9).

HANKIN, B. D. and Wright, R. A. (1958) Passenger flow in subways. *Operational Res. Quarterly*, **9**(2).

HEANUE, K. E. and PYEN, C. E. (1963) A comparative evaluation of trip distribution procedures. *Publ. Rds.*, **34**(2).

HEWING, R. B. and MOHMAN, M. L. H. (1969) *An Explanation of the Transient Algorithm.* Research Memorandum, Department of Highways and Transportation, Greater London Council.

HIGHWAY RESEARCH BOARD. *Traffic Assignment*, H.R. Record 6; *Travel Forecasting*, H.R. Record 38; *Origin and Destination: Methods and Evaluation*, H.R. Record 114; *O. and O. Technology*, H.R. Record 250; *Choice of Travel Mode and Considerations in Travel Forecasting*, H.R. Record 369; *Transportation Demand and Analysis Techniques*, H.R. Record 392; *N.C.H.R.P. Data Requirements for Metropolitan Transportation Planning*, Report 120, Washington.

H.M.S.O. (1960) *The London–Birmingham Motorway; Traffic and Economics*. Road Research Technical Paper No. 46.

LAMB, G. M. (1970) Introduction to transportation planning. *Traff. Engng. and Control*, **11**(11–12) and **12**(1–4).

LANE, R., POWELL, T. J. and PRESTWOOD SMITH, P. (1971) *Analytical Transport Planning*. Gerald Duckworth & Co., London.

L.G.O.R.U. (1968) *Modal Split*. The Local Government Operational Research Unit, Reading.

MALTBY, D. (1970) Traffic at manufacturing plants. *Traff. Engng. and Control*, **11**(2).

MARTIN, B. V., MEMMOTT, F. W. and BONE, A. J. (1961) *Principles and Techniques of Predicting Future Demand for Urban Areas Transportation*. Department of Civil and Sanitary Engineering, Massachusetts Institute of Technology, June.

MAYER, J. K., KAIN, J. and WOHL, M. (1965) *The Urban Transportation Problem*. Harvard Univ. Press, Massachusetts.

McINTOSH, P. T. and QUARMBY, D. A., Mathematical Advisory Unit, M.A.U. Note 179. *Generalised Costs and the Estimation of Movement Costs and Benefits in Transport Planning*. Department of the Environment.

MILLS, L. S. (1972) *Implementing the Report of the Urban Motorways Committee*. Department of the Environment, Circular 56/72. H.M.S.O.

MINISTRY OF HOUSING AND LOCAL GOVERNMENT (1970) *Development Plans—a Manual on Form and Content*. H.M.S.O.

MISHAN, E. J. (Ed.) (1971) *Cost Benefit Analysis*. George Allen & Unwin.

NEWLAND, R. M. (1971) Transport studies in Staffordshire—data collection and traffic models. *Traff. Engng. and Control*, **12**(11) and **13**(1).

NICHOLLS, B. A. (1971) The time function iteration trip distribution method. *Traff. Engng. and Control*, **13**(5).

OI, W. Y. and SHULDINER, P. W. (1962) *An Analysis of Urban Travel Demands*. Northwestern Univ., Chicago.

OLDER, S. J. (1968) Movement of pedestrians on footways in shopping streets. *Traff. Engng. and Control*. **10**(4).

OVERGAARD, K. R. (1966) *Traffic Estimation in Urban Transportation Planning*. Danish Academy of Technical Sciences, Copenhagen.

PAILING, K. B. and SOLESBURY, W. (1970) The future proportions of non-car owning and multi-car owning households. *Traff. Engng. and Control*, **12**(5).

PREST, A. R. and TURVEY, R. (1965) Cost benefit analysis, a survey. *The Economic Journal*.

PRICE, W. L. (1971) *Graphs and Networks*. Butterworth, London.

PUBLIC ADMINISTRATION SERVICE, CHICAGO (1959, 1960, 1962) *Chicago Area Transportation Study*. Vols. 1, 2 and 3. U.S.A. (see also Transportation studies of all major British cities).

QUARMBY, D. A. (1967) Travel mode for journey to work. *J. Transport Econ. and Policy*, **1**(3).

RICHARDS, M. G. and WILLIAMS, G. (1967) City of Worcester study techniques. *Traff. Engng. and Control*, **9**(3) and (4).

SCHWARZ, H. (1963) Methods for determining trip distribution. *Traff. Engng. and Control*, **4**(11).

STAIRS, S. W. (1966) *Bibliography of the Shortest Route Problem*. L.S.E. Transport Theory Network Unit.

TANNER, J. C. (1961) *Factors affecting the Amount of Travel*. Road Research Technical Paper No. 51. H.M.S.O.

TAYLOR, M. A. (1968) Studies of travel in Gloucester, Northampton and Reading. RRL Report LR 141. The Road Research Laboratory.

U.S. DEPT. OF COMMERCE, Bureau of Public Roads, *Procedure Manuals*, 1958. 2A *Origin/Destination and Land-Use*. 2B *Conducting a Home Interview Origin and Destination Survey. Calibrating and Testing a Gravity Model for any sized Urban Area*, 1965. Traffic Assignment Manual, 1964, Washington.

VARIOUS. *Transportation Studies in Very Big Cities*, P.T.R.C. Symp. Proc., 1969; *Public Road Transport Analysis*, P.T.R.C. Symp. Proc., 1970; *Urban Traffic Model Research*, Symp. Proc. 1970 and Seminar Proc. 1972.

WARNER, S. L. (1962) *Stochastic Choice of Mode in Urban Travel: a Study in Binary Choice*. Northwestern University Press.

WILSON, F. R. (1967) *Journey to Work*. Maclaren & Sons, London.

WOOTON, H. J. and PICK, G. W. (1967) A model for trips generated by households. *J. Transport Econ. and Policy*, **1**(2).

Direct Interview

Individuals parking in the area are interviewed about their origin and destination and the purpose for parking. This information, together with the length of time the car was parked, enables the major parking characteristics to be determined.

The survey area is divided into a number of sections, each being of such a size that it can be covered in one day by the available team of interviewers. Interviewers are given a specific length to keep under surveillance, and are responsible for recording each parking incident in that length. A brief preliminary study will determine a suitable length of kerbside for each interviewer and is based on parking density and turnover, but in typical city centre parking conditions is not likely to exceed 100 m.

Off-street parking facilities are covered by interviewers stationed at the entrance, who question each entering or leaving driver. Such facilities are likely to be used by long-term parkers and to generate high morning and evening peaks requiring a larger number of interviewers than during the rest of the day. Again the conditions must be assessed by a preliminary investigation.

For each vehicle the interviewer records the following information:
1. Registration number: for identification purposes.
2. Vehicle classification: car, taxi, lorry, etc.
3. Nature of the parking: legal, illegal, kerbside, off-street, garage, etc.
4. Time at which vehicle stopped.
5. Time at which vehicle started.

Then, after polite questioning of the driver, he further records:
6. Last point at which driver made an essential stop.
7. The driver's destination after he has left the vehicle.
8. The purpose for the stop: shopping, work, business, off-loading, etc.

A simple interview form, suitable for recording this information, is shown in Fig. 4.2, completed as an example. The items marked with an asterisk are for subsequent entry in the office. Blocks on the right-hand side of the form are used in coding the information for transfer to punched cards or tape for analysis. Each batch of forms used by an interviewer should have a cover form giving the location at which he carried out the interview, his name, the date and other information common to all his forms.

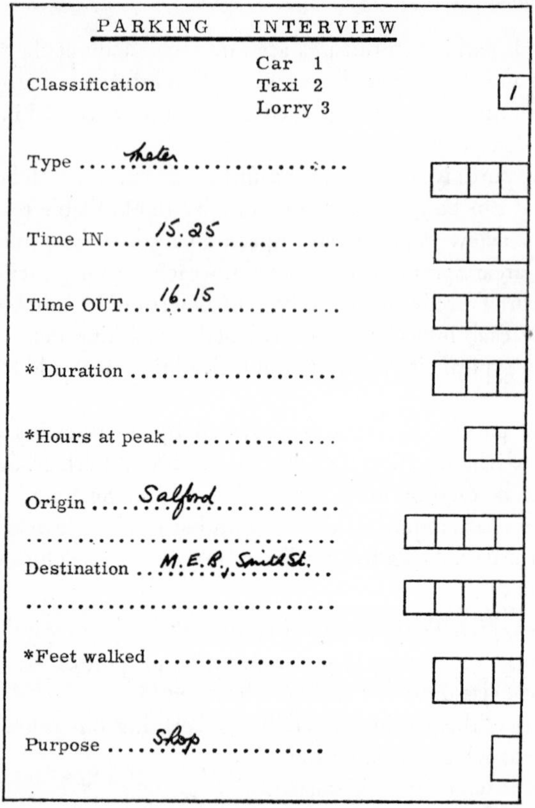

PARKING INTERVIEW

Classification — Car 1, Taxi 2, Lorry 3 — 1

Type ....Meter.......

Time IN.......15.25.......

Time OUT.......16.15.......

* Duration ....

*Hours at peak ....

Origin ....Salford.......

....

Destination .......M.E.B., Smith St.......

....

*Feet walked ....

Purpose ....Shop.......

FIG. 4.2. Parking interview form.

The direct interview provides the core of the parking study, revealing the parking characteristics, the use being made of the facilities and the locational demands.

Patrol Survey

The study area is divided into sections sufficiently small for each to be toured once every half-hour, hour or other suitable interval. On each patrol the number of parked vehicles in the section is counted, thus revealing the parking accumulation for the hours of the survey. If, in addition to counting the parked vehicles, the enumerator records the registration number of each vehicle it is possible to see for how many trip intervals a vehicle is parked and, hence, obtain information on parking duration.

The sections may be patrolled on foot or, in the case of kerbside parking, by car. Each section must be of such a size that the enumerator can cover its length and return to the start of the section in the selected trip interval. If it is possible to divide the area so that different sections complete a circuit, the time used in returning to the beginning of a section can be eliminated, enabling longer sections to be used, as illustrated in Fig. 4.3. The enumerator, on reaching the end of his section, carries on into the next section instead of returning to the start. When the patrols are completed, the records of the several enumerators have to be collated before analysis. Patrolling by car enables a longer section to be covered in the same trip interval, but extra people are needed. For making a simple count, one enumerator, together with the driver, is sufficient and, assuming a typical city centre, the car may be driven at the speed traffic conditions permit. The enumerator, using suitably mounted tally counters for each vehicle category, records the number of parked vehicles. If registration numbers are being noted, it is necessary to have two enumerators, one calling out the registration numbers and classification and the other recording them, unless a tape recorder is used. The speed of the vehicle, with normal close parking, should not exceed 15 km/h.

Selecting a suitable trip-interval depends upon the amount of time, money and labour available to make the survey, and upon the likely characteristics of the parked vehicles. Any vehicle which has arrived, parked and then been driven away between successive visits of the observer will be missed, and a long trip interval, although saving in survey time and analysis, will consequently overlook a proportion of short-term parkers. Preliminary surveys, or knowledge of the area, will indicate suitable trip intervals. Where short-term parking is likely, as in shopping streets, 30 min is a commonly used interval, and where parking is predominantly long-term, as in back streets and off-street parks, a trip interval of 1 h or even 2 h is usually suitable.

Fig. 4.3. Patrol survey.

Assessment of Suppressed Parking Demand

The techniques of study so far described are all associated with the vehicle. They can reveal relevant statistics concerning parking use, but they cannot reveal parking demand that is suppressed due to insufficient facilities. Estimating this suppressed demand requires market research techniques involving interviewing samples of the population. Transportation surveys can usefully include questions on parking but, to obtain data statistically satisfactory for use in a small area, large samples are normally required.

An alternative technique is to interview users of the area by sampling on footpaths and at entrances to shops, restaurants, hotels, cinemas, theatres and in offices and other places of work. Figure 4.4 summarises the results of a survey of workers in various office premises in the centre of a large British city. The difference between the present and desired uses represents the demand suppressed due to lack of parking accommodation.

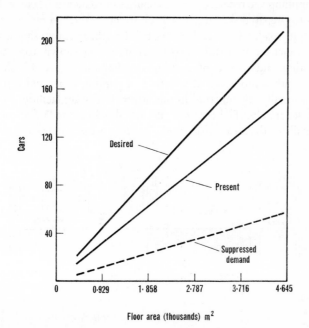

FIG. 4.4.   Car use by office employees.

Survey of Existing Facilities

Parking surveys must necessarily include an inventory of the space available in the area where parking is possible or where it would be possible with suitable development. The inventory should detail the type of parking, whether street or off-street, using all, or some, of the subdivisions shown below:

(i) Location and control: street parking—kerbside, unilateral, bilateral, parallel, and oblique parking; off-street parking—open space, covered parking, ramp and type, mechanical, layout of stalls, and entrance and exit arrangements; private or public.

(ii) Time restriction: duration and restrictions by time of day; free and metered, and rates charged.

In compiling the record of street facilities the data can be entered in the field on to prepared sketch plans. Each street is sketched on graph paper as a straight road, true to scale as regards length, and, by using a suitable key, the exact location and type of parking can be shown, together with the location and nature of parking restrictions. Figure 4.5 shows an example with a more varied selection of parking types and restrictions than is normally encountered in one street. Off-street facilities should be detailed separately. The location of each should be recorded on a plan with details of the area, capacity, the parking pattern, entrances, exits and charges.

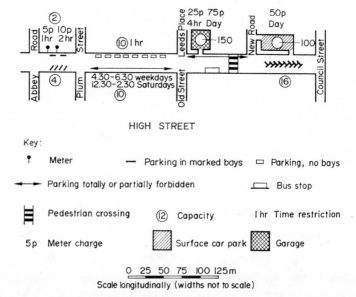

Fig. 4.5.   Parking surveys—completed field sheet showing existing parking facilities.

The parking inventory, together with the details of restrictions, enables the theoretically available space hours of parking to be evaluated. Depending on the ratios of turnover of parking, at the different facilities, the available space hours can be determined for comparison with the demand revealed by the parking use study.

PARKING CHARACTERISTICS

Because parking surveys in Great Britain have not been centrally collated, it is more difficult to assess the national parking characteristics in the way that has been done, for instance, in the U.S.A., by the Bureau of Public Roads who issue the *Parking Guide to Cities*. However, U.K. parking characteristics are similar in form to those of the U.S.A., but differ in magnitude. For instance, they agree that the average number of cars parked in the central area of a city or town per thousand of population decreases with increased size, but the actual number of vehicles parked per thousand population is still lower in this country. Due to this similarity, it is considered justifiable to use U.S. data alongside United Kingdom information when discussing characteristics and, in any event, may be looked upon as upper values which may be attained at some future date.

Parking Measurements

The major items of measurement used in parking surveys are:

(i) Parking accumulation is the number of parked vehicles in an area at any specified moment and can be divided into journey purpose categories, as shown in Fig. 4.6. The integration of the parking accumulation curve, over a specified period, determines the parking load in vehicle hours per specified time period.

(ii) Parking volume defines the number of vehicles involved in a parking load (i.e. vehicles per specified time period, usually per day). The time a vehicle spends parked, in minutes or hours, is the parking duration.

(iii) Parking turnover is a rate of use of parking spaces, and is obtained by dividing the parking volume by the number of parking spaces for a specified time period.

(iv) Parking index is another measure to determine the use of a street length and is expressed as a percentage of the theoretically available 6 m lengths of kerb space actually occupied by parked vehicles.

Parking Accumulation

Figure 4.7 shows characteristic accumulation curves for the central

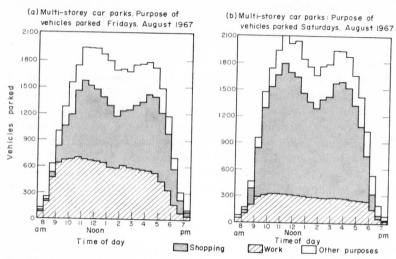

FIG. 4.6.   The use of multi-storey parking space in Coventry (Coventry Transportation Study: Report on Phase 1, 1968, City of Coventry).

area of Coventry. The cordon accumulation curve rises steeply between 8 a.m. and 9 a.m. with the entry into the area of people going to work. It continues to rise, but less steeply later as incoming workers are replaced by shoppers and those engaged on other journeys. The curve reaches a peak approaching mid-day, after which the accumulation starts to decrease as some people leave the area during the lunch period. Between 1 p.m. and 2 p.m., the curve starts to rise again with the return of workers from lunch, and the entry into the area of fresh shoppers. The afternoon generally attracts more visitors than the morning and the accumulation peak for the whole day is often reached between 2.30 p.m. and 4 p.m. After this time the major exodus from the area starts as people return home and the accumulation declines. If the area contains evening entertainment facilities there may well be a minor peak later as people return to the area. The lunch-time dip in accumulation is most pronounced in small towns, decreasing as town size increases, and is unlikely to be present at all where population exceeds 500,000. The figure also shows the effects of changes in parking charges.

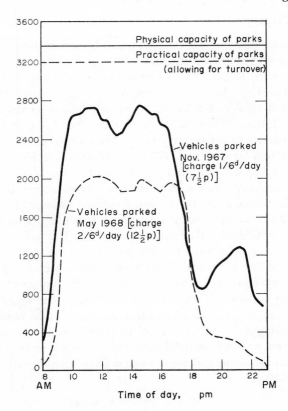

Fig. 4.7. Coventry central area: vehicles parked in public car parks (Coventry Transportation Study: Report on Phase 1, 1968, City of Coventry).

The parking accumulation is similar to the cordon accumulation but is necessarily below it by an amount representing the vehicles in motion in the area. Figures show that some 15–30% of vehicles, accumulated in an area, are on the move at times of peak accumulation, and a larger proportion when the accumulation rate is greater (see Fig. 4.1). The integration of the parking accumulation curve, over a period of time, gives the parking load for the period and, hence, the average accumulation. The ratio of peak-to-average accumulations is a measure of the efficiency with which facilities are used.

Parking Duration

The main duration characteristics are to be seen in Figs. 4.8 and 4.9 and Table 4.1 (based on U.S. data).

Figure 4.8(a) shows typical duration curves and compares street with off-street parking. As would be expected, the duration of street parking incidence is considerably less than that of off-street parking. Whereas 63% of all street parking had a duration less than 1 h, only 12% had a similar duration for off-street parking. The median duration is approximately 40 min for street and 140 min for off-street, or 3·5 times greater.

Figure 4.8(b) differs from Fig. 4.8(a) in that the latter refers to all parking incidence whereas the former is concerned with the numbers of vehicles parked at any one instant. As stated previously, 63% of street parking incidence had a duration less than 1 h, but Fig. 4.8(b) shows that only 30% of vehicles parked stayed less than 1 h. This indicates, in effect, that 70% of occupied street parking places are not in use for short-term parking and that, if the vehicles occupying those places were parked off-street, many more spaces would be available for a greater number of short-term parkers. This is characteristic of situations where off-street parking is inadequate and unattractive, and where time restrictions on street parking are poorly enforced, or pricing policies are unrealistic. The changes resulting from the introduction, over a number of streets, of restrictions limiting parking to a maximum of from 1 to 2 h are shown in Fig. 4.10.

TABLE 4.1. PARKING DURATION

Population group (thousands)	Length of time parked, h			
	Shopping and business	Work	Other	All purposes variation
<50	0·6	3·3	0·9	1·2
50 to 250	0·9	3·8	1·1	1·5
250 to 500	1·2	4·8	1·4	1·9
>500	1·5	5·2	1·6	2·6

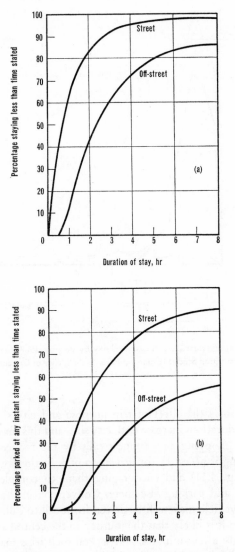

Fig. 4.8. Cumulative frequency curves of street and off-street parking durations.

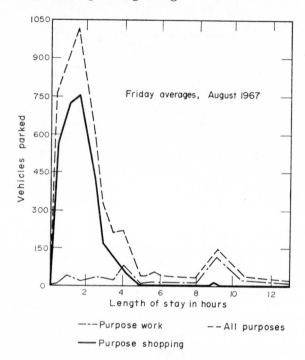

FIG. 4.9. Multi-storey car parks: duration of stay by purpose 1967, Coventry (Coventry Transportation Study: Report on Phase 1, 1968, City of Coventry).

Table 4.1 shows the effect of trip purpose and city size on parking duration. The durations increase with city size, and this may be explained in the case of shopping and business calls by the reduced freedom of parking, making it necessary for drivers to park further away from their destination (Fig. 4.11) and encouraging them to complete more calls before leaving and parking elsewhere. Conversely, in the smaller cities or towns, the vehicle may well be driven from call to call. Furthermore, in a small town it is likely that the journey to the central area is a minor one, taking only a few minutes, and several such trips may be made in the course of the day with each involving a separate, but short, parking

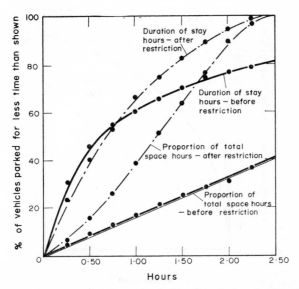

Fig. 4.10. Changes in parking characteristics resulting from the introduction of meters.

event. The increased duration of parking for work in larger cities is probably largely due to the tendency to park all day rather than to leave the area for lunch as in smaller cities.

Walking Distances

It is seldom possible for a driver to park his vehicle immediately adjacent to his destination in the central area of a town or city. Normally, he has to accept a walk from a place of parking and sometimes will deliberately incur such a walk in order to save the expense of parking nearer. There is, however, a limit to the distance at which most people will park, and the relationship between the distance parkers will walk an city size is illustrated in Fig. 4.11. It can be seen that in the small town, 90% park within 185 m (600 ft) of their destinations, while only 66% park so close in the large city. It is also found that the longer people intend to park the further they are prepared to walk.

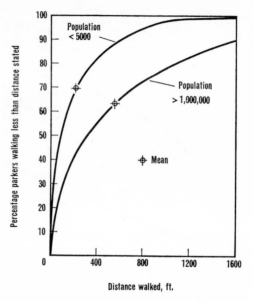

Fig. 4.11. Distance walked by parkers (U.S. data).

Land Use

Parking demand is generated according to the distribution and type of land uses in an area, together with the levels of accessibility provided by competing modes of transport. Whether a car park is provided as an integral part of a building or at some distance from it and its size, related to the generation, depend on the overall transportation policy for the area. Car parks can be sited at transport interchanges and walkways, travellators and bus services connected directly with the land use destinations, dependent on the distances involved and the trip purpose. Various standards for car parking provisions are laid down by authorities, but these vary considerably and should only be established as part of a comprehensive plan which includes a pricing policy. Current values usually allow one space per dwelling and range from one space for every 3–20 workers in industry, 2–10 workers in offices, 10–50 seats in theatres and cinemas, 1–5 bedrooms in hotels and from 20 to 200 m² of shop floor area. Some authorities no longer allow a parking provision in central offices and others are seeking control over all central area parking.

PARKING GENERATION

Parking generation studies in two towns, each under 50,000 population, indicated the parking demands for shopping and a market as shown in Table 4.2. Values from a survey of 65 industrial premises, in a Midland county, are also given in the table.

It can be seen that there is a larger variability in the industrial premises when floor area is used alone. Linear regression analysis indicated the following relationship:

$$P = 0.087 + 0.819C$$

where P is the number of parking spaces required and C the number of cars owned by employees ($r = 0.997$, significant at the 0.1% level). A multiple regression established the following equation:

$$P = 0.72 + 0.42\ E_m\ (1) + 2.71^*\ E_m\ (2) + 0.45^*\ E_m\ (3)$$
$$+ 0.04\ E_m\ (4 + 5) + 0.75\ E_f\ (1 + 2) - 0.05\ E_f\ (3\ \text{to}\ 5)$$

where E_m and E_f are the number of male and female employees. The variables (1 to 5) are, respectively, professional, intermediate, skilled, partly skilled and unskilled occupation categories. ($r = 0.970$; *variables significant at 0.1% level.)

STREET PARKING

The most obvious and, usually, the most convenient place to park for the driver is at the kerbside, but this has several disadvantages. First, the flow of traffic along the street is hampered, leading to congestion and delay to all travellers. It has been shown that where the parking index is of the order of 20% or less (that is, approximately 60 veh/km of street) the reduction in traffic speed in a typical city street is of the order of ¾ km/h for each ten additional parked vehicles.

With close parking the slowing down of traffic is more pronounced. Experience with the introduction of unilateral parking has suggested that the effect of an unbroken line of kerb-parked vehicles is to reduce

TABLE 4.2. PARKING GENERATION—AMOUNT OF GIVEN SPACE USE
GENERATING ONE CAR SPACE

Type of shop	Existing	Future (estimated)	Industry	Mean	Coefficient variation
	One car space for given area (m²)				
Food shops	21	10	Food	550	2·32
Clothing	65	30	Metal	130	0·69
Chemists, confectioners, newsagents	30	15	Engineering and electrical	55	0·61
Hardware	40	25	Vehicle	90	0·56
Restaurants	35	20	Other metals	150	0·74
Banks and post offices (public floor area)	2·5	1	Textiles	185	0·57
			Timber	210	0·92
			Paper	21	0·32
Market	25	12	Distributive	65	0·55
Mean (all)	40	20	Mean (all)	175	2·60

speeds by more than 20%, and street capacities are also markedly reduced. A 20 m wide street, with parking on both sides, has the same capacity as a 12 m street where parking is prohibited, thus representing a loss in effective width of over 4 m for each line of parked vehicles. This figure is considerably in excess of the width of a standing vehicle. Street parking also results in an increased number of accidents. In 1947/8, road accidents in London showed an overall increase of 8%, whereas in several miles of road where no-parking regulations were introduced accidents fell by 31·5% indicating an effective reduction of nearly 40%.

The increased delay due to slower speeds, the decreases in capacity and increases in accidents are due to the physical occupation of road space, parking manoeuvres, opening of car doors, erratic behaviour of cyclists, the appearance of pedestrians from between parked cars and to the other activities associated with parking and the parked vehicle.

Despite these disadvantages some street parking is necessary and there are circumstances in which it may be permitted. In streets about 10 m wide, where the two-directional flow does not exceed 400 veh/h, or in a one-way street, where the flow is less than 600 veh/h, parking on one side may be permitted if the adjoining footpath is not overcrowded and pedestrian crossing movements are few. On streets where the flow varies during the course of the day it may prove practical to permit parking where the flow falls below a critical level (Fig. 4.12), but care must be taken to ensure that associated intersections are not impeded and no undue delays are caused. Allowance may have to be made for the flow characteristics of the street and due attention paid to the effects of special days (market days, etc.). Total prohibition or selective hour prohibition may apply to both sides or to only one side of the street. When unilateral parking is permitted the ban should, preferably, be on the side carrying the predominant flow, although, in the interests of shopkeepers, it is often alternated.

Time Control

If no limit is placed on the length of time a vehicle may be parked in those areas where street parking demands are high, many available spaces are completely used up by the comparatively few long-term parkers to the detriment of a greater number of short-term parkers. In general it is often the latter who contribute to the prosperity of an area. The long-term parker is usually employed in the area and if he cannot park near his work he may be prepared to park at a greater distance, or to use public transport. The short-term parker is often a shopper, or business customer and, if there is no convenient parking place, may well take his custom elsewhere. One investigation in America revealed that a kerbside parking space, adequately controlled to permit a frequent changeover, was worth £6000 per annum in sales at an adjacent store.

Two factors to be considered in establishing time limits are the nature

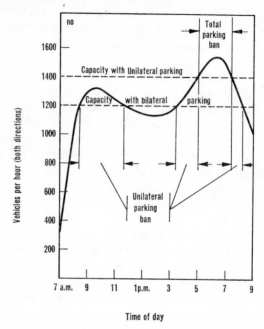

Fig. 4.12. Selective parking prohibitions by hour.

of the business carried on in the immediate area and the size of the city or town. Post offices, banks, newsagents, tobacconists and other "errand" type generators call for short 15 or 20 min limits, whereas departmental stores, car and furniture showrooms and such premises generate longer parking durations, which should be met with longer time limits. Furthermore, as seen in Table 4.1, cities with populations greater than 500,000 have shopping and business parking durations two and a half times greater than towns with populations less than 50,000 and, in establishing limits, consideration must be given to city size. Ideally, the correct time limit has been established when there is at least one car parking space available in 60–100 m of kerb, but to achieve this in most city centres would call for absurdly low limits impossible to enforce.

Parking enforcement in Britain used to depend entirely on the police, causing overwork and harming police public relations. Methods to overcome these disadvantages are numerous, but two principal ones include the disc and parking meter systems supervised by traffic wardens.

Disc System of Time Control

This system was first introduced in Paris but has since spread to other countries. In France, an area called the Blue Zone is a designated zone, inside which street parking is limited to 1 h for the greater part of the day. When parked, a vehicle must display a cardboard disc consisting essentially of a cardboard cover with two apertures backed by a rotatable disc. When parking, a driver rotates the disc so that the time of his arrival shows in one aperture while the other automatically indicates the time at which the vehicle must be moved. A patrolling policeman can detect, by inspection, vehicles which have overstayed the limit, and issue a ticket imposing a monetary penalty.

Parking Meters for Time Control

London was the first city in Great Britain to introduce parking meters. Any vehicle parking in the street in a designated area must do so in a marked bay governed by a parking meter. The meter consists of a timing mechanism started by the insertion of a coin. The period paid for is indicated by a pointer which gradually returns to zero as the time elapses. When zero is reached, a device appears, which indicates to a traffic warden that the vehicle has overstayed its limit and a fixed penalty ticket or summons can be issued.

The marked bays are usually 6 m long, which facilitates quick parking and unparking. This reduces interference with traffic flow and the accident potential to crossing pedestrians walking between closely parked vehicles. It does, however, considerably reduce the number of vehicles which can park in a given length of street. In a metered area in London, the introduction of meters resulted in a 54% reduction in the peak number of parked vehicles, but journey and visit times in the area were lower by 10% and accidents were significantly reduced.

Comparison of Discs and Meters

The disc system does not use marked bays, thus enabling more vehicles to be parked in a given street length, but requires over twice the number of attendant personnel to supervise than a metered system parking the same number of vehicles. Meters are expensive, and a considerable capital outlay is necessary to start a scheme, whereas the cost of cardboard discs is negligible. On the other hand, there is no direct revenue from discs, although profits from British meter schemes have mainly been negligible.

Portable Parking Meters

A device to obtain some of the advantages of both meters and discs is the portable meter which is carried in the vehicle. When parked, the meter is engaged so as to record the parked time. The meter is taken to an authorised place for opening, at regular intervals, and a charge made for the total parked time recorded. The device can allow differential parking charges to be made, according to the area in which the vehicle is parked.

OFF–STREET PARKING

In most central areas, street parking is limited and it is necessary to augment the parking capacity by the provision of off-street parking facilities. These may be generally classified into (a) surface parks, (b) multi-storey garages, (c) underground garages, (d) composite development, (e) mechanical garages and (f) drive-in facilities.

The design standards for parking structures and surface parks are based on the dimensions of vehicles in current use, as there is little indication that the size of cars is changing radically. The recommended stall width, for long-stay parkers, is 2·30 m which allows 0·55 m between two 90th percentile width cars parked centrally in adjacent stalls. It is recommended that this is increased to 2·5 m for convenience shopping and other high turnover parks. A stall length of 4·75 m is generally suitable, with an adjacent aisle width, for 90° parking, of 6·00 m. The minimum width between columns is then 15·50 m for 90° parking, obtained from adding the aisle width to twice the stall depth, a dimension known as the bin width. The gap between fixed obstructions, occupied by one or more stalls, is termed the bay width.

The presence of walls, posts and other obstructions close to a stall discourages drivers from parking their cars overhanging the low end kerbs, and correctly positioning their vehicle within a stall. Greater stall depth is utilised where side line markings are painted for a length of 3·50 m instead of marking out individual rectangles.

Surface Car Parks

Depending on the layout adopted and the shape of the site, a surface park can accommodate 350 to 500 cars/ha. Construction costs are at a minimum, but compared to the other and more expensive types of park less efficient use is made of land.

The layout should be such that a vehicle may be parked in one distinct manoeuvre without reversals of the steering lock. The most efficient use of the parking area is made if this is achieved by backing into the stall, using a 90° parking angle, as illustrated in Fig. 4.13(a). Using an aisle width of 6 m (which permits two-way traffic flow) and a stall size of 5·50 m by 2·50 m, the area required for each car, including half the area of the access aisle adjacent to the stall, is 21·25 m². For the simpler manoeuvre of a forward drive into the parking bay, maximum efficiency is obtained using a parking angle of 45°. Either of the herring-bone patterns, shown in Fig. 4.13, with an aisle width of 3·50 m, requires an area of 22 m (not allowing for wasted areas at the end of each row of bays).

The basic requirements of traffic circulation are that routes to all parking stalls should be as short as possible and that traffic movements should be sufficiently dispersed to prevent lock-ups, particularly at peak periods. Parking space may have to be sacrificed to improve operational efficiency, as shown in Fig. 4.14. Sites are often irregularly shaped and several trial layouts may be required before a final design is selected. Awkward areas and heavy slopes, not suitable for parking, can be used for landscaping.

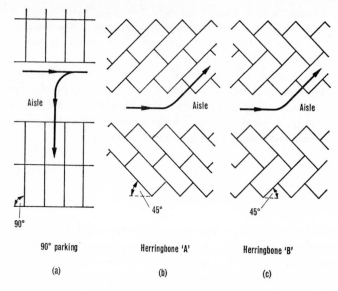

90° parking

(a)

Herringbone 'A'

(b)

Herringbone 'B'

(c)

FIG. 4.13. Parking stall layout.

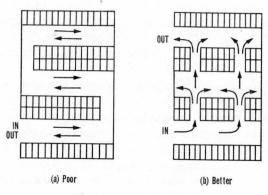

(a) Poor

(b) Better

FIG. 4.14. Traffic circulation.

Multi-storey Car Parks

As land values rise, more cars have to be parked over a given area. Multi-storey car parks consist of a tier of platforms supported by columns, spaced to permit an efficient arrangement of stalls and aisles with pedestrian ways. The buildings may be clad externally for aesthetic reasons or to permit a future change of use, but, when used solely for parking, guard rails reduce construction costs. Good design enables cars to be stored efficiently, with a minimum floor area per car, and to speed up the operation of entry and exit and parking manoeuvres to minimise delays in a safe and convenient manner.

Ramp and Floor Systems

Access ramps, interconnecting floors, should have a maximum gradient of 12% but generally should not exceed 10%, if straight, and 8% if curved, with an absolute minimum inside radius of 5·5 m. Staggered floors can be used to halve the difference in level between successive parking platforms, as shown in Fig. 4.15. There are several types of staggered floor designs permitting two-way travel on floors and ramps, or separating movements directly on the ramps. In other cases, complete directional segregation is made of travel both on floors and ramps. In these cases of shortened ramps, the gradients can be steepened to a maximum of 14%, provided that the approaches are well graded. One-way ramps are preferable and should have minimum width of 3 m. Two-way ramps, if used, should be divided, particularly where curved or at turning points, to prevent head-on collisions by drivers cutting corners or swinging wide at bends.

An alternative to the normal type of ramp is the sloping floor, either in the form of a complete spiral, from ground level to roof, or as split floors, in the manner shown in Fig. 4.15. Floors of these types form parking ramps with cars parked on either side of the access aisle. Gross floor space per car is less with the parking ramp but against this advantage must be offset the delays caused to circulating vehicles by parking manoeuvres, and also by the extra distances that have to be travelled. Floor gradients should not be steeper than 5% and, preferably, flatter.

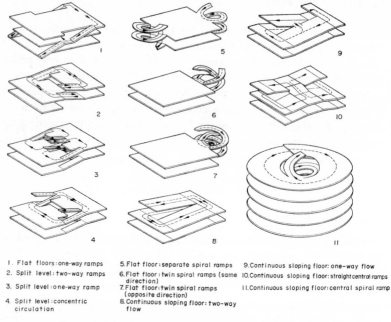

1. Flat floors: one-way ramps
2. Split level: two-way ramps
3. Split level: one-way ramp
4. Split level: concentric circulation
5. Flat floor: separate spiral ramps
6. Flat floor: twin spiral ramps (same direction)
7. Flat floor: twin spiral ramps (opposite direction)
8. Continuous sloping floor: two-way flow
9. Continuous sloping floor: one-way flow
10. Continuous sloping floor: straight central ramps
11. Continuous sloping floor: central spiral ramp

FIG. 4.15. Layout of floors and ramps in multi-storey car parks.

Headroom should be limited to 2·25 m to keep ramp lengths to a minimum, but it may be advisable to have 3·75 m on the ground storey to accommodate high vehicles and to allow its use for other purposes. Flat slabs eliminate the loss of height due to beams, and lift-slab methods of construction lend themselves to parking structures.

Self-parking garages should be limited to five storeys because of the extra travel time and inconvenience to customers. With attendant parking the driver leaves his vehicle at a reception point and from there it is driven to its parking place by an attendant. The attendant parking system permits narrower access aisles, smaller parking stalls and steeper ramps, thus reducing the gross floor area. Such garages may exceed five storeys but have major disadvantages of additional labour costs incurred in operating the system, and some of the parking area saved is needed as reservoir space in the reception area where customers leave and collect their cars. If there are heavy peak demands this can be considerable. Some customers also dislike handing over the control of their vehicles to the attendants.

Parking Operations

The principal factors in car parking capacity are the inflow rates, parking manoeuvre time and discharge time, and each of these components must be matched and balanced with the fee paying system. Entrance and exit gates are often the lifting barrier-arm type with a "take-a-ticket" machine at the entry, limiting the flow to between 300 and 500 veh/h, depending on the approach conditions. Payment exit gates normally have an attendant in a kiosk processing the ticket and receiving the fee, which limits discharge rates to less than 250 veh/h.

Table 4.3 gives a summary of mean manoeuvre times, for stall parking, obtained in a controlled experiment. The values allow for the full manoeuvre time from a mark 6·1 m from the bay until the handbrake was set, and Table 4.4 illustrates the inside time (a time measured from setting the handbrake to the operation of the door catch), and the outside time (a time required for the driver to leave the vehicle, lock the door and walk to the edge of the aisle). Parking times were shortest with 45° stalls and 3·66 m aisles and longest with 90° stalls and 5·49 m aisles. Driver errors tended to obscure the relationships to bay widths and the higher mean parking times showed larger variance.

Capacity

Ellson showed in *Parking: Dynamic Capacities of Car Parks* (R.R.L. Report LR 221, 1969) that the regression equations expressing inflow and outflow capacity (C_{IN} and C_{OUT}, cars/h) are:

$$C_{IN} = 55x_1 + 425x_2 + 150x_3 - 10 \cdot 24x_4 - 849$$
$$C_{OUT} = 66x_1 + 242x_2 + 52x_3 + 7 \cdot 7x_4 - 136x_5 - 690$$

where x_1 and x_2 = aisle and stall widths respectively (m),

$\quad\quad\quad x_3$ = stall depth (m),

$\quad\quad\quad x_4$ = % reversing into stalls,

$\quad\quad\quad x_5$ = 0 for one-way aisle or 1 for cul-de-sac aisle.

TABLE 4.3. SUMMARY OF MEAN PARKING MANOEUVRE TIMES (SECONDS)

	Bay Size								
	1·98 m (6′–6″)			2·13 m (7′–0″)			2·28 m (7′–6″)		
	P	U	T	P	U	T	P	U	T
I 90° Bay Angle 16·71 m (22 ft) Aisle Width									
Forward	13·5	19·7	33·2	11·0	20·5	31·5	7·9	21·1	27·0
Reverse	24·2	7·7	31·9	21·0	6·9	27·9	18·4	7·1	25·5
II 90° Bay Angle 5·49 m (18 ft) Aisle Width									
Forward	22·2	23·3	45·5	10·5	24·7	35·2	10·1	19·1	29·6
Reverse	25·6	9·7	35·3	20·2	9·0	29·2	18·4	8·2	26·6
III 45° Bay Angle 3·66 m (12 ft) Aisle Width									
Forward	8·0	13·9	21·9	7·3	13·9	21·2	6·4	12·2	18·6
Reverse	18·6	6·7	25·3	17·5	6·8	24·3	15·8	6·1	12·9
IV 45° Bay Angle 2·74 m (9 ft) Aisle Width									
Forward	9·3	14·1	23·4	7·5	13·6	21·5	7·3	13·8	21·1
Reverse	26·9	7·8	34·7	20·8	6·5	27·3	17·1	9·0	26·1

P=parking time.   U=unparking time.

T=total manoeuvre time (parking and unparking time).

TABLE 4.3   *(continued)*

| | BAY SIZE | | | | | | | | |
| | 2·44 m (8′–0″) | | | 2·59 m (8′–6″) | | | 2·74 m (9′–0″) | | |
	P	U	T	P	U	T	P	U	T
I 90° Bay Angle 6·71 m (22 ft) Aisle Width									
Forward	7·9	18·2	26·1	7·2	15·0	22·2	9·0	14·1	21·1
Reverse	18·8	6·7	25·5	17·7	6·3	24·0	16·0	6·2	22·2
II 90° Bay Angle 5·49 m (18 ft) Aisle Width									
Forward	7·8	16·2	24·0	6·9	15·5	22·4	6·2	15·0	21·2
Reverse	16·8	7·6	24·4	16·7	7·5	24·2	15·9	6·9	22·8
III 45° Bay Angle 3·66 m (12 ft) Aisle Width									
Forward	5·9	12·1	18·0	6·4	11·6	18·0	5·8	11·7	17·5
Reverse	15·5	6·4	21·9	14·3	5·9	20·2	14·7	6·2	20·9
IV 45° Bay Angle 2·74 m (9 ft) Aisle Width									
Forward	6·4	12·8	19·2	6·4	12·1	18·5	6·0	11·8	17·8
Reverse	19·8	6·8	26·6	17·2	6·1	23·3	16·8	6·4	23·2

P=parking time.   U=unparking time.

T=total manoeuvre time (parking and unparking time).

G

TABLE 4.4. SUMMARY OF MEAN INSIDE AND OUTSIDE TIMES
OF PARKERS (SECONDS)

	I		II		III		IV		Mean without basket		Mean with basket	
	P	U	P	U	P	U	P	U	P	U	P	U
Inside	3·8	7·0	4·7	9·0	2·9	7·3	3·7	9·6	3·4	7·0	4·1	9·2
Outside	7·4	5·6	9·3	6·0	7·6	5·5	10·9	6·0	7·6	5·5	10·2	6·0

I   = 90° bay angle, 6·71 m aisle, Forward Parking without basket
II = 90° bay angle, 6·71 m aisle, Reverse Parking with basket
III = 90° bay angle, 5·49 m aisle, Forward Parking without basket
IV = 90° bay angle, 5·49 m aisle, Reverse Parking with basket
P   = inside time while parking
U   = inside time while unparking

The equations are based on 90° stalls and if parallel cul-de-sac aisles are used the capacity (C) is reduced because drivers looking for a vacant stall travel slowly past each junction. Ramps and aisles have similar maximum capacities to those of equivalent lanes on a street. The average maximum capacity of a 3 m ramp is between 1800 and 1900 cars/h and, for one-way aisles of the same width or greater (w), the relationship is $C_A = 15w + 1800$ (cars/h). The capacity of a bend (C_R) is $C_R = 1850/(1+100/r^3)$ (cars/h), where r = radius of curve in metres with a single file of cars. Reservoir space, between the exit gate and the adjacent road junction, will be frequently required, and is based on the maximum entry flow (q_{max}) possible from the minor road into the major road, as follows:

$$q_{max} = \frac{Q(1-Q/S)}{e^{(0·0015Q-Q/S)}[1-e^{-Q/s}]}, \quad Q \neq 0 \text{ and } S \geqslant 667 \text{ cars/h}$$

where Q = flow in near-side lane of major road, veh/h,
      S = saturation flow, near-side of major road, veh/h,
      s = maximum discharge of cars from the minor road, ranging from 1250 cars/h for turning left with no other major road traffic, 760 cars/h for left turns

with Give Way signs and some major road traffic, and to 620 cars/h with Stop signs. The assumed acceptable gap in the major road is 5·4 s.

Parking requirements are diverse, and automatic systems need to be flexible in operation, presenting easy and rapid entry to the park, by conforming to the logic requirements, and subsequent pedestrian movements. Payment is ideally made by the returning driver to a machine in the entrance hall giving change and an exit gate token. Variable charging rates are often required to allow for both parking duration and time of arrival or exit. These rates can then be used to regulate the use of the park and adjacent streets by a simple pricing mechanism. With the fuller control systems now developed, automatic floor counting is available with linked signs to indicate a particular floor for a selected parking duration, or the availability of spaces on all floors. These control systems can be linked into remotely switched signs, parking space indicators and direction signs on the adjacent approach roads.

Lighting Car Parks

Good lighting is an essential design feature where vechicles are manoeuvring, particularly in the presence of pedestrians. Poor lighting leads to dangers of assault, vandalism and theft. Uniform levels of illumination are difficult to achieve because of the relatively low ceiling heights which help to reduce costs and ramp gradients. It is not only necessary to have well-lit roadways and ramps but also stall areas, where vehicles are manoeuvring and passengers are alighting and moving in shadow. Overall consistency of illumination is best achieved by using low-powered units more frequently. A standard of one 40 W fitting for every two or three stalls is suitable, with additional lamps sited at the ends of ramps. Efficient operation is aided by well-sited and maintained illuminated direction and regulatory signs.

Lock-up Garages

The minimum width of a lock-up garage needs to be greater than that of a stall, to allow for ease of entry, and greater manoeuvring width is also required in aisles serving a row of garages.

Underground and Roof-type Parks

Underground types have the advantages that they allow the surface amenities to remain or to be restored after construction. They fit under public squares and parks as, for example, the Hyde Park underground garage for one thousand cars. However, because of the form of retaining walls and usual alteration to underground services they are expensive and cost three to four times as much per car space as multi-storey garages.

Rooftop parking, with access either by ramp or lift, depending on site conditions, has a twofold attraction. First, individual roof parks, spread throughout an area, can contain in aggregate as many as a multi-storey facility, but with all the advantages of dispersion to reduce peak hour discharge over many streets. Secondly, a rooftop park can be constructed over an area which is already giving an adequate investment return. An example of this type is over the covered market at Coventry and the method is readily applicable to such sites as railway stations, theatres and swimming pools. It is possible to link a number of roof tops together, reducing the cost of several access ramps.

Mechanical Garages

Mechanical garages are usually multi-storey. They vary in complexity from the use of lifts, to accommodate vertical travel between floors, to a combination of vertical and horizontal movement by mechanical means. In the simple case, the vehicle to be parked is driven on to the lift, taken to the required floor, driven off and parked.

In a fully mechanised garage the car is stopped over a mechanical pallet and left by the driver. A push-button control enables the pallet to lift the car and transfer it to a lift, which moves both vertically and horizontally to align itself with "pigeon holes" on either side of the shaft. The car is transferred to the pigeon hole until called for by the driver, when the automatic process is reversed. In other systems the loading point remains stationary and the stall moves past it for vehicle loading, either grouped round a "fairground" wheel or batched horizontally.

Mechanical parking by eliminating ramps, and in some cases aisles, increases accommodation by a quarter for an average site. They can be adapted to sites with a frontage too narrow for a structure with ramps and there is less limitation on heights. While they have been built on sites as narrow as 6 m and rising to 16 storeys, their main disadvantage is the rate of vehicle handling. Ramp capacities are high, when compared to lifts, and reservoir space is needed at peak times to enable cars to be lifted to their final positions later, and can be used, in reverse, for customers who have notified the operator of a collection time. Further disadvantages include the danger of breakdowns, power failures and expensive maintenance.

Drive-in Facilities

Facilities can be provided which permit a driver a brief business transaction without leaving his car. A person carrying out an "errand", such as depositing money in a bank, may have to spend time cruising around in congested streets looking for a place to park and then walk a distance which is disproportionate to the time spent on business. Drive-in facilities reduce the time loss and have been built for post offices, newsagents, tobacconists and banks to relieve the parking congestion in some areas (Fig. 4.16).

LOCATION OF OFF-STREET PARKING

Ideally, an off-street park should be located at the centroid of the destination requirements of those whom the park is intended to serve. This centroid may be determined by the method of moments as shown in Fig. 4.17. The technique can be refined by using weighted distances to allow for the indirectness of pedestrian routes between the proposed car park and the parker's destination. In redevelopment areas the car park can be suitably located, taking into account the required accessibility levels for vehicles and pedestrians. Where areas are not being redeveloped, the destination centroid may fall on a site which is not available. Large car

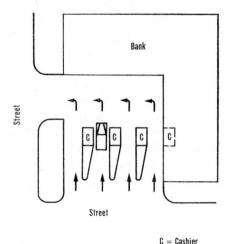

C = Cashier

FIG. 4.16. "Drive-in" bank.

parks also generate considerable traffic which may not be wanted at a location, particularly if surrounding streets are narrow or flanked by shop fronts and crowded footpaths, increasing the danger of accidents. It may be that the location requires entrances at or near a junction where there is a possibility of parking vehicles, waiting to enter, causing it to block up unless special control is provided.

Entrances and exits to garages are best situated on one-way streets, since this simplifies traffic movement and eliminates any need to cross the main stream of traffic. On streets with higher speeds, deceleration and storage lanes should be provided for entering traffic, and acceleration lanes for those leaving. Pedestrian safety must be considered and, where the exits and entrances are wide, pedestrian refuges may also be needed with traffic-light control.

ON- AND OFF-LOADING OF GOODS

Most goods start and finish their journeys by road and the provision of loading facilities is essential; although the use of the kerbside may still

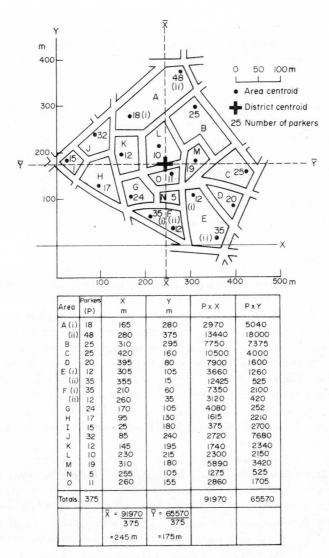

Area	Parkers (P)	X m	Y m	P x X	P x Y
A (i)	18	165	280	2970	5040
(ii)	48	280	375	13440	18000
B	25	310	295	7750	7375
C	25	420	160	10500	4000
D	20	395	80	7900	1600
E (i)	12	305	105	3660	1260
(ii)	35	355	15	12425	525
F (i)	35	210	60	7350	2100
(ii)	12	260	35	3120	420
G	24	170	105	4080	252
H	17	95	130	1615	2210
I	15	25	180	375	2700
J	32	85	240	2720	7680
K	12	145	195	1740	2340
L	10	230	215	2300	2150
M	19	310	180	5890	3420
N	5	255	105	1275	525
O	11	260	155	2860	1705
Totals.	375			91970	65570
		$\bar{X} = \frac{91970}{375}$	$\bar{Y} = \frac{65570}{375}$		
		=245 m	=175m		

Fig. 4.17. Method of moments to locate parking **garage**.

be necessary it must be controlled and fairly shared. Existing back alleyways to shops should be investigated to see whether improvements could be made to them for loading purposes, and all new areas should be constructed with full rear access roads with turning spaces or underground service roads.

Generally, loading bays should provide approach widths to permit single manoeuvre positioning for the selected design vehicle, taking into account the turning circle characteristics of commercial vehicle types and off-tracking when siting street furniture. Loading and unloading is usually most efficiently carried out with a raised loading platform, which is preferably slightly lower than the floor level of the truck or van to prevent damage to the vehicle by dropping loads. These levels vary, in general, from 1 to 1·20 m and a platform height of about 1 m is usually suitable.

Lorry Parks

The three principal problems created by indiscriminate lorry parking on streets and open spaces in towns are loss of amenity in residential areas, safety hazards and the crime value of loads. Orders banning such parking in residential areas can only be effective if proper provision is made for the accommodation of lorries and their drivers in purpose built and controlled lorry parks. The problem is an extensive one; in the West Midlands alone, nearly 3000 heavy vehicles are parked uncontrolled overnight. Thus a national network of lorry parks, designed to appropriate standards, is being developed. Lorries are divided into three parking categories; local based (local use), local based (long distance use) and away based (long distance use).

The lorry park should be sited close to the major road network with good access to industrial areas, docks and town centres but away from residences, schools, shops and, obviously, amenity areas. Site access roads must be structurally sound and routes comprehensively signed throughout the area. A primary concern in the park itself is the security of high value loads, and perimeter fencing is usually 3·5 m high surrounded by a ditch and crash barrier with single entry and exit points. High standards of overall lighting are needed and closed-circuit television is a useful surveillance system.

Within the park provision is made for a service and reception area containing fuel supply and workshops and overnight accommodation for drivers with full restaurant facilities and recreational rooms. Economic factors indicate a minimum size of about 100 vehicles (2·50 ha), ranging up to 300 vehicles (5 ha) maximum on traffic and environmental considerations.

The proper regulation and identification of vehicles carrying dangerous and inflammable materials must be envisaged when designating suitable areas for lorry parks and the siting of water supplies for fire fighting.

Service Areas

On long distance journeys, the traveller requires service facilities sited at regular intervals, either on or adjacent to the route, for refreshment, rest and vehicle service. Access routes to recreational areas and places of scenic or historic interest also need amenity stopping and picnic points.

The spacing and size of a service area is interrelated, and influences the number and types of restaurant seats and meals, parking spaces (by vehicle types) and the number of fuel points. Layout partly depends on topography and the standardisation of the service operations (familiarity with the flow pattern aids efficiency and safety) and also predicted traffic flows, distributed by daily, weekly and seasonal patterns. As many sites tend to be remote, staffing requirements and access have to be carefully assessed in relation to the type of services provided, and it is usual to construct the work in stages to match the traffic growth. British practice on the motorways has been to build full facilities at twice the final intended spacing of about 20 km. Typical European standards are between 25 and 50 km, depending on route importance. Because service areas generate similar amounts of traffic to interchanges, they should normally be sited away from important junctions.

The amount of traffic stopping on motorways varies with site location and route type, being least immediately before a large city, unless information and booking offices are sited there, and greatest at those first reached after the city. In Britain, about a quarter of the traffic is likely to stop, a much higher proportion than in Germany, but a tenth will solely take on fuel, although in total about a third will refuel. About two-thirds of those stopping will make use of the toilets.

Parking is related to vehicle occupancy and eating habits, i.e. the length of stay for particular activities. Average vehicle occupancies range from 1·75 cars, 1·20 lorries and 27·5 for coaches, while an equivalent seating accommodation per parking stall is about 1·5 cars, 1·0 lorries and 20 for coaches. Average duration of stay varies from a minimum of 3 min for toilets, to between 15 and 35 min for standing and seated restaurant meals respectively. A typical parking provision, for a single flow direction with a high proportion of commercial vehicles, would allow stalls for 100 cars, 50 lorries and 5 coaches.

Amenity Parking Areas

These vary from a simple pull-in and parking area, generally provided at good viewpoints, to sites with simple tables, seats and toilets. Facilities at the approach to tourist towns and National Park areas may be large fully landscaped sites, accommodating tourist offices, map and information rooms, motels and accommodation booking facilities. Parking space provision generally ranges from 50 to 250 according to the type of area, and sometimes access is provided to the local countryside with adjacent picnic areas.

FURTHER READING

BELL, R. A. (1970) Traffic parking and the regional shopping centre. *Traff. Engng. and Control* **134**(5).

BRIERLEY, J. (1972) *Parking of Motor Vehicles* (2nd ed.). Applied Science Publishers, London.

BRIGGS, M. (1969) Multi-storey car parks. *Surveyor*, **cxxxiii** (3999).

BRITISH PARKING ASSOCIATION (1970) *Car Parking* 1968; *Off-Street Parking* 1970; Technical Note No. 1, *Metric Dimensions for 90° Parking*; *Parking Policies in Urban Areas*, and *Making Parking Pay*. Reports of the British Parking Association, London.

BRITISH ROAD FEDERATION. *Car Parking a National Survey* (series) 1961, 1964, and *Car Parking* 1968. British Road Federation, London.

BUREAU OF PUBLIC ROADS (1956) *Parking Guide for Cities*. U.S. Dept. of Commerce, Washington.

BURRAGE, R. H. and MOGREN, E. G. (1957) *Parking*. Eno Foundation, Saugatuck.

BURTON, M. J. (1973) Parking policy as an instrument of traffic restraint. *J. Instn. Highway Engrs.* **xx**(1).

DAWKES, F. W. (1968) Multi-storey car park design. *Parking Supplement, Municipal Engng.*, May.

ELLSON, P. B. (1969) Parking: Dynamic capacities of car parks. RRL Report LR221. The Road Research Laboratory.

ELLSON, P. B. *et al.* (1969) Parking: Effects of stall markings on the positioning of parked cars. RRL Report LR 289.

GLANVILLE, J. (1971) *The Provision, Location and Design of Parking Facilities in Europe.* The International Road Federation, Washington.

KLOSE, D. (1965) *Multi-storey Car Parks and Garages.* The Architectural Press, London.

MARSHALL, P. and ALLEN, G. P. (1965) Layout of multi-storey car parks. *J. Instn. Municipal Engrs.*, **92**, August.

MINISTRY OF HOUSING AND LOCAL GOVERNMENT AND MINISTRY OF TRANSPORT. *Parking in Town Centres*, H.M.S.O., 1965. *Better use of Town Roads*, H.M.S.O., 1967. *Traffic Management and Parking*, H.M.S.O., 1969. *Cars in Housing No. 2*, Design Bulletin No. 12 (1967).

NATIONAL COMMITTEE ON URBAN TRANSPORTATION. *Conducting a Limited Parking Study*, Procedure Manual 3C; *Conducting a Comprehensive Parking Study*, Procedure Manual 3D. Public Administrative Service, Chicago.

RICKER, E. R. (1957) *Traffic Design of Parking Garages.* Eno Foundation, Saugatuck.

VARIOUS (1971) *Car Parking.* Proc. P.T.R.C. Summer, Planning and Transportation Research and Computation Co. Ltd., London.

VARIOUS (1970, 1971, 1972) Focus on parking. *Traff. Engng. and Control* **11**(12), **12**(7) and **13**(11/12), and Car parks: design and construction, *ibid.* **12**(12).

WHITESIDE, R. E. (1957) *Parking Garage Operation.* Eno Foundation, Saugatuck.

WILBUR SMITH & ASSOC. (1965) *Parking in the City Center.*

WILLIAMS, T. E. H. and LATCHFORD, J. C. R. (1966) Prediction of traffic in industrial areas. *Traff. Engng. and Control*, **10**.

CHAPTER 5

Traffic and Environmental Management

TRAFFIC MANAGEMENT

The principal aim of traffic management is to maximise the use of the existing street system and improve road safety, without impairing environmental quality. It is analogous to work study and production control in industry and is most appropriately applied to short-term and low capital cost improvements, thus improving, in economic terms, the supply. Management measures may relate to a single traffic category, such as pedestrians, or to mixed traffic and the close operational control of feeder routes to urban motorways. Most forms of traffic regulation produce some disadvantages which must be more than offset by the advantages gained.

The definition of a study area will not only include a particular length of facility but also adjacent parts that may be affected, e.g. servicing frontages, rescheduling bus routes and stops, adjusting signals, erecting signs and signals on intersecting streets, etc. Detailed inventories are prepared of existing layouts, control devices, street furniture, adjacent land uses, environmental factors and traffic flows, delays and speeds. If accurate economic assessments are needed, some origin and destination information is necessary, particularly where traffic will be rerouted or diverted. Alternative schemes are prepared and evaluated and it may be necessary to try out parts of the scheme before final implementation. The aims and objectives of the proposals must be widely disseminated to the affected public through the media, and at public meetings.

Traffic management may entail alterations to the geometric layout, provision of additional guidance and control devices such as bollards, signs, signals, pedestrian guard rails, pedestrian crossings and lighting. Standing vehicles may also require the construction of ancillary pavement areas, such as bus draw-ins and loading and unloading bays for commercial vehicles. Moving traffic is assisted by the coordination of traffic signals, adjustments to controllers and reducing conflicts by the use of one-way streets, reversible flow lanes for roads with directional flow peaks, and the limitation of selected turning movements at intersections.

ONE-WAY STREETS

Land uses are usually serviced by traffic approaching from all directions and thus, when designing one-way schemes, complementary streets are required with suitable frequencies of interconnecting streets. Grid iron layouts are ideal, as they allow paired streets with similar capacities. Terminal points of one-way streets are critical areas needing careful design of the resulting conflict points imposed by the demands of additional turning traffic. At sites with high flows, one-way working of the cross streets is advantageous. Elongated systems, with a separation of less than 500 m between street pairs, reduces the likely journey kilometres run on the network. Reversible one-way systems can partially overcome capacity limitations of a network but need complex, purpose designed signs to display appropriate messages and automatic switching of control devices. Special arrangements can be made for buses to minimise walking distances to passengers by constructing counter-flow bus lanes where there are suitable street widths. The principal advantages and disadvantages of one-way systems are set out in Table 5.1.

The major costs of one-way systems lies in the provision of traffic signs, which are comparatively inexpensive compared to new road construction and some of the savings can be allocated to the improvement of junctions, and the provision of more complex signalisation. By increasing capacity, one-way streets often allow a continuation of metered parking, which may be essential to the life of an area. Finally, besides providing signs, careful road markings and the channelisation of junctions, to prevent incorrect movement, are always essential. However, greater visual intrusion generally results from one-way schemes and higher traffic

TABLE 5.1.   ADVANTAGES AND DISADVANTAGES OF ONE-WAY STREETS

Advantages	Disadvantages
(i) Potential increase in capacity at and between junctions and possible improvements in traffic distribution.	(i) Longer journey distances and increased traffic volume on parts of the network leading to more turning traffic at end points.
(ii) Fewer pedestrian and vehicle conflicts, generally reducing accident rates and eliminating severe head-on collisions.	(ii) Difficulty of routeing traffic through an area, particularly for strangers. Loss of amenity for residents in areas of one-way streets and possible environmental deterioration.
(iii) Improved kerb parking conditions and less interference from bus stops, and loading and unloading vehicles.	(iii) Diversion of public transport loading points and affects on bus scheduling and route coverage.
(iv) Improved utilisation of streets with odd numbers of lanes.	(iv) Increased walking distances for public transport passengers.
(v) Easier application of progressive systems of traffic signal control.	(v) Opposition from commercial interests along one-way routes.
(vi) Better connections to and from ramps at urban motorway interchanges and simplification of traffic distribution to the local street system.	(vi) Difficulties of driver and pedestrian familiarisation during initial phases of scheme.

speeds tend to exacerbate community severance by creating greater difficulties in crossing the street, isolating one side from the other.

Traffic Studies in Management

Full traffic studies are required before taking management decisions, and this is particularly the case in considering one-way systems. Inventories must be compiled of the layout, siting of existing signs, signals, pedestrian crossings and the land use of frontages. Volumetric classified counts must be taken throughout the area by hour and direction, together with the types and numbers of turning movements at intersections. Speed and delay measurements are also required, and data on parking character-istics. Finally, information is required on the total movements of pedes-trians, including those to and from public transport stops, and the routes and frequency of services.

The area study results will allow the theoretical assignment of traffic to the possible alternative one-way routes and these can be evaluated with new capacity computations. Uni-directional volumes and journey speed are then estimated and compared with existing speeds. By making due allowance for increased journey distance, it is possible to select the most advantageous scheme. The new one-way streets must allow for rerouted bus services and the changes in pedestrian movement. Subsidiary in-vestigations into accidents on the existing and proposed network will also influence choices. Commercial interests have to be convinced of the wisdom of the measures if severe opposition and delay to a scheme are to be prevented.

As one-way streets are only one method of increasing traffic flow and reducing delay, other measures, such as parking and unloading restric-tions and progressive signal systems, should be considered at the same time. Compromise will often be necessary, and some or all of the above improvements may be included in a phased programme. Once all these types of measures have been effected, new road construction becomes inevitable if further capacity is needed. If serious traffic dislocation is to be avoided in the future, adequate planning and execution of new work must be made before the final restriction is operated.

The general application of one-way street principles is more difficult to achieve in British cities than in many countries because of basic diff-erences in street layout. However, sensibly applied, these measures result in higher flows, improvements in safety, and often there will be decreases in journey time due to higher running speeds. Flow conditions are normally more stable and less subject to breakdown. Figure 5.1 shows a number of applications of one-way street systems.

TURNING TRAFFIC

Each turning vehicle at a junction imposes an additional delay, over and above that of a through vehicle, varying from zero for a diverging

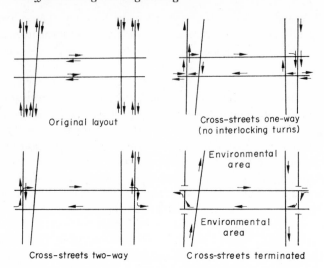

Original layout

Cross-streets one-way
(no interlocking turns)

Cross-streets two-way

Cross-streets terminated

Fig. 5.1.   One-way street systems.

vehicle leaving a route at a speed equal to that of through vehicles, to a value tending to infinity for a right-turning vehicle, causing a lock-up of the junction. The limitation of capacity and the reduction of total delay from these causes is controlled by banning, completely or partially, selected turning movements. It must be borne in mind, however, that delay may be incurred additionally when the turning movement is made in several stages and it must be shown that the aggregate overall delay for all vehicles is minimised. Exit left turns are dealt with by ensuring adequate radii for the class and speed of traffic. Right turns across traffic streams can be replaced by T–, G–, and Q–turns as illustrated in Fig. 5.2. With most traffic management schemes, certain vehicles, such as public transport, can be given favoured treatment by permitting turns banned to the other vehicles or other operating advantages.

CLEARWAYS

Whereas clearways were first introduced on rural roads mainly to enhance safety, they now have important traffic management advantages

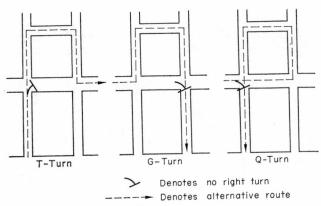

FIG. 5.2. Right-turn traffic diversions.

on urban roads. The principal objective is to improve traffic flow by restricting waiting and loading. While rural routes do not require road markings, and usually only the provision of occasional laybys, those in urban areas generally restrict the control to specified peak periods and need extensive signing and enforcement. Pedestrian accidents have been reduced by up to a half and traffic flows improved by up to 10% on roads without previous controls. While no benefits are gained at junctions their use enables signal progression schemes to be instituted. Besides enforcement difficulties the major disadvantage is usually to small traders who are likely to lose important custom.

TIDAL AND REVERSIBLE FLOW

With heavy inward or outward peak flows there is an advantage in utilising additional lanes in one direction, particularly where the directional split is over 70%. The ratio of directional flows should match the lanes available; theoretically, three lanes permit the operation of tidal flow but, in practice, one lane may be frequently blocked for short periods, causing excessive delay and dangerous manoeuvres by other vehicles. Similar considerations apply to standard width four-lane highways, but in some circumstances the two outer lanes can be increased in width to allow, in effect, a "squeeze lane" while the two central lanes are narrowed by a similar amount. For widths in excess of 16·5 m of pavement, lane marking configurations for reversible flow are straightforward.

The operation of reversing flows needs very careful control, preferably with physical separation of the reversed flow lane. It is achieved by signs and signals and occasionally movable barriers and bollards. Overhead signs on gantries consist of illuminated red crosses (fluorescent or neon tubing) sited over each lane, or signs with legends painted on rotating slats. Newer secret signs, using a large panel containing a matrix of about 150 lamps, can be lit separately from a control centre computer, to show a variety of messages and speed indications. A special purpose programme sets up a consecutive sequence of instructions for various control modes and in-built checks prevent erroneous messages and sequences. Combinations of flashing amber and red lights are additionally illuminated to signal hazards and stop traffic respectively. In the design of high cost facilities, such as urban motorways and for bridges and tunnels, considerable operating savings are possible by providing for directional flow demands, but it is often difficult to ensure adequate levels of safety.

MANAGEMENT FOR THE PEDESTRIAN

The improvements of pedestrian movements and safety are no less important than for other traffic. The reduction of delay and the avoidance of lengthy detours, particularly for those routes serving public transport operations, are best determined by the examination of main user routes. The most appropriate crossing points of vehicular traffic routes can be selected, and then measures implemented to control, channelise and segregate conflict points. The type of facility required is based on the availability of gaps in the traffic stream and the resultant delays likely to arise for road crossing by pedestrians (see Fig. 5.3). The major provisions include crossing points, with or without central refuges, traffic signals with pedestrian phases, independent pedestrian signals and complete segregation by bridge or subway. At main pedestrian crossing points, the road surfaces need careful selection, and the drivers should be presented with good visibility and as few other conflicting demands as possible competing for theit attention. Guard-rails can be used to define routes and also protect pedestrians.

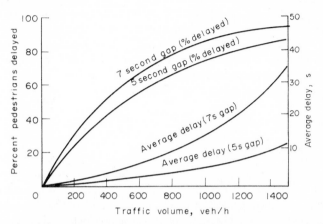

Fig. 5.3.   Proportion of pedestrians delayed, and average delay to pedestrians, in crossing the road.

Education and instruction are an important aspect of all management programmes and no less than with the pedestrian. The Green Cross Code has been developed to teach people, and particularly children, to cross the road safely. It sets out a sequence of six logical steps to be taught and understood, but it is not suitable for children less than school age. Children are extremely limited in their ability to judge both speed and distance, and also sounds directionally up to about 10 years of age. Furthermore, they experience difficulty in distinguishing between left and right. The Code defines safe crossing places and the process of judging whether or not traffic is far enough away to cross safely. However, the inculcation of a correct approach to road use can only be developed through experience gained in the company of adults and in specific road-side classes.

The alignment of pedestrian routes must be made attractive to the users and avoid badly lit and recessed areas. Ramp gradients should not exceed 10% and by careful siting the total rise and fall along a route should be kept to a minimum.

GENERAL MANAGEMENT MEASURES

The review of legislation, enforcement methods, the improvement in the flow of information, the presentation of easier decision-making tasks and the observation and monitoring of accident rates are all a basic part of traffic management studies and policy. Congestion often arises from stopped vehicles, and the introduction of box junctions, to prohibit vehicles entering a junction, unless their exit is assured, is indicated by yellow cross diagonal striping. Clearways similarly prevent traffic stopping on the carriageway.

TRAFFIC MANAGEMENT IN PUBLIC TRANSPORT

An increasingly important task in traffic management is the improvement of public transport services. A primary objective of current transportation planning strategy is to encourage more public transport use and this can be achieved by restraint of personal vehicles and better service levels of public transport. It is necessary not only to improve services but also to provide additional facilities for travellers transferred, or restrained, from other mode use if the viability of an area is to be safeguarded. Once the specific objectives of the transport plan have been derived, for the respective areas in terms of movement requirements, standard traffic study methods are applied to a number of case studies. These include the location of potential transport interchanges on bus and rail systems and the siting and size of appropriate car parks. Estimates of existing and future traffic are required to determine generated and diverted traffic. Because catchment areas are likely to be changed, and route patterns affected, particularly for the remaining car drivers, schemes must be carefully assessed for environmental consequences before making changes to the road network. In most cities and towns, the principal public mode is the bus and most of the improvements will be directed to improving their priority over other vehicles. Longer term measures may include feasibility studies to build entirely new bus routes and where these are only likely to be utilised at peak hours, commercial vehicles could be permitted to use them at other hours, and so improve their economic viability.

Measures to Improve Bus Routes

The principal methods include the adoption of bus-only lanes on suitable roads, either with-the-flow lanes or contra-flow lanes, bus-only streets and bus precincts. While these changes improve the flow and journey times between junctions, additional management measures are needed to reduce delays at traffic signals, regulate or prohibit parking or loading by operating bus clearways, banning turns for other traffic and granting exemptions to buses. It is often customary in Britain to physically segrate countra-flow lanes by a median, which also may be required or widened for with-the-flow lanes where loading and unloading is needed to service frontages alongside the bus lanes.

Traffic Studies for Bus-only Lanes

For a comprehensive scheme a coarse study is made of all routes to identify operating conditions and congestion points. Detailed studies are then made of selected routes likely to yield suitable benefits. Observations are usually made by travelling observers equipped with stop watches and tape recorders to record a sample of bus journey times and the distribution of delays due to stops, junctions and congestion. Mean journey times, journey and running speeds are calculated from the data, together with the statistical attributes of the services. The number of runs required for a given level of accuracy is determined from the variability of the observations. Normally, about ten runs are sufficient, and these are spread over the days of the week, but avoiding special occasions such as school holidays and roadworks.

Figure 5.4 illustrates the main features of bus lanes. It is essential that the routes are clearly defined by adequate signs and bold road markings to improve safety for all road users. Minimum lane widths are established from vehicle characteristics but are currently not less than 3 m. Contra-flow lanes are often designed particularly to prevent lengthy detours of buses in one-way systems; in these cases, it is usually infeasible to permit taxi and cycle use, but is possible for them to share lanes in other cases. In congested lineal shopping streets, often found on important radial

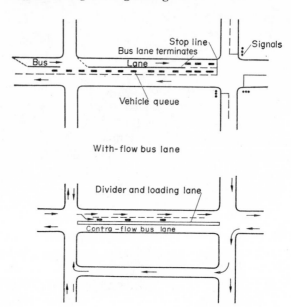

Fig. 5.4.   Bus lanes: with-flow and contra-flow arrangements.

through routes, bus precincts may be a preferable alternative to pedestrian-only precincts. However, pedestrian safety must be carefully considered, and it is paramount where contra-flow lanes are operated.

Bus lane operations may be restricted to selected hours of the day, for example, 8.00 to 10.00 a.m. and 4.00 to 6.00 p.m. While a primary objective of bus lanes is to enable buses to pass queues and slow-moving traffic, it is often necessary to maximise the saturation flow at traffic signals and prevent other traffic queues overlapping upstream junctions. It is therefore normal practice to terminate bus lanes 20 to 60 m upstream of the stop line and this also enables other traffic to make safer left turns. Where it is probable that peak flows may cause queues to extend over the preceding junction, it is necessary to install queue detectors to adjust the signal controller's cycle time and phase split.

Signal Pre-emption

In order to further improve the bus priority, by ensuring that the bus clears the next signal ahead with minimum delay, it is possible to install special loop detectors in the carriageway which are activated by an onboard bus signal generator. The detector relays a command to the signal controller which either terminates the cross flow early, or extends the running green on the approach to enable the bus to clear the junction. To prevent queues building up on the side road additional running time can be subsequently allocated, when no bus is present on the main road, thus restoring some of the time lost to other traffic. Emergency vehicles can be similarly equipped to receive priority.

Design of Bus-only Lanes

From the data analysis the principal causes and frequencies of delay will be located, and consideration can next be given to potential improvements which yield net community benefits. These may be the introduction of forms of signal priority, banned and permissible turns for all vehicles and bus laybys, besides the introduction of bus lanes. Bus laybys may also be required on bus-only lanes to prevent unnecessary stops where there is a high frequency service. The effects of bus schemes on pedestrians must be carefully assessed, and zebra crossings may need replacing by the pelican type. Frontages may also be adversely affected by the operations and diversions of traffic onto unsuitable roads. This causes environmental deterioration and increased hazards and effects on parking, if this has been previously permitted. Particular attention must also be given to enforcement and regulation problems.

Assessments

It is usually essential to undertake a comprehensive cost–benefit analysis, taking into account bus passengers, and the costs and benefits to transport operators. By considering only operator benefits, in the case of one-man bus operation, heavy disbenefits have been incurred by other groups of users due to the increased delays imposed by longer stopping times.

Cost–benefit analysis is used to compare the relative net benefits of alternative schemes and the before-and-after effects on vehicle operating costs, crew costs and passenger costs. The coordination between transport operator, police and traffic engineer is essential to achieve maximum community benefit from management measures.

CONGESTION AND RESTRAINT

The alleviation of congestion is a growing problem, because of its effects on trade, public transport viability, and the inevitable environmental consequences to society. Traffic management measures, if soundly based, permit greater traffic flows to be accommodated more safely on the existing road system with some benefits in time savings to travellers. While some management schemes have been detrimental to the environment from their inception, the overall deterioration has been due to the steady growth in personal travel generated by car ownership. This traffic growth has steadily eroded the benefits obtained from the original management measures; often the opportunities and necessity of building a primary urban motorway network have been lost and with it the creation of environmental areas. Consequently there has been a steady and spreading deterioration of unsuitable conditions to all parts of the city.

Current objectives in management are to seek for ways in which to impose restraint in traffic growth and use. The principal economic methods under discussion include supplementary licensing, proposed on a period basis for the use of specified areas, and road pricing, whereby a driver is charged for the use of the roads. Road pricing may be effected in a large number of ways varying from simple time expendable meters to complex variable rate systems, where the charges are automatically metered. An alternative to road pricing is to extend parking charges, but it is estimated that parking charges have to be relatively higher to achieve the same results because they only restrain journeys ending at a particular destination and do not directly discourage the use of roads generally. Road pricing affects the proportion of through journeys in an area. Similar discriminatory problems arise with differential fuel tax policies.

Finally physical restraints can be placed on the principal routes, particularly the main radial roads, by introducing a "throttle point", with signals or turn prohibitions, and permitting only public transport and emergency vehicles unrestricted access.

Traffic planning strategy should encourage a more positive approach, creating suitable alternatives by long-term changes in urban layouts, encouraging some types of journey and discouraging others, while investing in alternative forms of transport. Restrictive policies in isolation tend to induce enforcement and administrative problems. Since the introduction in London of controlled parking schemes (in 1960) the issues of the fixed penalties has risen almost tenfold from under 100,000 to nearly a million and the number of wardens has increased from less than 200 to over 1500. At the same time courts and police have become overburdened and a large number of offenders escape the consequences of their disdemeanours.

SEGREGATION MEASURES

Traffic Segregation

While the principles have been widely applied to segregating vehicles and pedestrians its potential utilisation for other purposes has not been adequately realised. Segregation not only permits the designer a more specific brief in meeting the basic requirements of particular categories of user more precisely, and with less compromise, but ensures a more amenable and comfortable environment for their needs and encourages a better performance of a less taxing nature. A purpose-built facility is often more cost effective and can be located, and integrated with surrounding land-uses, with the least intrusion and disturbance.

Pedestrian Segregation

Complete segregation of pedestrian and vehicle is often difficult to achieve in existing urban layouts but all new development should permit a design, for each type of use, taking special account of individual characteristics and requirements. In central areas, for acceptable pedestrian operation, shops, offices, public buildings and entertainment places must have direct and rapid access to public transport and car parking facilities. Differences in vertical level for the main walkways should be kept to a minimum. Where height differences are unavoidable they should be catered for by ramps, escalators and moving walkways rather than steps. Generally many of these requirements demand the regrouping of individual units into single blocks offering full access facilities. Provision for loading and unloading by rear access or underground connections to premises will, together with the removal of parked street vehicles, considerably reduce the accident potential within commercial developments.

New residential areas must depend to a large extent on the design of suitable road systems fulfilling their special function. Centres of gravity of individual parts of the large estate must be close to a major feeder route carrying public service vehicles into the town's main road system and connected at stopping points by special bus draw-ins constructed with pleasantly designed enclosed shelters and seats, timetable displays and directly connected to the main covered walkways. Where neighbourhood centres are provided with shops and recreational buildings there should be separately located and segregated footpaths to the various parts of the estate. Other roads should specifically only provide access to and from an individual's residence or garage, and not permit through access. An example of a segregated residential area is shown in Fig. 5.5.

The design problems for traffic in new areas (see Fig. 5.6) are far more easily dealt with than those in the existing towns built without the numbers of present-day road vehicles and levels of activity in mind. In old towns segregation of pedestrian and vehicle can only be accomplished on a more limited scale. However, many examples of pedestrian streets have been introduced into a variety of towns and cities reducing accident rates and improving amenity and, often, trade. This is achieved by diverting through traffic away from pedestrian areas, constructing peripheral parking facilities and providing new public transport routes and interchanges. Servicing premises is sometimes difficult and best overcome by constructing rear service access or underground roads, but if these alternatives are not possible regulation is resorted to by restricting servicing to times outside the principal shopping hours. In such circumstances very careful design, warning, and control has to be introduced to

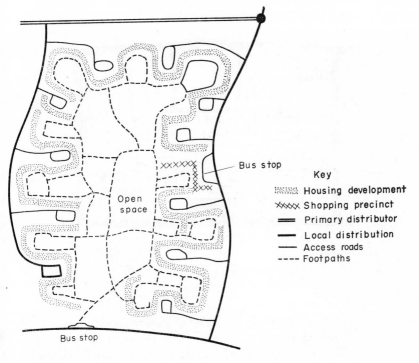

Bus stop

Open
space

Key

▦ Housing development
×××× Shopping precinct
═══ Primary distributor
━━ Local distribution
━ Access roads
---- Footpaths

Bus stop

FIG. 5.5.   Segregation in a residential area.

prevent accidents to pedestrians conditioned to a vehicle-free environment. An alternative method that is practical, provided that distances are not too great, is the breaking down of loads into small lots and trolleying the consignments to individual shops and offices, where these are not too large.

In areas where vehicular traffic is unavoidable, and particularly at junctions, it is possible to install a limited measure of segregation for reasons of safety by erecting guard railing. This prevents crossing at other than selected points and pedestrian controlled lights can be installed to further separate vehicular and pedestrian movement. At sites with very heavy crossings of pedestrians it will often be desirable, both because of delays to traffic and the safety of pedestrians, to construct subways,

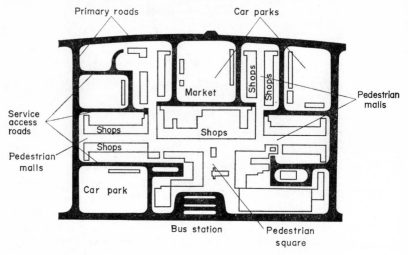

Fig. 5.6.   Pedestrian town centre (Stevenage).

with suitably located ramps to encourage their convenient use. A major site difficulty is inevitably the high cost of modification to services, but this can be minimised and at the same time pedestrian ramp gradients reduced if the road is raised relative to the adjacent footpath. The major objection to this method is generally not the cost but difficulties in narrow streets of obstructing frontages and the discharge of exhaust fumes at a particularly annoying height, but this can be overcome by constructing walls. Separation of turning and directional vehicular movements enables the engineer to locate refuge areas across the main lines of flow and so assist road users by simplifying their decisions and improving safety. In a similar manner, one-way streets can reduce accident potential by a reduction in the number of types of conflicts present at a junction.

Cyclist Segregation

Segregation of the cyclist is no less important than of the pedestrian. Whatever proportion of a car passenger unit is considered appropriate the fact is that the road width occupied by cyclists, often in pairs, is effectively nearly a lane, and, due to their relatively low speed and instability, they are a potential danger to themselves and to drivers. Cyclists on their own tracks need less space because of the lower relative speed differences present than on the road and, like the pedestrians, require less than a quarter of the construction depth of road pavements. This represents a considerable saving in construction costs. In view of high accident rates careful consideration should be given to the provision of multi-purpose cycle tracks accommodating pedal cycles, mopeds and scooters but with some form of effective speed control.

Vehicle Segregation

Reduction in exposure risk, by the segregation of pedestrian, cyclists and motorists, can further be achieved by the segregation of vehicular traffic. External and internal traffic to towns can be separated by the construction of by-passes and ring roads within towns; through and stopping traffic can be separated by the provision of through and local routes, creating environmental areas. Small towns and villages, astride important routes, are often made intolerable by through traffic. Motorways can often replace a number of such routes through a region, allowing the existing network to revert to local use, and improving safety and environment simultaneously.

With an increasing proportion of cars within the total traffic flow the case for car-only roads is emphasised. Considerable construction cost savings can be made because lane widths can be narrower, headrooms beneath structures can be lowered by about a third and by using steeper gradients the total interchange requirements in land, roadworks and structures are minimised. Structural and pavement costs are reduced and the visual impact on the environment is less. Better opportunities are created for inserting new roads into urban areas as curvature and greater route diversion are not so dependent on benefits from the time savings of commercial vehicles. Similar benefits can be granted to public transport by the purpose building of new bus routes, possibly shared with commercial vehicles. Both categories of vehicle generally need to penetrate to the core of activities whereas this is not a basic requirement for the majority of private cars. Fortunately, from a traffic viewpoint, the peak uses of the two categories do not coincide and thus road space is capable of maximum use over an extended time period. The likely joint benefits would justify such purpose-built roads which presently are not economically viable when considered individually.

Other important segregations of traffic are made by direction (central dividing strips), by turning movement (storage lanes), by speed conditions (speed change lanes), traffic signals (separation in time) and by other traffic control measures such as one-way streets.

ENVIRONMENTAL STUDIES AND ASSESSMENTS

The demand for greater travel results in increasing traffic flows, which may arise on existing roads or be accommodated on new routes, particularly urban motorways. Both situations can lead to environmental problems caused by traffic noise, visual intrusion, air pollution and vibration. The insertion of new motorways into urban environments can also generate secondary traffic effects which radiate outwards from interchanges, along feeder routes, and cause a marked deterioration in environmental conditions to people not previously affected. Traffic management schemes may also have marked environmental consequences. It is thus more than ever necessary for the engineer to estimate, by careful study, the impact of traffic measures on the overall quality of life, and to ensure that steps are taken to ameliorate the disturbances to individuals. Finally, that in the aggregate the result is of total benefit to society. For the assessment of each type of disturbance, there are four principal categories of investigation, dealing with generation, propagation, possible effects and methods of reduction or control.

Noise

Noise is best described as unwanted sound and its measurement therefore imposes considerable difficulties, as it will vary with individuals and between situations. Sound is energy transmitted in a longitudinal wave travelling at a velocity of about 340 m/s through air at sea level. The energy carried by the wave, whose length in time is the frequency (f cycle/s – hertz), is conveniently measured as a pressure (P μN/m^2). Sound waves cause an oscillation of the ear drum, whose sensitivity varies with age, sex and frequency. The minimum sound perceived is 20 μN/m^2 and the maximum, at the pain threshold, is about 100 N/m^2. The difference between the two pressures is in the ratio of $1: 5 \times 10^6$ and, for practical reasons, sound pressures are usually expressed in a relative scale of decibels. The decibel is defined as ten times the logarithm to the base ten of the ratio between two quantities of power. Because the sound power is related to the square of the sound pressure a suitable noise scale is defined as follows:

$$\text{sound pressure level} = 10 \log_{10} \left(\frac{P_1^2}{P_0^2}\right) = 20 \log_{10} \left(\frac{P_1}{P_0}\right) \text{ dB,}$$

where P_1 is the sound pressure being measured and P_0 is the reference pressure based on the threshold of hearing. The range is now from 0 dB to 134 dB. Because the scale is a multiplicative it is necessary to add together the intensities (powers) and not pressures in order to sum the loudness of sounds, e.g. two almost equal sounds increases the level by about 3 dB while ten almost equal sounds increases it by 10 dB. Each time the sources are increased tenfold, add 10 dB to the sound level.

The loudness of a tone is given in phons (P); an equivalent loudness of n phons equals that of the standard tone at n decibels above its zero. A subjective scale of sones (S) is formed so that the apparent loudness ratio of two sounds assessed by observers is given by the ratio of their sone values and $S = 2^{(P-40)/10}$. Most traffic noise measurements are weighted with respect to the response characteristics of the human ear.

Sound Level Measurements

A suitable microphone and amplifier will respond to sound pressure levels and indicate frequency levels. By attaching a filter, which nullifies or screens frequencies outside those to which the ear responds, a scale of equivalent values, for human hearing, are obtained by the so-called A, B or C weighting levels. For traffic noise measurements the A weighting is used and measurements are made in dB(A), with little weight given to low-frequency sounds. There are a variety of instruments available ranging from simple peak recorders to meters with statistical distribution analysers. Each type can be set up at sites alongside the road and observations taken at predetermined time intervals, or recorded on a chart by means of a pen, either in the field or the laboratory as shown in Fig. 5.7. Statistical analysis enables the field records to be fed, at set time intervals, to a counter for up to twelve ranges of sound levels. From the counter record, a cumulative frequency curve can be drawn, enabling percentile

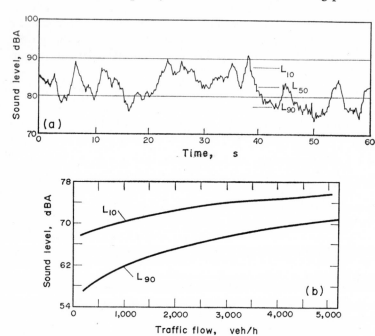

Fig. 5.7.   Noise levels near motorways.

values to be deduced, as shown in Fig. 5.8. The percentile values L_{10}, L_{50} and L_{90} refer to the sound levels which are exceeded 10%, 50% and 90% of a specified time.

In practice the L_{10} levels are important and have been used to specify disturbance (indoor levels) by the Wilson Committee. These are also used in the computation of the Traffic Noise Index (TNI), developed by the Building Research Station, to indicate noise annoyance by a composite weighted variation, as follows:

$$\text{TNI} = 4\,(L_{10} - L_{90}) + L_{90} - 30.$$

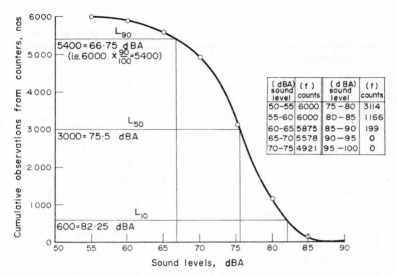

FIG. 5.8. Sound levels, cumulative frequency curve.

It is usually obtained by measuring levels for 100 s in each hour for 24 h.

Subjects generally suffer greater annoyance from high peaks occurring in low background levels, e.g. a motor cycle accelerating at night in a quiet residential area. Table 5.2 indicates the effects of noise with examples.

Other studies have also quantitatively related physical measurements of traffic noise to resulting dissatisfaction. The average of L_{10}, from 0600 to midnight, outdoors on a weekday is a useful approximation of dissatisfaction. A Swedish study has indicated the following relationship, based on the level equivalent (L_{eq}) to the energy mean of the fluctuating sound levels:

$$L_{eq} = 10 \log \tfrac{1}{100} \Sigma 10^{L_i/10} f_i$$

where L_i is the median sound level of the 5 dB(A) interval i,

f_i is the percentage time that a sound level is in the ith interval.

Robinson has developed the Noise Pollution Level (LNP), applicable to general noise disturbance, including aircraft and road traffic:

$$LNP = L_{eq} + 2 \cdot 56s$$

H

TABLE 5.2.   EFFECTS OF NOISE AND EXAMPLES OF NOISE LEVELS

	Noise effects	Decibels	Typical examples
Damage	Blast deafness	150	Explosions
	Pain	140	Engine tests
	Threshold of feeling	120	
		110	Thunder, gunfire Pneumatic drill Aeroplane
		100	
Annoyance	Reduced working efficiency	90	Underground railway Busy street
	Occupational deafness	85	
			Noisy factory
		80	
	Interference with normal speech	70	Noisy office Suburban train
		65	
	Annoyance		Factory
		60	
Acceptable background levels	Typing office		Large shop
	Restaurant or general office	50	Quiet office Average house
	Private office	45	
	Lecture room & suburban living room	40	
			Country road
	Suburban bedroom & library	30	Quiet conversation
			Whisper
		20	
			Quiet church
	Very faint	10	Sound-proof room
			Threshold of hearing

where s is the standard deviation of the instantaneous sound level considered in time over the specified period.

Vehicle noise increases with its size, power and speed and is influenced by such operating conditions as gradient, surface texture and manoeuvring. While exhaust noise predominates up to 40 km/h as speed increases, aerodynamic and tyre noise form a greater proportion of the total emissions. The volume, composition and consistency of the flow are predominant factors in the general noise climate, as shown in Table 5.3.

TABLE 5.3. MEAN VALUES OF L_{10} IN dB(A) AT BUILDING FAÇADE FOR
TABULATED DISTANCES FROM SOURCE

Speed (km/h) at flow 5000 veh/day	Without barrier. Distance from source (m)			With 2 m high barrier. Distance from source (m)			Traffic flow correction. Add to all values in table	
	10	25	50	10	25	50	Veh/day	Add dB(A)
50	70	65	60	58	52	46	10,000	2
70	75	70	65	63	57	51	20,000	4
100	80	75	70	68	62	56	50,000	7·5

Energy is dissipated in doing work and thus sound pressures are reduced by atmospheric absorbtion, ground wave, wind, buildings and land form. As an approximation, each doubling of the distance causes a drop of about 6 dB(A) in L_{10} and L_{50} levels, but for background levels, L_{90}, the approximation is about 3 dB(A) for each doubling of the distance. A further rough guide of the subjective impression of noise indicates that each reduction of 10 dB(A) corresponds to a halving of the apparent loudness.

Noise control can be achieved in three principal ways. The first is by reducing the noise at the source by better vehicle design and more stringent legislation to ensure that vehicles are operated and maintained within the relevant levels, as shown in Table 5.4. Secondly, because traffic characteristics also affect noise levels, design and management of traffic can be effective in reducing noise levels at critical sites. Finally, by planning areas with sufficient shielding and designing buildings with adequate

TABLE 5.4.   MAXIMUM PERMITTED NOISE LEVELS FOR MOTOR VEHICLES
(see BS 3425: 1966)

Vehicle type	Construction limit, dB(A)	Use limit** dB(A)	EEC recommendation
Motor cycles > 125 cc capacity	86	90	84
Passenger vehicles (< 12 passengers)	84	87	82
Goods vehicles not exceeding 3½ tons	85	92	84
Goods vehicles > 3½ tons & buses	89	92	89–91*

*Depends on B.H.P.   **Use limit 3 dB(A) above construction limit for vehicles registered after Nov. 1970.

sound insulation, noise intrusion can be controlled (see Table 5.5). There are many ways of achieving this, varying from siting the road in cuttings, earth mounding and contouring, constructing carriageway edge barriers, siting less noise-sensitive buildings such as warehouses, garages and factories alongside the line of route, or by cladding buildings with a noise shield. Figures 5.9 and 5.10 illustrate the relationships between noise, motorway construction and the siting of buildings.

The *Noise Insulation Regulations 1973*, made under the *Land Compensation Act, 1973* (Sec. 20), provide rights to insulation, for residential properties, against traffic noise from new and improved roads, and include a 15-year provision. Methods of prediction and measurement are given in a technical memorandum *Traffic Noise Prediction and L10 Measurements*. The specified level adopted is an L_{10} of 68 dB(A), obtained as the mean of all hourly L_{10}'s between 0600–2400 h on a working day.

Vibrations

Traffic vibrations are usually too low to cause structural damage to buildings but may create unpleasant and worrying sensations, as can be experienced when standing on a footbridge crossing a major traffic

TABLE 5.5.   AVERAGE NOISE REDUCTION VALUES

Window	Reduction in noise level, dB(A)
Open (single)	5 – 10
Closed (single)	15 – 20
Fixed (single)	20 – 25
Fixed plate glass (6 mm) sealed	25 – 30
Sliding (double) (twin 4 mm)	30
Fixed (double) 200 mm gap	40
Walls (no windows)	
115 mm (4½ in.)	45
230 mm (9 in.)	50

route. Generally, because many surfaces are relatively smooth, the vibrations from motorways are less than those on corresponding urban main roads.

Vibrations are described by the amplitude, velocity and acceleration of the particles or surface affected and the number of completed cycles in a time period, i.e. the frequency. Peak values are usually measured and, in the case of a phenomenon with a sinusoidal relationship, are related as follows, although approximately for most vibrations:

$$2\pi \times \text{frequency} = \frac{\text{acceleration}}{\text{velocity}} = \frac{\text{velocity}}{\text{amplitude}} \,.$$

Measurements are generally made with instruments recording amplitude, velocity and/or acceleration by using a transducer to convert the energy into a direct reading electrical or mechanical signal.

Traffic vibrations are caused by variations in the load transmitted to the road by the vehicle's suspension and by impact with surface irregular-

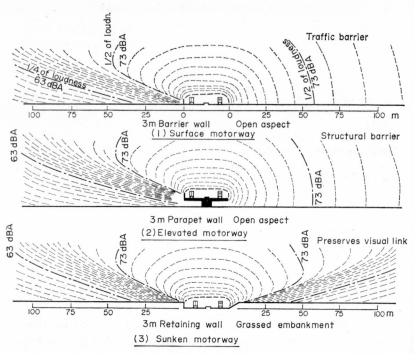

FIG. 5.9. Noise levels from motorways.

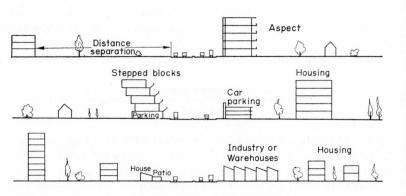

FIG. 5.10. Building near motorways.

ities. The frequency (f) of vehicle-induced vibration is represented by the formula:

$$f = \frac{1}{2\pi} \sqrt{\frac{M}{m} \times \frac{g}{d}}$$

where M = total vehicle weight,
$\quad\quad m$ = unsprung weight,
$\quad\quad d$ = static deflection of tyre,
$\quad\quad g$ = acceleration due to gravity.

Most frequencies from vehicles are in the range 7–20 c/s and resonance is likely to occur with silty soils resulting in larger amplitudes, but these,

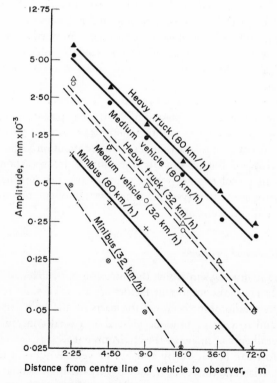

Fig. 5.11. Vibration amplitude by distance and type of vehicle.

in any case, are small. Most vibration is transmitted through the road pavement directly to the supporting soil mass. Because of the complexity of the systems involved there is a considerable variability in results, due to the differences in materials and the relationship with distance, but it is generally accepted that for short distances amplitude and velocity varies inversely with distance as shown in Fig. 5.11.

Air Pollution

The effect of air pollution is felt by a deterioration in the health and performance of man, animals and plants and can create an intolerable or poorer environment. It is generated by homes, industry and motor vehicles and, while the Clean Air Acts have had a marked effect on background levels, that of traffic is increasing and becomes more noticeable. The concentration of emissions is reduced in proportion to increased distance from the source, although in unfavourable meteorological and topographical conditions photochemical smog may be formed as in Los Angeles.

Traffic pollution has been measured at a number of sites in Great Britain as shown in Tables 5.6 and 5.7. Different pollutants are emitted by diesel and petrol engines and the concentrations vary with operating conditions. Whereas smoke has directed public attention to diesel engines, it is the invisible pollutants of carbon monoxide, hydrocarbons and lead emitted from petrol engines which seriously threaten health. The only real safeguards are to strictly control the emission of engine pollutants by legislation and enforcement.

Visual Intrusion and Severance

There are many ways in which the intrusion of vehicles and roads can be reduced. The most important factors are those of scale relationships and the interrelationships between the parts of the built environment; landscape and townscape must be viewed as a total concept concerned for the overall enhancement of the environment.

Discomfort can be caused by a flicker of vehicle lights at night, both to the pedestrian and the resident, and also by the high standards of street lighting provided on major routes. These conflicts are best resolved by

TABLE 5.6. AIR POLLUTION

Pollutant	Blackwall tunnel	Fleet street	London av. background levels	London smog 1957
Sulphur dioxide (μg/m^3)	—	384	—	—
Smoke (μg/m^3)	202	430	35	670
Lead (μg/m^3)	27·2	3·2	2	5
Carbon monoxide (ppm)	120	23	11	360
Nitric oxide (pp 100 m)	121	—	3·3	
Nitrogen dioxide (pp 100 m)	10	—	2·4	
Hydrocarbons (μg/1000 m^3):				
Fluoranthene	110	—	2·5	407
1:2 Benzpyrene	18	26	2·0	74
Pyrene	98	—	2·5	317
Coronene	22	20	1·0	28
Anthranthrene	7	6	0·5	38
1:12 Benzperylene	51	46	2·5	106
3:4 Benzpyrene	31	—	5·0	222

segregation policies and locating facilities with compatibility uppermost in the evaluation.

Severance results from the division of an area by roads and traffic. The worst effects of separation can be minimised by careful design and often additional costs. These may be incurred during construction, i.e. elevating a route to prevent interference with the local movement pattern or depressing it to facilitate overbridging; or during operation by increasing vehicle distances, i.e. locating routes on the boundaries of areas. Tunnelling, while expensive, permits land to be developed without interference or areas to be left undisturbed.

The incompatibility of pedestrian and vehicular environments is obvious, both from a consideration of amenity and for safety reasons. In many respects the pedestrian has been neglected in design, and certainly in cost–benefit analysis, and it is probably right that they should be considered more favourably than any other group of traveller.

TABLE 5.7. POLLUTANTS (Source: Colwill, D. M., Atmospheric pollution from vehicle emissions: measurements in Reading 1971, TRRL Report LR 541, 1973)

Pollutant	Regression equation	
Average carbon monoxide concentration, C, ppm (3 h period)	$C = 2\cdot96 + 0\cdot00032V + 0\cdot0000005V^2$	$V =$ total number of vehicles passing in 3 h period.
Nitric oxide concentration, N, $\mu g/m^3$ (1 h period)	$N = 46\cdot9 - 0\cdot036T + 0\cdot00004T^2$	$T =$ hourly traffic flow.
Smoke level, S, $\mu g/m^3$ (3 h period)	$S = 9\cdot49 + 0\cdot022V$	$V =$ total number of vehicles in 3 h period.
Lead concentration, L, $\mu g/m^3$ (3 h period)	$L = 0\cdot000249P + 0\cdot0431$	$P =$ total number of petrol-engine vehicles in 3 h period.

FURTHER READING

BROCH, J. T. (1969) *Application of B & K Equipment to Acoustic Noise Measurements*. Bruel and Kjaer, Copenhagen.

BUCHANAN, C. and CROMPTON, D. H. (1968) Objectives of traffic management. *Traff. Engng. and Control*, **10**(1).

BUILDING RESEARCH STATION (1971) *Motorway Noise and Dwellings*. Dept. of the Environment Building Research Station, Digest 135.

BURT, M. E. (1972) Roads and the environment. TRRL Report LR 441. The Transport and Road Research Laboratory.

CHU, C. (1972) Environmental effects of urban road traffic. C.E.S. Info. Paper 26, Centre for Environmental Studies.

COLWILL, D. M. (1973) Atmospheric pollution from vehicle emissions: measurements in Reading, 1971. TRRL Report LR 541. The Transport and Road Research Laboratory.

DELANEY, M. E. *et al. Propagation of Traffic Noise in Typical Urban Situations.* NPL Acoustics Report AC 54. National Physical Laboratory.

DEPARTMENT OF THE ENVIRONMENT (1972) New housing and road traffic noise—a design guide for architects. Design Bulletin 26, H.M.S.O.

DIECKMANN, D. (1958) A study of the influence of vibrations on man. *Ergonomics,* **1**(4).

FISHER, C. H. (1969) Petrol engine emissions – what next? *Automobile Engr.,* April.

GREATER LONDON COUNCIL. *Traffic Noise.* Greater London Council, 1966; and *Traffic Noise, Major Urban Roads,* Urban Design Bulletin No. 1, 1970.

HAYNES, C. D. and SOUTHALL, M. (1968) Atmospheric pollution from petrol engines. Motor Industries Research Association Report No. 1968/5.

HOPKINSON, R. G. (1972) The evaluation of visual intrusion in transport situations. *Traff. Engng. & Control,* **14** (8).

HOUSE, M. E. (1973) Traffic induced vibration in buildings. *J. Instn. Highway Engrs.* **xx**(2).

JOHNSON, D. R. and SAUNDERS, E. G. (1968) The evaluation of noise from freely flowing road traffic. *J. Sound and Vibr.* **7**(207).

KERENSKY, O. A. (1968) *Urban Motorways and their Environment.* Rees Jeffreys Triennial Lecture, Town Planning Institute, London.

LANGDON, F. J. and SCHOLES, W. E. (1968) *The Traffic Noise Index: a Method of Controlling Noise Nuisance,* Building Research Station Current Paper 38/68; and *Subjective Response to Road Traffic Noise,* BRS Current Paper 37/68.

LEONARD, D. R. (1966) Human tolerance levels for bridge vibrations. RRL Report LR 34. The Road Research Laboratory.

MAYCOCK, G. (1971) Implementation of traffic restraint. Symp. on Traffic Restraint. Instn. Highway Engrs., April.

MILLARD, R. (Chairman) (1970) A review of road traffic noise. The Working Group on Research into Road Traffic Noise. RRL Report LR 357. The Road Research Laboratory.

MILLAR, A. and COOK, J. A. (1968) *Pedestrians and Vehicles on Housing Estates: a User Study.* Building Research Station Current Paper No. CP 23/68.

MINISTRY OF TRANSPORT. *Urban Traffic Engineering Techniques,* H.M.S.O., 1965. *Traffic Management and Parking,* 4.134 Circular, 1969. *Traffic and Transport Plans,* Roads Circular 1/68.

MINISTRY OF TRANSPORT (1967) *Cars for Cities—a Study of Trends in the Design of Vehicles with Particular Reference to Their Use in Towns.* H.M.S.O.

MINISTRY OF TRANSPORT (1970) *Roads for the Future: the New Inter-urban Plan for England.* Cmnd. 4369, H.M.S.O.

NATIONAL SOCIETY FOR CLEAN AIR (1967) Air pollution from road vehicles. Report by the Technical Committee of the National Society for Clean Air, London.

O'LEARY, J. D. (1969) Evaluating the environmental impact of an urban expressway. *Tr. Quarterly,* July.

OLIVER, W. T. (1968/9) Practical emission control systems—air injection into exhaust manifold. *Proc. Instn. Mech. Engrs.*, **183** (3E).

PAGE, E. W. M. and SEMPLE, W., Silent and vibration-free sheet pile driving. *Proc. Instn. Civil Engrs.*, **41**, 19.

REED, L. E. and BARRETT, C. F. (1965) Air pollution from road traffic—measurements in Archway Road, London. *Int. J. Air Water Poll.*, **9**. Pergamon Press.

REED, L. E. (1973) Environmental pollution. Paper No. 6 at 100th Annual Conference, Instn. of Municipal Engineers.

RIDLEY, G. (1973) Bus lanes in London. *J. Instn. Highway Engrs.*, **xx** (7).

ROBINSON, D. W. (1969) *The Concept of Noise Pollution Level*. Ministry of Technology, N.P.L., Aero Report AC 38.

SHERWOOD, P. T. and BOWERS, P. H. (1970) Air pollution from road traffic—a review of the present position. RRL Report LR 352. The Road Research Laboratory.

THE NOISE ADVISORY COUNCIL (1972) *Traffic Noise: The Vehicle Regulations and their Enforcement*, H.M.S.O.

TROTT, J. J. and WHIFFIN, A. C. (1965) Measurements of the axle loads of moving vehicles on trunk roads. *Rds. and Rd. Constr.* **43** (511).

VARIOUS. *Traffic Management*, Proc. PTRC Seminar, 1971; and *Traffic Management*, Proc. PTRC Seminar, 1973. Planning and Transport Research and Computation Co. Ltd.

WALLER, R. A. (1967) *Environmental Quality, its Measurement and Control*. Int. Symp. on Urban Renewal, Brussels.

WATKINS, L. H. (1972) Urban transport and environmental pollution. TRRL Report LR 455. The Transport and Road Research Laboratory.

WEBSTER, F. V. (1971) Priority to buses as part of traffic management. TRRL Report LR 448. The Transport and Road Research Laboratory.

WEEB, J. (1973) Noise studies related to motorway alignment. *J. Instn. Highway Engrs.*, **xx** (5).

WHITTIN, A. C. and LEONARD, D. R., A survey of traffic induced vibrations, RRL Report LR 418, Building Research Station. Cracking in building, BRS Digest No. 75 (1966); Vibrations in building – 1 and 2, BRS Digest Nos. 117 and 118 (1970), Building Research Station, H.M.S.O.

WILSON, SIR ALAN (Chairman) (1963) Noise. Final Report of the Committee on the Problem of Noise. Cmnd. 2056, H.M.S.O.

CHAPTER 6

The Road User, The Vehicle and The Road

THE ROAD USER

The effective design and control of the road system by engineers demands a close study of human behaviour with an understanding of the limitations of human performance in the varied circumstances of the road environment. Individual elements to be considered are the road user, the vehicle and the road environment; these form a complex interactive system whose performance is measured in terms of output efficiency, safety and amenity. Creating the right environmental condition is a worthwhile investment leading to user confidence and acceptability which, in turn, enables a balance to be drawn between physical and legislative control. The need for restrictive legislation, with its attendant enforcement difficulties, can then be reserved for a minority of users who do not measure up to some minimum standard.

PHYSIOLOGICAL FACTORS

Before turning to the complexities of behaviour it is necessary to consider, in simple terms, basic human physiology and the perception system. Each individual has certain basic physical attributes such as hearing, vision, strength and mobility, all of which are amenable to measurement. Under different circumstances, and at different times, the measured values of these characteristics may well vary with an individual according to imposed conditions such as fatigue, cramp, cold or a changed psychological state. Some of the elements relevant to the traffic situation are shown in Table 6.1. Well-designed roads and vehicles, suitable for their operating environments, help to limit human variability and, together with better education, reduce the possibility of poor perform- ance. Minimum road user standards can thus be set by legislation and regulation.

The functions and relationships of human organs, responsive to external stimuli, are briefly described below.

THE SENSORY SYSTEM

The central part of the nervous system, containing some two thousand million interconnected cells, is located in and protected by the skull and vertebrae. Intercommunication must be maintained at all levels between these individual cells (grey matter) which are connected together by long fibres (white matter). Different parts of the brain are primarily concerned with specific tasks like vision, hearing, memory, motor coordination (muscular movement), taste, and smell, and through connections in the vertebrae with movement in arms, trunk and legs. There is not a single master central control; the whole system is maintained by the effectiveness of their intercommunicating links.

The unit structure of the nervous system is the neurone consisting of a cell and connecting fibres known as dendrites and axons; the former maintain inter-cellular contact while the latter are insulated fibres which pass signals directly from one part of the body to another. Sensory neurones relay impulses from sensory cells and motor neurones deal with control signals to muscles. A reflex defines the basic unit of activity within the system and the response to a perception stimulus and resulting trans- mission of a motor signal is called a reflex arc. Certain reflexes, such as breathing and blinking, are inborn (unconditioned), but other reflexes are being continually learnt (conditioned). As in all communications systems time is an important element if it is to work precisely and effectively (see Table 6.2). The transmission of sensory signals (small electrical impulses) to and from sensory organs also activates cells in the brain, where coordination and assessment are often required, before responses are induced in muscles and other organs. Time of varying amounts is re- quired, with small stimulii, under adverse conditions, needing longer recognition periods than correspondingly larger stimuli. Conditioned

TABLE 6.1.   HUMAN FACTORS IN ROAD USER PERFORMANCE

Factors and effects	Defects developed	Possible corrective measures and controls
Visual: intake of information of drivers and pedestrians	Incorrect situation interpretation due to:	
	(i) Faulty visual acuity	(i) Standards of visual acuity with and without glasses
	(ii) Stereoscopic defects	(ii) Simplifications of road layout, improved road markings and access control
	(iii) Poor adaptation of eye to varying illumination and impaired night vision	(iii) Improved street and vehicle lighting. Reduction of glare
	(iv) Colour blindness	(iv) Careful colour selection of control devices and shape regularity
Hearing: intake of information, particularly important to elderly pedestrians	Lowered perceptual performance, serious at nights for pedestrians	Pedestrian segregation measures; guard railing to prevent sudden movements into carriageway. Improved crossings. Better street lighting. Surface irregularities causing vibrational warnings to drivers
Other physiological	Posture and operating conditions leading to fatigue and impaired performance	Improvements in vehicle design, control layouts and equipment carried. Higher road design standards, control devices signs and lighting

TABLE 6.1 *(continued)*

Factors and effects	Defects developed	Possible corrective measures and controls
Psychological	Aggression, risk taking exhibitionism, lack of concentration, attitudinal instabilities. Task overloading leading to incorrect responses or event sequencing	Standards of licensing raised; improved educational programmes; convicted persons to have psychological investigation and corrective treatment or licence withdrawal

TABLE 6.2.   STIMULUS RESPONSE TIME

Stimulus	Response time (s)
Sound	0·14
Touch	0·14
Light	0·18

responses to simple well learnt situations result in minimum reaction time as the higher thought processes are not called upon, but as new and complex situations arise more call is made on the higher thought planes leading to greater time needs before comprehensive action can take place.

VISION

The eye is the most important sensory organ for road users. The sensations produced by light waves on the retina enable a person to judge size, shape, colour, estimate distances and speed within the general perception of the external world. The images received are not always focused on the retina in the right plane. Where parallel rays are brought to focus in front or beyond the retina, the malfunction causes short or long sight.

Anomalies in the curvature of the eye also affect vision (astigmatism), but these, and other defective conditions, can be readily corrected by the use of optical aids. Where artificial aids, of any type, are required to raise performance to acceptable levels then legislation should ensure that the aid is efficient, appropriate to the use and worn.

Physical Features of the Eye

Figure 6.1 illustrates the main parts of the eye and the position of the optic nerve which transmits the perception of light to the brain. The two important types of retinal cell are cones and rods. Cones are distributed in greater numbers around the focal point and while they are less light-sensitive they are able to discriminate fine detail. The eye has a remarkable ability to discern detail and with normal visual acuity, under good lighting and contrast conditions, an object can be seen which subtends a visual angle of 1 minute. However, to detect moving objects and gauge their speeds and directions requires identifiable positional markers within the field of view and these are more prominent in the vertical rather than the horizontal plane. The rods, spread over the retina, are responsive to the lower levels of illumination but cannot discern colour. Contraction and dilation of the pupil affects the amount of light admitted to the retina but, unfortunately for the night driver, adaptation covers a relatively small range of illumination. Dark backgrounds interspersed with bright light sources markedly impairs visual performance, resulting in temporary blindness. Response times for maximum dilation to minimum contraction typically takes 3 s, while minimum contraction to maximum dilation (light to dark) has the much longer full recovery time of about 3 min, making correct steering difficult after glare.

Peripheral Vision

Because of the variation in types of cell in the retina, the ability to distinguish detail in the field of view falls for zonal areas located away from the focal point. While the total visual field for normal sight is approximately 180° horizontally and 145° vertically, anything outside the central $2\frac{1}{2}°$ of the force rapidly becomes indistinct, deteriorating towards

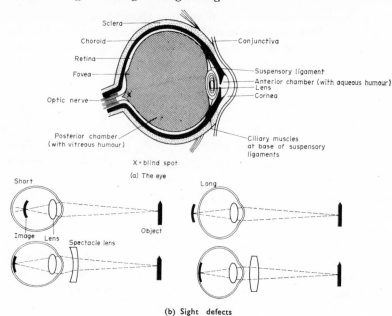

FIG. 6.1. (a) The eye. (b) Uncorrected and corrected eye sight deficiences.

the peripheral limits, as shown in Figs. 6.2 and 6.3. However, the movement of objects or subjects of high stimulation are readily detected on the peripheral field, causing the eye to shift and focus on the point of activity. A child running from a pavement and observed as a peripheral stimulus may enable a driver to take avoiding or braking action. Detrimental effects also occur; for example, a compelling advertisement may cause a driver to shift his gaze from the vehicle ahead and cause an accident. Obstruction of peripheral vision leads to a deterioration in steering and speed judgement, whereas loss of the central cone of vision has little affect on control but obviously, as in fog, increases the likelihood of impacting obstacles in the vehicle path.

Time is required by the driver to scan the field and focus on points of detail within it. His view in a vehicle is restricted to about one-fifth of his total surroundings. Situation appreciation is assisted by the depth of field and colour discrimination and, hence, visual performance at night is much reduced even without the impairment caused by light

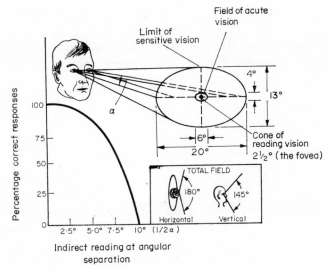

FIG. 6.2. Visual field.

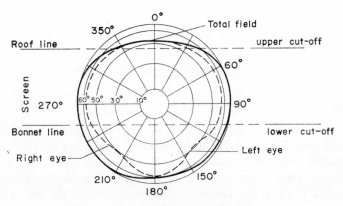

FIG. 6.3. Total field of view.

source glare. Vision is poor as the eye moves from one fixation point to the next and is also lost for about 0·3 s during blinking, which tends to increase with eye movements. Concentration reduces the normal blink rate of 5 per minute but results in eye fatigue.

Vision is affected by movement; as speed increases, the peripheral view shrinks with a corresponding increase in the focal point distance. At 40 km/h these are 100° and 180 m, and at 100 km/h 40° and 500 m respectively, as indicated in Fig. 6.4. Concentration also increases with

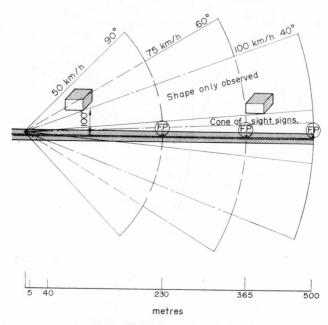

Fig. 6.4.   Visual fields to driver in motion.

speed and detailed scanning is reduced. The road alignment and control devices must be revealed at distances ahead and within the visual cone compatible with the operating conditions. Less time can be afforded in high speed and complex situations for the continuous shifting of the eyes to and from the traffic stream and, to overcome this, the size of signs must be increased and sited to lessen the visual angle. On motorways this factor may often entail the use of over-lane mounted signs.

Streaming is also caused by vehicle motion; every object within the peripheral view has a relative movement with respect to the driver's line of sight. The amount of displacement increases with the separation from the centre of vision. If the driver is looking ahead, the expansion is linear but becomes spiral when attention is directed at roadside objects. In the case of linear streaming, moving objects, within the visual field, will appear as marked discontinuities; but where a driver's eyes are directed sideways to signs or signals, while moving forward, detection of movement is difficult unless it is within the immediate vicinity of the point of focus. This factor probably accounts for some of the higher accident rate in the vicinity of crossings and traffic signals.

Distance Judgement

The judgement of space and distance is assisted by stereoscopic vision. A pedestrian crossing a road in the presence of vehicles must make a correct assessment of the arrival time of the next vehicle. This appears to be made in relation to both time and distance rather than just an assessment of speed. Pedestrians tend to overestimate the approaching vehicle's arrival time as its speed increases, i.e. underestimate higher vehicle speeds.

HEARING

The ear is the organ of perception which locates and senses sounds. While man responds to auditory and tactile stimuli more quickly than to those of light, hearing is generally less important to the road user. However, the sound of tyres on pavements, wind, engine noise, horns and other traffic noise are useful additional indicators and particularly so to elderly pedestrians who may hear rather than see vehicles, particularly at night. As shown in Fig. 6.5, sound waves cause oscillations in a taut membrane and these are transmitted, by three small bones through a further membrane, to a fluid within a canal in the inner ear.

OTHER SENSES

The vestibular organs, located within the inner ear, are sensitive to acceleration orientation and, unlike visual stimuli, cannot readily be ignored. Many of the refinements in vehicle control are made as the result of this static sensory information concerned generally with balance

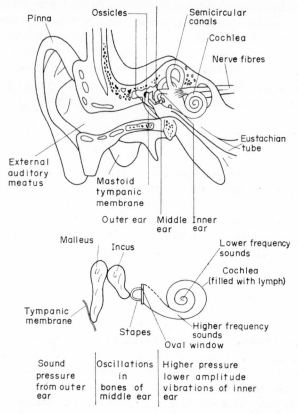

FIG. 6.5. The ear and diagrammatic functioning of middle and inner ear.

and stability. Kinaesthetic senses are perceptual indicators of the relative spatial position of head and limbs, important to vehicle control operation. Such emergency situations as fire and overheated engines or brakes may first be detected by smell, through the olfactory senses. The thermal senses respond to climatic and environmental conditions while the tactile sense is important in ergonomic design of control switches. Finally pain may have important effects on other senses and also concentration causing the onset of fatigue. It may be induced by other conditions such as those occurring in cramped and overheated environments and due to cold and

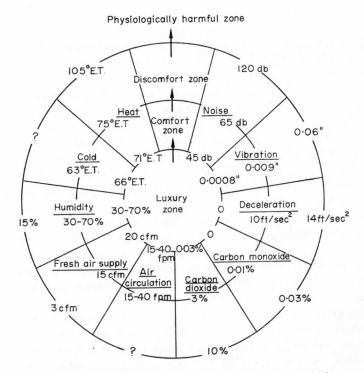

FIG. 6.6. Physical variables influencing driver comfort. (Source: McFarland, R.A., An epidemiological approach to the control of motor vehicle accidents, Sun Life Insurance Company, Montreal, 1955.)

glare. Environments must be within comfortable operating limits, as shown in Fig. 6.6, if task performance is to be adequately maintained over normal operating periods.

APPLICATIONS

Generally the visual senses are overloaded, while the highly significant auditory and vestibular senses are under-utilized in the driving task. The use of audio signs, electronically triggered at dangerous sites, can now be supplemented by audio direction signs. Information from recorded tapes is transmitted by roadside apparatus to vehicle mounted receivers tuned to the correct frequency. More sophisticated systems allow traffic controllers to interrupt car radios and to broadcast emergency messages on breakdowns, accidents or weather hazards ahead of the driver. Vibratory effects can be induced by road surface changes such as raised markers (jiggle bars) and other devices. Generally uncomfortable sensations are required at dangerous sites, although devices conducive to accidents must always be avoided. Speed control can be effectively introduced where the majority of vehicles are of a similar type by constructing road surface warping which makes driving, outside the specified speed, uncomfortable. Both visual and vibratory stimulators can be used together to highlight colour and surface contrasts and where bad weather may obscure one or other type at certain times.

Psychological factors influence the physiological state through glands secreting hormones, which control heartbeat, breathing rate, sweat rate and muscle state and have an important bearing on performance under conditions of stress and drugs. A number of research studies have made use of these physiological changes to investigate stress conditions while driving, seeking to understand which conditions and combinations of them are conducive to stress. While individuals may accommodate for certain deficiencies in one sensory aspect by placing more reliance in another, a sensory channel may be masked by temporary or permanent blocking like that arising from the motor cyclist's crash helmet, excessive tyre or engine noise or other visual obstructions.

PERCEPTION

Events in the external world, of sufficient stimulus, awaken consciousness in the brain in a process of perception. Recognition and response to event stimuli are far more complex than the simple images projected on the retina, or other unsifted sensory information. While objects are seen as a certain shape and size, through the experience of relating them by scale and position within a background, their interpretation is a complex association between the conscious physical and unconscious psychological world. Perception is thus dependent on introspection where psychological aspects, conditioning and acclimatisation are very important aspects of experience.

An event (or stimuli) only impinges on the receptors at some minimum level, known as the absolute threshold. The proportional change required in a stimulus for awareness to be awakened is termed the differential stimulus. Both are dependent on the nature and environment of the stimulus, the degree of user concentration, viewing conditions, the type of task and the sensation. The sensation of deceleration does not vary linearly with stimulus and car following or braking tasks are constantly subject to over- or under-correction. Thresholds are determined for an individual and vary according to many factors such as age and state of health and mind. If a driver is presented with the same information repeatedly, the threshold condition can be determined. For example, in overtaking where the speeds and distances of the overtaken and oncoming vehicles are such that on half the occasions he overtakes and on the remainder he refuses then his overtaking threshold has been established.

There are two principal factors which prevent a stimulus registering. The first is associated with the level of arousal; activity in the brain is continuous but varies from deep coma through relaxed wakefulness to extreme excitement, creating both physical and mental tension. High levels of arousal induced by large stimuli or the building of one stimulus upon another are normally followed by a period of low response or recuperation. Regular stimuli of repeated magnitude impose rhythmic sensations on the normal oscillatory brain waves leading to hypnotic states. The second reason for the loss of a stimulus occurs where there are stronger signals competing for attention. In a constant state of an environment a discontinuity is immediately apparent, like the flashing light in a continuous display, but more difficulty is experienced in detecting a new single flashing light from a background containing a large number of such sources.

Reaction time and Responses

In the case of a subject undergoing a simple test, where he anticipates the receipt of a signal stimulus and is required to operate a switch, the time measurement is known as response time. Reaction time is defined as that time which elapses between the reception of an external stimulus and the taking of an appropriate action and necessarily includes perception time, referred to above. The simplest forms of reaction are of short duration and do not fully involve higher thought processes because of previous learning. This conditioning occurs after frequent experience and leads in repeated situations to more consistent patterns of response. Reaction to the appearance of a red stop light is a typical example. More complex and new situations require more thought and association with past experience. This thinking process is known as intellection and some intermediate action may take place preparatory to a final decision.

Decision making is not necessarily a rational process and driving decisions are often called for at or near an individual's threshold limit where mistakes can be made. Such decisions are difficult to take and weighing up such a situation needs longer response time, perversely reducing the time left for action. Consequently lower speeds generally allow safer margins for decision. Decision time is also influenced by individual motivation and situation risk. Many actions result from unconscious decisions but others require a deliberate act of will before they are undertaken. In driving situations, where stimuli are generally predictable and the driver is experiencing a regular or monotonous journey, the level of awareness may fall, giving way to an automonitoring and an autoresponding performance. It is in these circumstances, when an unpredictable event arises that the accident risk is greatest. Awareness levels are also affected by the elapsed period after sleep (lowest arousal is 4/5 h after the last sleep) and predriving activity.

Volition, the will to act, varies between individuals and can be seen in the inability of some drivers to overtake correctly or select the appropriate lane at a junction, while other road users may vacillate for a time before acting, thus endangering both their own safety and that of others. The amount of information a road user can deal with at one time is obviously finite and related to its complexity. Human capacities also vary between individuals and, from time to time, with the same person. Simple events can be perceived at the rate of about 2 per second for very short periods of time, although the average rate is about half this and reduced by conditions such as darkness or rain. Automonitoring control decisions, affecting adjustments to the vehicle's position or speed, may have a repetition rate of about 1 per second.

Some typical response and reaction times to the appearance of a light stimulus in a simulator and also in a vehicle under test conditions are shown in Tables 6.3 and 6.4 for various conditions.

TABLE 6.3. RESPONSE TIME IN LABORATORY TEST

Position of hand relative to switch	Response time(s)								
	Position of light stimulus relative to visual cone								
	Central			Peripheral			Peripheral with task distraction		
	Mean	Min.	Max.	Mean	Min.	Max.	Mean	Min.	Max.
Hand on switch	0·37	0·31	0·46	0·42	0·34	0·50	0·59	0·44	0·82
Hand on steering wheel	0·53	0·42	0·36	0·57	0·47	0·75	0·68	0·54	0·87

TABLE 6.4. RESPONSE TIME IN TEST VEHICLE

Vehicle path	Response time(s) in test vehicle. Peripheral stimulus		
	Mean	Min.	Max.
On straight	0·75	0·51	1·03
On curve	0·82	0·62	1·27

The tests show that there is an increase in response time for stimuli in the field of peripheral vision or where the movement of limbs are involved and, where tasks become more complex, increased thought is needed. Individual variance also increases as visual and mental situations become more complex and whereas the influence of alcohol always lengthens response time there is considerable variability in its effects between subjects. The peak increase in time is about 1½ h after drinking, but it is affected by such factors as type of alcohol consumed and the stomach contents. Motivation and emotion are often overriding factors in reaction time, both modifying the thought process and changing the outgoing messages. Although these two factors may be interrelated, the emotional state of an individual will often solely determine his behaviour. Anger, frustration, worry, exhibitionism, or fear will pervade the decision-making process, Correct decisions and actions are fostered by a purpose designed environment conducive to well-mannered and unemotional behaviour. The traffic engineer needs to study the factors which are influential in a variety of road conditions if design is to minimise erratic behaviour.

Typical brake reaction times for individuals vary from about 0·25 s to about 1·0 s in ordinary traffic conditions. The time is likely to be halved if the stimulus is expected, and doubled for a weak stimulus. For instance the brake reaction time, for a driver following another vehicle, on the appearance of the brake light, averages 0·8 s, whereas if the preceding vehicle has defective brake lights the time increases to 1·7 s. Most individuals establish a working rhythm after time spent at an activity; this improves their performance, but, if the period is too extended fatigue may set in. Steering response has been shown to be sharper than a brake response. The time to look right and left at junctions before manoeuvring ranges from 2 or 3 s to 5 or 6 s and at night, under street lighting, the road user requires nearly half as much time again.

Simulators

The study and measurement of responses, under controlled conditions, is important and simulators are often used. These vary from such simple apparatus as a device for arresting the drop of a coin, the operation of a switch on the appearance of a light signal to more complex apparatus which includes the use of screens with varying background contrasts and tasks. The subject is often faced with a decision or choice made by operating one of a group of switches, for instance in matching the position of various light signals. Real simulators of road conditions are difficult to design because the "feel" of a vehicle has characteristics quite different from those capable of reproduction in laboratory conditions. The most advanced simulators of a vehicle and controls are mounted on rollers to reproduce road surface and braking conditions, with a projector screening a film of a road action sequence. Simulators are also useful both for control familiarisation and for some aspects of driving instruction.

THE DRIVING TASK

Continuous observations are made in each sensory aspect although some, for the reasons given above, may be unresponsive. Attention can be focused on only one event at a time and as the event rate increases the driver resorts to sampling. A finite number of observations can thus be made in the available time; these may be related or unrelated to the driving task. The information flow process is shown in Fig. 6.7.

Unobserved events can occur due to vehicle design, environmental obstruction, environmental conditions, lack of attention and an event rate greater than the driver's capacity. The first two types are controllable through adequate design of the vehicle's forward or rear visibility (see Fig. 6.8), and avoiding restricted sight lines caused by bridge abutments or alignment defects. The second is partly controllable by attention to surface characteristics and the all-weather nature of vehicle and roadside devices. The remainder are also influenced by design; for instance, by reducing the number of manoeuvring vehicles or through better education and warning systems.

Information received by a driver may be either immediately discarded or used, retained momentarily for future action, or permanently retained as part of the learning process. Mental triggers are important in information retrieval, certain messages are better verbalised than portraying them as abstract symbols. An example of the former is STOP and of the latter the use of a directional arrow to indicate keeping left. Traffic information is obtained from three environments comprising the external (the road and its margins), the internal (the vehicle and passengers) and the overall environmental conditions. All of these generate both continuous and discrete information such as the width of pavement, lane markings, curves, signals, instruments, talking, sun, rain, glare, parked vehicles and the vehicle stream itself.

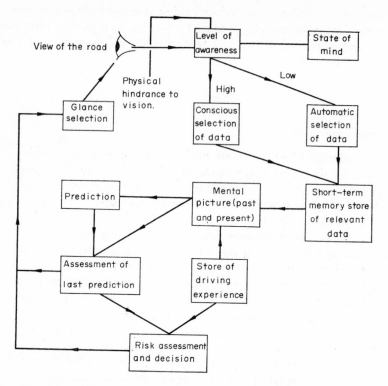

Fig. 6.7. A description of the information flow process. (Source: R. L. Moore, Some human factors affecting the design of vehicles and roads, *Journal of the Instn. Highway Engng.*, Aug. 1969, vol. **xvi**(8).)

The principal task of the driver is to manoeuvre his vehicle in relation to the highway geometry and other traffic. This tracking entails continuous adjustments to the steering, brakes and accelerator controls in repositioning the vehicle in both space and time with the additional task of displaying signals, as appropriate, for other drivers. A refined sensori-motor control mechanism is an essential element of good tracking and signal response in the closed loop feedback system of the driver, vehicle and road situation. Tracking is accomplished by reference to a

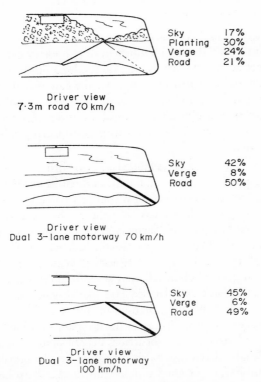

Sky	17%
Planting	30%
Verge	24%
Road	21%

Driver view
7·3m road 70 km/h

Sky	42%
Verge	8%
Road	50%

Driver view
Dual 3-lane motorway 70 km/h

Sky	45%
Verge	6%
Road	49%

Driver view
Dual 3-lane motorway
100 km/h

Fig. 6.8. The driver's view at different speeds and for different road types.

zero axis, generated through the plane of the eyes in the direction of movement, and static ancillary markers, which are continuously set up and discarded as the vehicle moves forward. All other traffic is then related to this basic reference and the key markers at that point in time. By moving the head away from the reference plane additional information is gained, partly through parallax, which assists in making performance precise. Generally, tracking performance is improved by continuous rather than intermittent displays. Spasmodic control information must be displayed with uniformity, simplicity and clarity.

MODIFYING FACTORS IN PERFORMANCE

Many factors modify the basic physiological characteristics of the driver and may be either of a permanent of temporary nature. Examples of the former are age, injury and disease resulting in permanent physical deterioration and impairment. It is often the case that the individual is able to adjust and accommodate to some extent for a disability. Perhaps more important and difficult to control are those of a transient nature because of their effect on the performance of normally able individuals. These include the following:

(a) *Fatigue.* This may be exhibited in two forms, either physical or mental. The purely physical condition can often be attributed to lack of sleep, incorrect posture induced by cramped conditions and impaired muscular movement, drowsiness brought on by overheated vehicles, rhythmic vibrations, glare and inability of the eye to accommodate different levels of light and known as poor residual adaptation. These factors can all contribute to mistakes leading to loss of vehicle control. Secondly, operational fatigue or lack of skill may severely affect performance when applied to a complex and detailed task like driving, particularly over extended periods. The deterioration manifests itself in many ways, causing lapses of attention, incorrect situation appreciation and omission to carry out task detail. The right actions may be performed in the wrong sequence. Fatigue may cause a driver to miss a traffic signal, turn before signalling, misjudge space and time or turn into a sharp bend too late. Poorly designed roads, or those with a monotonous alignment and situations conducive to rhythmic sensation, induced by regular patterns of tree or fence layout, will also reduce performance and lead to drowsiness.

Combinations of fatigue types may occur towards the end of long driving periods and there is a need for both comfortable posture and the proper siting of controls. However, some investigations have shown that a high proportion of accidents on long-haul goods vehicle journeys arise during the first few hours of driving.

(b) *Alcohol and Drugs.* Alcohol and certain drugs act as depressants on the central nervous system. Increasing amounts adversely affect judgement and attention, lengthening reaction time and eventually leading to a breakdown of coordination between muscle and senses with complete inability to perform the simplest task. Drugs of a stimulating nature lead to wild and erratic behaviour also affecting judgement and vehicle control.

(c) *Illness.* Even a minor ailment, such as the common cold, disturbs the normal emotional and physical state, resulting in impaired performance. Maladjusted and psychopathic states, blood pressure and epilepsy are a few illnesses associated with accident proneness, but the control of these serious diseases is difficult and must be left to the medical authorities and government to prescribe suitable tests and legislation.

(d) *Weather.* Modifications to the normal state occur due to external conditions like weather. Excessive heat and cold particularly affect temperament but can be overcome with adequate vehicle design.

(e) *Posture.* Driver position within the vehicle should be taken into account in the layout of roads, and the optimum siting of devices at the roadside determined from actual measurements. These include eye height, lateral and transverse positioning of the vehicle.

FACTORS WHICH INFLUENCE BEHAVIOUR

An important function of the nervous system is to integrate the whole range of human activity. Unity of judgement, thought and action are processes continually demanded in the traffic stream, and breakdown, malfunction or confusion occurs if situations become too complex. This unity is influenced by continuing but transient modifications to the psychological state, due to motivation, environmental and other background influences briefly outlined below.

Motivation

Motivation has an important place in the determination of human activity. For a particular journey, the road user will usually have some end object in view which will influence his behaviour. The driving characteristics exhibited by a family outing in the country will be markedly different to those of the commercial traveller caught in a traffic hold-up and late for an important meeting; the window shopping pedestrian will

K

differ radically from the office girl rushing to the nearest bus stop. Those characteristics, induced by different motives, must be considered in detail by the planning engineer in the layout of towns if all types of movement are to be safe and comfortable.

Environmental Influences

These environmental factors follow naturally from a consideration of travel motives. Smooth orderly traffic movement, whether pedestrian or vehicular, sets the right context to travel. Heavy peak demands, which cannot be met on through routes except by long delays, causes traffic to divert to alternative routes usually of a different character and designed for a different purpose. They often pass through residential areas causing a disruption of community life with added danger to their inhabitants. However, the traffic stream itself has the greatest influence on user behaviour. Traffic study helps the designer to understand the interactive nature of these problems and to satisfy the diversity of needs for varying traffic circumstances. The limitation of noise, exhaust emissions and atmospheric pollution, by the application of control regulations, is a further step in the improvement of the total environment.

Education

The real gains from good educational programmes have been too heavily discounted; while good and bad practices can be learnt with equal facility, it is very difficult to eradicate bad habits. Many failures in the appropriate use of travel facilities and the cause of accidents can be attributed to a lack of knowledge and understanding of the situation. The mass media of the press, radio and television can improve both individual and community response to the needs of users of all ages and encourage more socially responsible attitudes. At the detailed level, instruction on road use is necessary at all levels and worthy of inclusion, not only in all levels of education but also at work and in social activities.

Conditioning

Some driving circumstances may encourage driver hypnosis, but careful design can avoid such conditions. One well-known form, called "velocitation", occurs on monotonous roads, often straight, level, high-speed routes. The danger arises when conditions change at the ends of long sections leading to sharp curves, roundabouts or narrower carriageways. While a driver may reduce speed, he will feel that he is moving much slower than he is in reality. This is due to the slow adjustment which is made to an extended focal distance developed at high speed, and this creates the deceptive impression of a slow progression rate per unit of time. Other conditioning takes place on major streets when a priority suddenly terminates on a more important route, or where a no-waiting ban is in force and the driver is conditioned to driving in a lane free from parked vehicles. Care must be exercised initially with the introduction of traffic management measures, such as one-way streets, because of this effect not only on motorists but on pedestrians. Some cyclists are conditioned to the kerb area as a region of safety and have difficulty in moving to the crown of the road when turning right.

Design Applications

Road user factors must be at the forefront of design and the following points should be noted. Higher operating speeds require more adequate warning devices located nearer to the central angle of vision. The general complexity of layouts must be reduced to a minimum, clearly demarcating intended vehicle and pedestrian paths. Roads and footpaths must be designed to avoid monotonous or arduous travel conditions. Advertisements and extraneous lighting must be strictly controlled to avoid driver distraction. A good maxim is not more than one decision at a time with an adequate time provided for its execution, compatible with the desired operating conditions. The impression should be created in the mind of the user that the designer has fully catered for the appropriate use of the facility by not leaving some elements to chance. This should instil in the user a feeling of well-being, without a sense of false security, and this is conveyed by traffic control commensurate with conditions. Typical examples are demarcating carriageway edges and lanes, adequate signs, lighting and roadside markers and by ensuring proper enforcement measures. Warnings of special dangers need particular care in their design and layout to be both effective and lasting. Street lighting is often a worthwhile investment helping to overcome the greater perception time required at night and thus improving road safety.

THE VEHICLE

Fortunately, for many purposes, the vehicle has less variable characteristics than road users and, in any event, these features can be legislatively controlled within defined limits. Legislation can impose limits on overall performance, weight and size, as well as specifying the minimum requirements for individual items of equipment such as brakes, lighting and indicators. This section deals mainly with the operation and performance of the vehicle on the highway, but design for the safe vehicle is important and major aspects are dealt with in Chapter 10. The current Statutory Instruments, *The Motor Vehicles (Construction and Use) Regulations*, H.M.S.O., should be consulted for detailed legislative requirements.

VISIBILITY

It has already been stated that situation perception is essential and thus the vehicle's body must interfere as little as possible with the driver's field of view.

Forward Visibility

Marked improvements have been made in vehicle design to increase visibility in normal weather conditions. Sloped and curved windscreens occupy a greater proportion of the total area, reducing the solid cut-offs due to body pillars, roof lines and bonnet shapes. In most vehicles lateral adjustment of the seats is provided, but relatively few are adjustable for height, despite the very great range of anthropometric variations between drivers. Typical fields of view are shown in Fig. 6.9 indicating the principal points of restriction. Door pillars often mask pedestrians, cyclists,

Forward field of view (cleared screen area dashed lines)

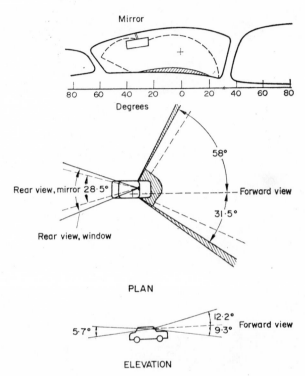

FIG. 6.9.   Fields of view—typical saloon car.

or other vehicles, and for relatively long periods when a vehicle is moving slowly or turning, as shown in Fig. 6.10. Particularly dangerous are intersection manoeuvres where a driver's attention may be concentrated on other moving elements in the traffic stream. However, while these aspects are important it is weather conditions such as fog, ice or rain which now mainly reduce visibility. Existing windscreen wipers are not wholly satisfactory as only part of the viewing area is cleared. Efficient methods of cleaning the whole screen and other windows, and the prevention of misting and icing, are still needed for most vehicles.

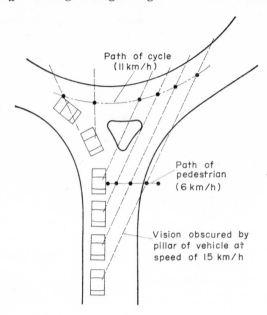

Path of cycle
(11 km/h)

Path of
pedestrian
(6 km/h)

Vision obscured by
pillar of vehicle at
speed of 15 km/h

Fig. 6.10. Collision paths shown are dependent relative speeds and paths in relation to the driver's obscured field of view.

Side and Rear Visibility

Side visibility is essential to the driver when manoeuvring. This becomes increasingly important at intersections, particularly as operating speeds are raised, if the driver is to position his vehicle correctly, safely and efficiently when merging with or crossing traffic streams. Rearward vision, except when parking, must be achieved by internal or external mirrors sited to determine the best field of view as shown in Fig. 6.9. Vision to the rear is still restrictive even with many modern cars but is even less satisfactory with many commercial vehicles. It is fortunate that purchase tax, financially restrictive to owners improving visibility in closed vans, has now been removed. Greater use of clear plastic in commercial vehicles instead of thin sheet steel or tarpaulins would effect some improvement. Particularly vulnerable are two-wheeled vehicles where the rider loses all forward vision, and often stability, when looking to the rear while turning. Some of these difficulties could be ameliorated by applying more rigorous legislative standards to ancillary vehicle equipment.

Finally all visual fields are dependent on the eye position of the driver in conjunction with the suspension and load characteristics of the vehicle. Fully adjustable seats are needed on all vehicles to cover the wide range in driver physiology. Established sight line standards are also effectively diminished with every eye height reduction and the continuing trend can be seen in Fig. 6.11 and Table 6.5.

LIGHTING

Vehicle lighting has two main requirements:

(i) To clearly define the vehicle to an external viewer from all approach angles and without glare discomfort to the onlooker.

(ii) To provide the driver with a suitably illuminated field of view consistent with operating speeds and road conditions at all times.

Inclement weather, particularly fog, must be considered when discussing lighting. Manufacturers have developed specialised lighting accessories but unfortunately, due to cost, there is often a tendency to compromise design by making a single unit incorporating more features than are satisfactory.

There are three conditions under which vehicles must be seen.

1. *Well-lit streets.* These will usually be traffic routes where external street lighting sources will provide enough illumination to show a clear outline of the vehicle and the parking and rear lights further help to define the width and length of the vehicle. Current British regulations permitting vehicles in certain streets to park without lights is not conducive to road safety. Drivers can proceed without the use of headlamps because pedestrians, vehicles, intersections and the road boundaries should be visible either directly or in silhouette. The vehicle itself will also be clearly visible to the onlooker.

2. *Poorly-lit streets.* These should only occur in residential areas, which are mainly lit for pedestrian convenience and as such do not provide a sufficiently continuous light background to make oncoming vehicles

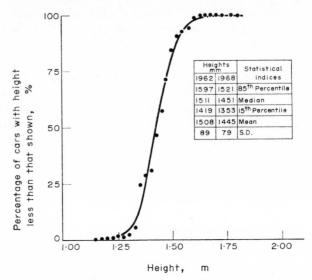

FIG. 6.11. Heights of cars in 1968 and comparison with 1962.

TABLE 6.5.   AVERAGE EYE HEIGHT FOR AN AVERAGE DRIVER (m)

Car type	Year of manufacture			
	1950	1955	1960	1965
Large saloons	1·38	1·36	1·26	1·20
Small saloons	1·34	1·28	1·19	1·11
Sports	1·16	1·10	1·05	1·02

visible or for drivers to detect other objects without the use of headlights. Because speeds on this type of road should be low, extended forward visibility is not required but a flat wide beam is needed to outline the road margins and, by depressing the beam, prevent glare to oncoming traffic. Pedestrians or other drivers are then adequately warned of the approaching vehicle and speeds of vehicles are more easily assessed by the size of the light source. Side lights used alone, partly because of their size and possible confusion with other small street sources, are difficult to detect quickly.

3. *Streets without lighting.* Some urban and most rural roads do not have street lighting and the approach of a vehicle is determined solely by its own lighting. Furthermore, the driver is dependent entirely for forward visibility on the size and power of his headlights. At high speeds on such roads, a long narrow, high-power beam is required, but as intensity is increased so does glare. Even low levels of glare disturb the eye and reduce seeing distance, as shown in Fig. 6.12.

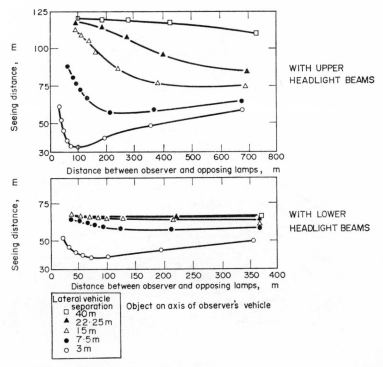

Fig. 6.12. Seeing distances on a straight road. (Source: *Road Research* 1961, H.M.S.O., converted to metres.)

Headlights

The general method adopted today is to provide upper and lower beam headlights to meet the needs of cases (2) and (3), or to provide individual units for each separate function. In the first case this is achieved by using double filament sources where the hot spot of high intensity is shifted in the dipped condition (lower beam) away from the approaching driver and in a downward direction, as shown in Fig. 6.13. For high-speed night driving, in excess of about 100 km/h, the range of standard headlights of 100,000 cd is restricted for adequate visibility. It must be

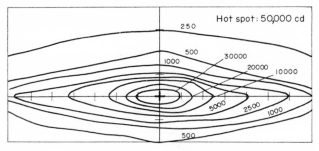

Main beam sealed unit 60W; 12V

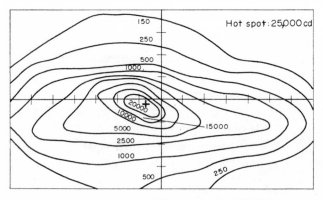

Meeting beam sealed unit 60W; 12V

FIG. 6.13. Typical headlight, upper and lower beam light distributions.

borne in mind that perception time at night under artificial lighting is longer than in daylight, but some improvement in seeing can be made with the new quartz halogen lamps, giving beams of high intensity with better vertical and lateral light control. The colour of light, for equal power, does not seem to be important for visibility, although most drivers seem to prefer to approach oncoming yellow light beams.

Lower Beam Light Distribution

The main requirements of lower beam headlights is to maintain the illumination along the nearside edge of the carriageway but reduce the offside intensities directed at the approaching driver. Two systems are employed, firstly those which dip and deflect both beam concentrations to the nearside and secondly those with a sharp top cut-off. The latter system has been improved by tilting the cut-off line at an angle of 15° to the horizontal from offside to nearside. Typical seeing distances are indicated in Table 6.6. Headlight adjustments are more critical with the

TABLE 6.6. RECOGNITION DISTANCES USING BRITISH AND EUROPEAN DIPPED HEADLIGHTS. (Source: *Road Research*, 1970, H.M.S.O.)

| | Recognition distances (m) | | | |
| | Nearside object | | Offside object | |
	British beam (B)	European beam (E)	British beam (B)	European beam (E)
Lit road, straight	217·7	225·0	145·4	152·0
Unlit roads, straight	51·4	50·4	22·1	24·8
Left-hand curve	37·5	32·6	40·9	40·9
Right-hand curve	25·8	27·6	15·6	21·8
Bottom of hill	26·5	26·8	16·8	16·7
Top of hill	48·5	42·3	23·7	24·6

latter (European) method but give improved offside visibility. In car meeting situations with lower meeting beams, seeing distances are often less than required stopping distances. In any event cut-off requirements impose visibility limits solely from an analysis of the geometry of head-lamp height and minimum beam deflection. The point at which a driver dips his headlamps is left to individual choice and to avoid possible glare lights may be dipped too early with a loss of effective seeing distance. Conversely a driver, through carelessness or other reasons, may fail to dip on the approach of other vehicles. This failure has been overcome on some cars by fitting photocell detectors which automatically actuate switches when certain levels of illumination are incident on their surface.

Fog Lights

In foggy conditions normal lights distract the driver's eye because of back glare and special lamps assist in providing a wide beam of light with a sharp upper edge cut-off. The light should be as far as possible uniformly distributed across the field of view to enable the road edges and reflectorised markings to be distinguished. The detection of vehicles in daytime fogs is much improved when headlamps or fog lamps are used and glare is not present because background illumination levels are high.

Glare

The problems associated with glare can be partly overcome by careful design of the lamp and by restriction of its use to the appropriate occasion. Adequate standards for checking the alignment and performance of lamps are also required and, as the tests are simple to perform, there seem to be good reasons for a regular test every 6 months. Some improvements to the adjusting mechanism, by the use of externally located screws, is desirable. The introduction of sealed beam units has assisted the alignment of beams as they can be set more accurately and there is also a slower deterioration rate in the optical system as shown in Fig. 6.14. No matter how well a system is presently adjusted it is still very sensitive to vehicle loading. Self-adjusting suspension and light systems have been developed and their general adoption would bring both

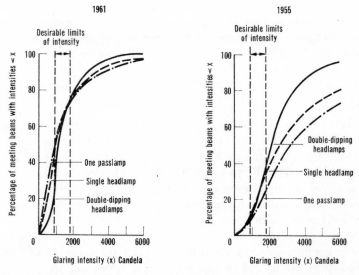

Fig. 6.14. Distribution of glaring intensities. (Source: *Road Research* 1962, H.M.S.O.).

lighting and other advantages. Besides improving the alignment of vehicle lighting and adopting more accurate control, for an extended life, it is still necessary to construct anti-glare screening on dual carriageway roads. Screening is also necessary on urban routes, particularly high-level roads, to avoid light disturbance to adjacent property.

Polarised Light

The possibilities for the use of polarisers and analysers on vehicles is interesting because of the reduction in apparent intensity of a beam when viewed by an approaching driver. However, certain major drawbacks to the system still await a satisfactory solution. Because the effective beam intensities are much reduced, the higher source intensities needed to obviate this would cause considerable distraction to external road users and some of the general illumination from oncoming headlamps would be lost. Further practical difficulties include the need to fit all vehicles with the more costly equipment at the same time, the problems of laminated windscreens and the breakdown of polarisers. Alternative developments to the use of polarised light include the design of variable beam pattern headlamps with electronically controlled shutters.

Rear Lamps

The worst occasion for seeing a rear light ahead arises when a high-powered light source is directed towards the driver's eyes from an approaching vehicle and the rear of a preceding or parked vehicle ahead may be lost to sight due to visual disturbance. However, a balance must be achieved, in the case of rear direction and brake light indicators, between brightness and glare. This can be partly overcome by using a two-level power system for day and night driving. Difficulty is also experienced where pedal cycles are moving or crossing high-speed routes; but light-coloured and reflectorised clothing assists identification.

Reflectors are needed to supplement rear lamps and are an added precaution where electrical failure may occur. Good viewing conditions require reflector characteristics giving apparently high intensities for large entrance angles at small observation angles, as shown in Fig. 6.15. As it is necessary to demarcate the width of vehicles, rear lamps and reflectors must be placed at the extremities, although whole reflectorised panels are useful for large vehicles both at the rear and on the sides. This arrangement assists trailing drivers in estimating distance although, for this purpose, it is necessary to see rear lights at an angular displacement from the longitudinal axis of the vehicle. Experiments have been conducted in which the degree of deceleration of a vehicle is indicated by a complex and variable lighting system but it does not appear to yield marked gains in performance.

The breakdown of vehicles on high-speed roads has led to many rear-end accidents and the equipping of all vehicles with a suitable light flashing system is urgently required.

VEHICLE WARNING AND INSTRUMENT SYSTEMS

Modern electronics, and the fitting of diagnostic equipment to vehicles

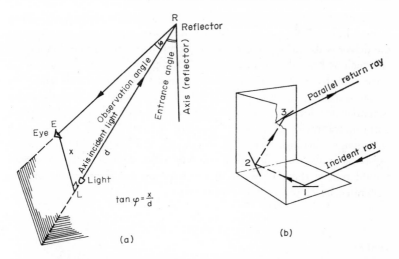

Fig. 6.15. (a) Reflector geometry, (b) Corner cube reflector—incident light ray redirected on the three faces successively.

for maintenance purposes, provides opportunities for the improvement of driver aids warning of the impending failure of important components. Although the style and positioning of instruments has improved over the years vision is lost, for 1–3 s, each time they are monitored. Head-up display instruments, which throw a light onto the screen, have now been developed to overcome this deficiency, although difficulties have been experienced in producing distortion-free images on curved windscreens. Besides head-up display speedometers the Road Research Laboratory has developed a station keeping indicator which directs two bright vertical lines onto the screen. The distance apart of the lines varies with speed and indicates a "safe" following distance. A driver keeps the vehicle ahead at the safe distance by keeping its apparent width narrower than the line spacing.

Route guidance instruments have also been tried in North America. In a General Motors system a driver inserts into the instrument a punched card containing destination and route information. Coded low-frequency radio transmitters, sited near junctions, respond to interrogation signals from the approaching vehicle and light up an instrument panel display indicating junction configuration and the sequence of required turns. Similar information can be given in voice instruction and in some systems the driver is able to speak directly to a central controller about emergencies such as breakdowns or accidents. Drivers can also be warned of ice formation by surface temperature measuring devices with audio or visual warning within the cab. It can be seen that there is considerable potential development for the use of vehicle radio devices to improve communication by providing a measure of route control together with emergency warnings of weather conditions and hazards. Some psychologists have also indicated that voice to voice contact between drivers would relieve them of some of the tensions and frustrations that are generated by closed vehicle confinement.

BRAKES

The ability to stop a vehicle quickly, and under full control, is an essential requirement of vehicle braking systems and a major factor in road safety. While the method and use of brakes varies, both with drivers and the nature of the traffic, stopping distances are principally determined by the efficiency and condition of the braking system and vehicle loading, weather conditions, road surface characteristics and tyre characteristics, and the road geometry. Most drivers, during normal braking manoeuvres, decelerate in two phases. First, when the foot is moved from the accelerator to the brake pedal they utilise the resistance to motion and the engine's braking effect, and secondly, by the application of an increasing braking force to the wheels. If the traffic engineer has correctly designed the road conditions, and the driver is competent, excessive braking is only used under emergency conditions.

Efficient modern braking systems allow greater retardation of the wheels than most road surfaces can provide and skidding of the tyre often results, particularly on wet surfaces. During braking a proportion of the total load is transferred from the rear to the front wheels and this affects which axles will lock with given surface coefficients of friction and vehicle centres of gravity. About two-thirds of the total braking force is applied to the front wheels of modern cars, a compromise between the conflicting requirements of various road surface coefficients. If all wheels are to be locked simultaneously, different distributions are required for different coefficients. Rates of deceleration usually range from 1 to 3 m/s² on initial slowing down with a final braking to a stop of up to 3·5 m/s². Rates in excess of this figure cause discomfort for standing passengers in buses and beyond 5 m/s² actual danger may occur due to loose objects sliding about the vehicle. Emergency stops, where rates exceed 6 m/s² and approach 10 m/s² on some surfaces, may cause injury to vehicle occupants.

Theoretically, maximum braking efficiency occurs the instant before the wheels lock. Some conditions and combinations of wheel lock can induce violent swerves and are a serious hazard to the driver's control of his vehicle. Figure 6.16 illustrates the principal combinations of wheel

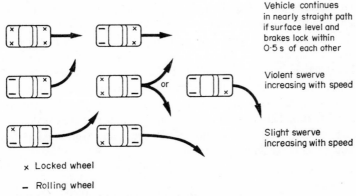

Vehicle continues in nearly straight path if surface level and brakes lock within 0·5 s of each other

Violent swerve increasing with speed

Slight swerve increasing with speed

x Locked wheel

— Rolling wheel

FIG. 6.16. Wheel lock and resulting vehicle path.

lock and the resulting vehicle path. The condition is caused either by faulty mechanism, incorrect adjustment or loading differences but these can be overcome, to some extent, by the use of transfer valves. Recent advances in the brake design field have led to the application of the "Maxaret" aircraft system to road vehicles. Drive shafts for the four units required are geared to each road wheel and through a spring clutch they rotate small flywheels. If the wheel locks, the flywheel continues to turn and, overcoming the resistance of the clutch, opens a pressure valve which releases the brake. There are other systems using anti-lock devices, one of which is governed by a pendulum which takes into account vehicle attitude at any instant and slightly releases any brake about to cause wheel lock, and hence the brakes can be fully applied without danger of this occurring. Such devices reduce braking distances very considerably by maximising tyre and road friction continuously and at the same time more safely because steering can be more accurately maintained.

Skidding Resistance

The brakes of modern cars are highly efficient and in adverse weather conditions it is often the road surface coefficient of skidding resistance which determines the maximum deceleration possible. If the vehicle is not equipped with an anti-lock device, even with a quite modest brake pedal pressure, a skid may be induced with the resultant loss of control, possibly more serious than the inability to stop. More than 20% of personal injury accidents have had skidding attributed as a factor by the police.

The friction developed between the area of tyre in contact with a road surface controls the forces developed during driving manoeuvres such as steering, accelerating and braking. Skidding occurs when the limiting friction between the tyres and the road surface is exceeded.

The braking force F, the sum of the front and rear braking forces (f_f and f_r) acting at the road surface, is:

$$F = \mu W$$

where μ =   coefficient of limiting friction between tyres and road surface (skidding resistance),

W =   weight of vehicle,

and $F \max$ = $f_f \max + f_r \max = \mu W_f + \mu W_r$

where W =   weight of vehicle (kg).

Also $$F = m \times a$$

where m =   mass of vehicle $= W/g$,

a =   resultant acceleration (m/s²),

g =   acceleration due to gravity (9806 m/s²).

Hence it follows that $\mu = a/g$ and values of μ are given in Table 6.7 for varying circumstances.

The braking force developed at the wheel equals the friction torque of the brakes divided by the rolling radius of the tyre but, for the reasons given above, the limiting conditions are those imposed by the adhesion between the tyres and the road surface. Typical skid resistance values for different weather conditions are also shown in Table 6.7.

TABLE 6.7.   WEATHER AND SKIDDING RESISTANCE

Weather	Skidding resistance as a proportion of g (locked wheels at 48 km/h)
Black ice	0·15
Rolled snow	0·25
Fresh snow	0·35
Rain (5th percentile of British roads): potentially slippery	0·45
Rain (70th percentile of British roads): accepted as safe	0·65
Dry	1·00

As would be expected, skid resistance varies considerably with weather, being very low on snowy or icy surfaces. In addition there is a variability of the road surface and it has been reported by the Road Research Laboratory that 5% of the roads in Great Britain have a skidding resistance of less than 0·45 (g) in wet weather and are therefore almost as slippery as fresh snow. The sites are very likely to be scenes of repeated skidding accidents.

The reason why particular sites have a low skidding resistance is that some road-making aggregates become highly polished with the passage of traffic. Any fine dust in a road will act as a grinding abrasive and since dust is present when there is little or no rain to wash the surface clean, surfaces frequently become slippery after a long dry spell in the summer. Some aggregates show less tendency to polish during the process of attrition because they continually expose a sharp irregular contact area. On wet roads the film of water tends to impede the contact between tyre and road and if a high skidding resistance is to be attained the water film must be expelled rapidly. Tyre tread patterns allow space for the water to escape from the smoother textured surfaces. The rate of escape will depend mainly on the contact pressures developed between tyres and surface, rapid expulsion occurring where the road aggregate has sharp projections inducing high contact pressures.

Measurements of Skidding Resistance

Skidding resistance measurement has, in the past, usually required a vehicle and often elaborate equipment. One of the earlier methods was to lock a vehicle's wheels by violent braking application usually for a period of 1 s at 48 km/h and to measure the skidding resistance directly with a decelerometer or indirectly in terms of stopping distance. This method has many disadvantages and cannot be used at many sites. A more suitable, although expensive, way is to use a fifth wheel which may be either:

(a) *A brake trailer towed behind a vehicle.* The wheel is locked by an electrically operated brake and deceleration is measured from a pressure capsule in the draw-bar. Tests at very high speeds can be made with this equipment. The ratio of the frictional force to the total load on the wheel is a measure known as the braking force coefficient.

(b) *A side-slipping wheel,* with a smooth tyre, is mounted within a car wheelbase or as the sidecar wheel of a motor cycle combination. In either case the wheel is rotated at an angle to the direction of travel. The sideways force, applied to maintain the wheel in its angular position, is measured and the sideways-force coefficient can then be expressed as the ratio of the sideways force to the total load on the wheel.

In order to measure the road surface coefficients the percentage wheel slip, with the braking force coefficient, and the wheel angle, with the sideways force coefficient, must exceed critical values. Slip is a relationship of the towed wheel's revolutions in a braked condition (R_B) to those in a freely rolling condition (R_F); the difference is taken up by tyre distortion and slipping:

$$S \text{ (percentage slip) } \% = \left(R_F - \frac{R_B}{R_F} \right) \times 100.$$

Both measurements refer to the dynamic coefficient of friction and are less than the coefficient of static friction. The maximum retardation is achieved between 10 and 20% slip, dependent on tyre and road surface conditions.

Neither of the fifth wheel methods are suitable for normal use by highway authorities and the Road Research Laboratory has developed a machine, code named SCRIM (Sideways-force Coefficient Routine Investigation Machine), which can measure and data log coefficients at regular intervals over networks of streets without interfering with normal traffic. The test wheel is side mounted, on a motorised tanker, with a spray nozzle to wet the surface under test. Accurate measurements can be taken for a range of speeds between 15 and 100 km/h and at the design test speed of 50 km/h some 80 km/day can be tested.

Portable Testers

For many years a portable tester, designed by the Road Research Laboratory, has been used for measuring skidding resistances in both the field and the laboratory. The apparatus is shown in Fig. 6.17 and

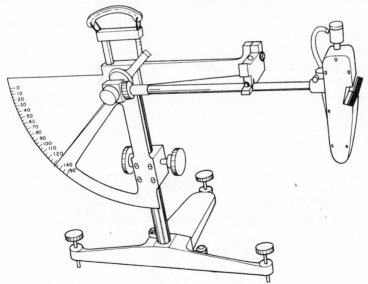

Fig. 6.17. Portable skid resistance tester.

consists of a small rubber slider, spring loaded, and mounted at the end of a pendulum arm. The angle of the pendulum at the end of its swing depends on the energy lost by the rubber slider when passing over a 5 in. (127 mm) length of road surface. A pointer passes over a scale calibrated to give a direct reading of skidding resistance and this value represents locked wheel braking at 30 mph (48 km/h). Tests are performed on wet surfaces and a small water supply is carried with the apparatus. Because the slider contact area is small, surface drainage is good and the tester behaves as a patterned tyre. Normal procedure is to measure at five test points along the nearside wheel track taking the mean as representative of the skidding resistance. Results from the apparatus have been extensively correlated with the results from other methods.

Braking Distance

The distance travelled by a vehicle from the instant the brakes are applied, and in some systems there is a considerable time lag between the initial depression of the pedal and the brakes operating, is defined as the braking distance. This measure is not as important in traffic engineering as stopping distance which includes the whole distance travelled during perception, reaction and braking. The figures indicated in the Highway Code are of a higher standard than can be used for normal design purposes. The computation of braking distance (s_B) from an initial speed v (m/s) at the instant of brake application, and assuming a constant frictional coefficient (μ), is then (neglecting resistances to normal motion):

Braking distance in metres $s_B = \dfrac{v^2}{2gf}$

where $g = 9806$ m/s^2.

This distance is considerably affected by gradient and a correction must be applied:

$$S_{BG} = \frac{v^2}{2g(f \pm G/100)}$$

where G = percentage gradient, positive when upwards.

STABILITY

The side force on the vehicle when cornering is $(Wv^2)/(gR)$, where R is the radius of the wheel path, and this is opposed by the lateral forces acting on the tyres. The angle between the plane of rotation and the direction of movement is termed the slip angle. The effective centre of forces lies at the neutral steer point and the distance between it and the vehicle's centre of gravity is the static margin. Understeering occurs when the vehicle turns away from the applied side force (positive static margin— front slip angles greatest) while the oversteering conditions occur when the vehicle turns towards the applied force (negative static margin— front slip angles smallest). A zero static margin has equal front and rear steer angles and this condition refers to a neutral-steer vehicle. Also important for cornering force conditions is the sideways weight transfer and the induced roll moment about the axis joining the front and rear roll centres. Suspension characteristics affect the behaviour of the sprung mass and the load on tyres, and it is the forces acting at the interface of road surface and tyre that finally determines control stability.

Developments in the use of synthetic rubbers, and design improvements in the tread patterns of tyres, has allowed shorter stopping distances because of the large energy dissipation characteristic of high hysteresis materials and the ejection of water from the road surface contact area. Incorrect tyre pressures cause marked deterioration in handling perform- ance and tyre bursts lead to serious loss of control. Both are important subjects for improved design, although the latter condition may soon be rectified by the marketing of a tyre which maintains steering conditions when ruptured.

VEHICLE DIMENSIONS AND WEIGHTS

The size and weight of vehicles are important considerations in the design of roads, intersections and parking facilities. Different proportions of the various vehicle categories present in the traffic stream necessitate different design standards. Tables 6.8 and 6.9 and Fig. 6.18 show some typical categories of vehicle together with leading dimensions. Figures 6.19a, b shows examples of turning circles.

TABLE 6.8. TRENDS IN THE DISTRIBUTION OF PRIVATE CARS BY
ENGINE SIZE (Great Britain)

Engine size (cylinder capacity)	Year		
	1961	1966	1971
less than 1000 cc	31·2	29·9	23·1
1000 – 1500 cc	40·4	40·4	45·0
1500 – 2000 cc	11·7	19·2	24·2
2000 – 3000 cc	14·3	8·7	5·4
more than 3000 cc	2·4	1·8	2·3
Total	100·0	100·0	100·0

TABLE 6.9. TRENDS IN THE DISTRIBUTION OF GOODS VEHICLES BY
UNLADEN WEIGHT (Great Britain)

Unladen weight	Year		
	1961	1966	1971
less than 1½ tons	56·8	57·2	60·5
1½ – 3 tons	23·7	16·7	12·2
3 – 5 tons	15·2	18·3	14·2
5 – 8 tons	3·4	5·9	8·9
more than 8 tons	0·9	1·9	4·2
Total	100·0	100·0	100·0

VEHICLE PERFORMANCE

Resistances and Power

The total resistance to traction on a level road can be divided into

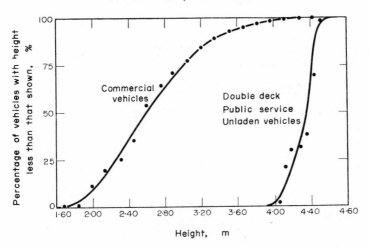

Fɪɢ. 6.18. Heights of commercial vehicles and public service vehicles.

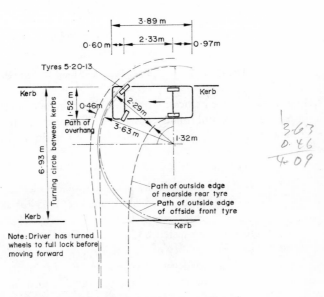

Fɪɢ. 6.19a. Turning paths of vehicle: Triumph Herald.

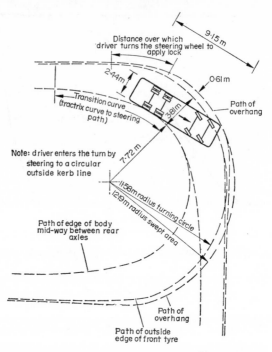

FIG. 6.19b. Turning paths of vehicle: 24-ton 8-wheel vehicle.

four parts: air resistances, mechanical friction and inertial resistances, impact resistance and rolling resistances. The resistances to vehicle motion from air resistance R_A is given, in standard air conditions, by the following relationship:

$$R_A = C_D \left(\rho A v^2 / 2g\right)$$

where C_D = dimensionless drag coefficient determined for body shape (0·25 for sports car; 0·45 for saloon; 0·80 for truck),

A = projected body area in direction of travel (m²),

ρ = density of air (km/m³),

v = velocity of vehicle in still air (m/s),

g = acceleration due to gravity (9806 m/s²),

or $$R_A = KAv^2,$$

where K is an experimental coefficient, depending on air conditions and body shape, with values ranging from 0·0012 for saloon car to 0·0005 for streamlined sports cars in Imperial units and 0·0022 to 0·0009 metric units.

Mechanical friction occurs in wheel bearings and in other moving parts and causes further resistance to motion. Energy is also dissipated in the movement of oil and heat losses. Initially a force is required to overcome inertia during acceleration to the required speed and, during motion, the inertial effects of the rotating parts.

Rolling resistance increases with speed and with rougher surfaces and decreases with higher inflation pressures, but power is also required to overcome impact and deformation of the tyres on loose and rough surfaces. Ambient air temperature and pressure also affects all of these resistances. The value of tractive resistance (sum of all resistances) varies with speed and type of surface. Some typical values for modern roads are shown in Table 6.10.

TABLE 6.10. TRACTIVE RESISTANCE

Speed (km/h)	Medium saloon car (kg/kg)	Truck (kg/kg) laden
30	0·014	0·009
65	0·029	0·018
100	0·054	0·029
125	0·087	0·054

The potential of a vehicle to accelerate, operate at given speeds and climb gradients depends, not only on overcoming resistance to motion, but on horsepower available. This can be determined from the general equation: $M = 2\pi r_f T_h N$ (horsepower = force × distance travelled in unit time divided by the rate of working where 1 hp = 550 ft lb/s (33,000 ft lb/min) in Imperial units, or in SI units, the metric horsepower, where 1 $hp_{(m)}$ = 75 kg m/s).

$$HP_{(m)} = \frac{2\pi r_f T_h N}{4500}$$

where M =   work done kg m/s = $2\pi r_f T_h N$,
$\quad\quad\quad HP_{(m)}$ =   metric brake horsepower,
$\quad\quad\quad r_f$ =   radius of flywheel (m),
$\quad\quad\quad T_h$ =   force (kg),
$\quad\quad\quad N$ =   number of revolutions per minute.

Where $r_f = 1$ m the equation becomes $BHP_{(m)} = 0.0014\,TN$ and in Imperial units $r_f = 1$ ft, $BHP_{(I)} = 0.00019\ NT$.

Tractive effort can be determined at the tyre rim of the rear wheel by taking into account the gear ratios of transmission and differential:

$$T_E = \frac{e\,TG_tG_D}{r_r}$$

where T_E =   tractive effort (kg),
$\quad\quad\quad e$ =   mechanical efficiency of transmission, usually about 0.9,
$\quad\quad\quad T$ =   torque (kg m),
$\quad\quad\quad G_T$ =   ratio of transmission gear,
$\quad\quad\quad G_D$ =   ratio of differential gear,
$\quad\quad\quad r_r$ =   loaded radius of drive wheel (m).

As horsepower is the rate of doing work the velocity (m/s) may be determined for any given tractive effort T_E,

i.e. $HP = \dfrac{T_E \times v}{75}$ (from $M = vT_E$)

and $v = \dfrac{75 \times HP}{T_E}.$

In addition, the total work (M) required to overcome the tractive resistances on a level road is obtained by summing the various resistances as follows:

$$M = R_R v\,W + 0.0416\,Av^3$$

where M =   work required to overcome tractive resistances (kg m/s),
$\quad\quad\quad R_R$ =   rolling resistance (kg),
$\quad\quad\quad W$ =   vehicle weight (kg),
$\quad\quad\quad v$ =   speed of vehicle (m/s),
$\quad\quad\quad A$ =   frontal area of vehicle (m²).

Additional requirements to overcome the gravitational effects on a gradient are:

$$M_i = vWi$$

where i is the gradient of 1 in x.

Given the general specification of a vehicle the various formulae can be used to compute the maximum gradient and velocity that can be achieved in a specified gear. Hence the need for, and length of, truck climbing lanes can be established for specific economic operating conditions. This is usually determined graphically by plotting on a speed basis the total resistances to traction on level ground and at maximum gradient and, on the same graph, plotting on the maximum tractive force available at the driving wheels in top and bottom gear thus obtaining the conditions of maximum speed and maximum gradient, as shown in Fig. 6.20.

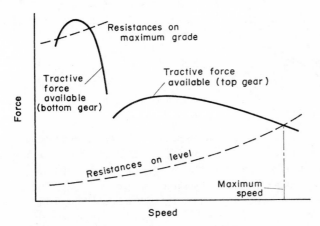

Fig. 6.20. Tractive forces in gears and vehicle speed.

Acceleration

Acceleration capability is dependent on vehicle mass, the resistance to motion and the available power, although most drivers will only use a proportion of the total engine output in any selected gear for acceleration purposes. Figure 6.21 shows typical maximum performance curves in various gears. The characteristic acceleration and deceleration modes adopted by drivers can be measured for different operating conditions

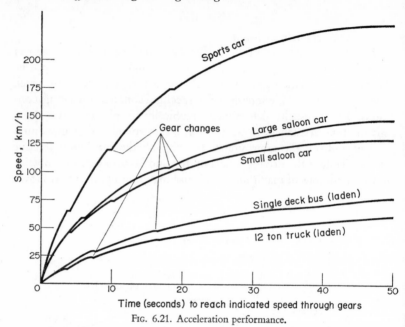

Fig. 6.21. Acceleration performance.

with suitable instruments. These can be of a simple type using pendulum U-tubes with a liquid spill device, etc., but they suffer from the disadvantage that only a maximum rate is recorded. The more complex recording types are expensive, but several types are available. One commonly used for traffic work has a three-channel marked trace which is actuated by the movement of weights longitudinally and transversely and a clock with $\frac{1}{10}$ s time units.

Typical acceleration rates in normal use are shown below:

Medium cars	3–8 km/h/s	(0·85–2·20 m/s²)
Sports cars	12–16 km/h/s	(3·33–4·50 m/s²)
Commercial vehicles	$\frac{3}{4}$–2 km/h/s	(0·21–0·56 m/s²)

Vehicle Testing

While it is the manufacturer's responsibility to produce reliable cars, designed to high standards of safety, the driver has an important duty to maintain his vehicle in an efficient state. Often through lack of knowledge, but in other cases because of negligence, deterioration of equipment occurs and it is necessary for the authorities to have powers to inspect and certify vehicle condition by a rigid and standard form of testing. Doubtless the introduction of vehicle testing in Britain has made an overall contribution to improving road safety, but severe component failure can still occur between the annual tests. However, further improvements can be made with inbuilt system monitoring, duplication of critical components, standardisation of qualities in such items as tyres and providing tread warning markers, and a greater frequency of roadside checks. Furthermore, a more stringent control and checking of vehicle loads is needed both in the interests of road safety and to prevent excessive axle loads on pavements.

Cycles

Cyclists have a high accident rate which may be partly attributable to faulty cycles and defective lighting. A small annual licence fee could well allow for an annual inspection and also the setting up of purpose designed cycle tracks where they are most needed between residential areas, factories and schools. The provision of 3 m two-way tracks would also allow the lower powered motor cycles and pedal cycles to be run together, although new regulations would be necessary. Cyclists normally occupy expensive road space where pavements have been designed for heavy vehicles. Space for cyclists could often be more economically provided in the form of individually located cycle tracks quite separate from other forms of traffic.

THE ROAD

ROAD ALIGNMENT

The alignment of a road is a major factor in determining how safely and efficiently it will meet the traffic demands. Alignments are dependent on the topography, the nature of the traffic and the functional use of the road. It is essential that their horizontal and vertical profiles are considered together in a three-dimensional process giving the road a flowing alignment which enhances both safety and visual appreciation. Examples of highway curvature, illustrating the effects of combining horizontal and vertical curves, are shown in Fig. 6.22.

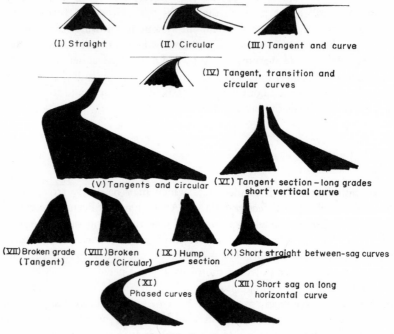

(I) Straight   (II) Circular   (III) Tangent and curve

(IV) Tangent, transition and circular curves

(V) Tangents and circular   (VI) Tangent section – long grades short vertical curve

(VII) Broken grade (Tangent)   (VIII) Broken grade (Circular)   (IX) Hump section   (X) Short straight between-sag curves

(XI) Phased curves   (XII) Short sag on long horizontal curve

FIG. 6.22. Curvature.

Horizontal Alignment

Circular curves. It can be seen from Fig. 6.23 that any imbalance in the forces H, W and P are counteracted by the frictional force fH. If the component of the reaction H is neglected and tan α equals i, the superelevation, it can be shown that for equilibrium:

$$f + i = \frac{v^2}{gR}$$

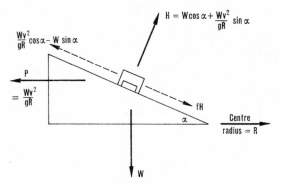

Fig. 6.23. Forces acting on a vehicle rounding a superelevated curve.

For a given speed, v, and the radius, R, the value of $f+i$ is fixed, but at low speed there is a limitation imposed by the steepness of i and at high speed there is the problem of how much friction, f, can be utilised while maintaining stability. In specifying a permissible maximum value of i consideration must be given first to slow moving or stopped vehicles, where there is a tendency for them to slide down the superelevated slope (particularly in conditions of snow and ice), for vehicle loads to move, and for a sense of improper balance to develop leading to steering errors. The value of the coefficient of friction, f, for a treaded tyre on an icy surface, is about 0·1 and this sets an upper limit to superelevation for such conditions (i.e. 1 in 10), but allowing a factor of safety, a value of 0·07 is generally recommended for roads liable to freezing and built without road heating.

The speed at which no frictional force is required to maintain the vehicle in the curve (i.e. $fH = 0$) is called the "hands-off" speed. Typical values for superelevation adopted in various countries are shown in Table 6.11. Maximum side friction factors are based on drivers' feelings of comfort with the higher values causing discomfort. U.S. practice recommends a reduction in the value of f from 0·16 at design speeds of 30 mph (48 km/h) and then decreasing linearly to 0·12 at 70 mph (113 km/h) as indicated in Table 6.12. Once the maximum superelevation and side friction factors have been set, then the allowable minimum radius is fixed for a given design speed. If $f = 0.12$, $i = 0.08$ and $v =$

100 km/h (27·78 m/s) and $g = 9\cdot807$ m/s², then from the relationship $f + i = v^2/gR$, $R = 393$ m. The normally recommended superelevation in Britain is 1 in 315 r/V^2, where V is the design speed in km/h. Table 6.13 indicates horizontal curve radii.

The alternatives for superelevating curves of less than the maximum curvature are shown in Fig. 6.24. In method (1) sufficient superelevation

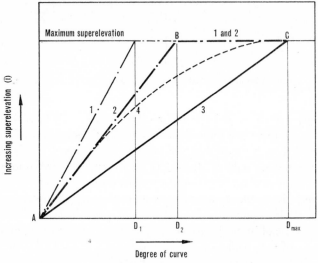

Fig. 6.24. Superelevation.

is applied to counteract all out-of-balance forces for a vehicle travelling at the design speed without using friction until the degree of curvature exceeds D, when maximum superelevation has been used. Friction requirements for curvature beyond D_1 increase rapidly and drivers are, in effect, presented with two different types of curves, those up to D_1 and those beyond D_1, and hence a more complicated judgement in negotiating a curve is necessary. Further, the majority of cars will be travelling at less than the design speed and these will experience negative friction on the flatter curves, i.e. they will be travelling at less than the "hands-off" speed and will tend to slip in towards the centre. This tendency will have to be counteracted by the irrational manoeuvre of steering out of the curve.

TABLE 6.11.   TYPICAL MAXIMUM SUPERELEVATION FACTORS

Country	Superelevation factor	Superelevation	Remarks
U.K.	0·069	1 in 14·5	Trunk roads
	0·067	1 in 15	Motorways
U.S.A.	0·08	1 in 12·5	Northern States
	0·10	1 in 10	Southern States
Germany	0·06	1 in 16·67	Autobahn
Malaya	0·10	1 in 10	Rural roads
	0·067	1 in 15	Urban roads

TABLE 6.12.   TYPICAL MAXIMUM SIDE FRICTION FACTORS

Country	Side friction factor f	Design speed V	Remarks
U.K.	0·15	100 km/h	Trunk road
	0·10	120 km/h	Motorway
U.S.A.	0·16	30 mph (48 km/h)	
	0·16	60 mph (96 km/h)	
Germany	0·04	160 km/h	Autobahn—lowland
	0·10	100 km/h	Autobahn—high mountainous
Malaya	0·15	60 mph (96 km/h)	Rural roads

TABLE 6.13.   HORIZONTAL CURVE RADII FOR URBAN AND RURAL ROADS

Design speed km/h	Urban radii				Rural radii	
	Normal (m)		Minimum (m)		Desirable (m)	Minimum* (m)
	4%	7%	4%	7%	4%	7%
120	—	—	—	—	960	510
100	—	—	—	—	660	350
80	500	300	260	230	420	230
60	275	170	150	130	240	130
50	200	120	90	80	—	—
30	75	50	35	30	—	—

* With maximum superelevation of 7%.

Method (2) overcomes this latter difficulty by applying superelevation to accommodate the average speed. This still suffers from the defect of giving two types of curves for the driver to judge—those flatter than D_2 and those sharper. Method (3), where i is proportional to D, is theoretically logical but does not allow for the common tendency to drive faster on shallow curves. Accordingly method (4) has been suggested in which the superelevation/curvature relationship is parabolic and tangential to the sides of triangle ABC as shown.

Transition curves. A vehicle cannot instantaneously change from a straight path to a circular one of constant radius, and it is usual practice to employ a transition curve changing the radius from infinity at the start to that of the circular one at the end. A transition length is also necessary in order to gradually apply the superelevation as the radius increases and to present a visually pleasing line without a disjoint at the tangent point. Many types of transition curves have been proposed such as the spiral, the lemniscate and the cubic parabola, but as road vehicles are not confined to a single path the differences between the curves, for most practical radii, are largely immaterial. The spiral is widely used and the leading dimensions given in this text refer to its characteristics, which are summarised in Fig. 6.25.

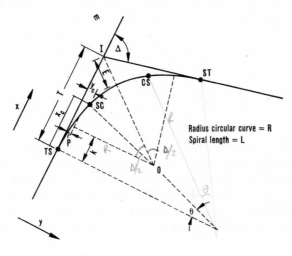

Radius circular curve = R
Spiral length = L

TS	Junction of tangent and spiral
SC	Junction of spiral and circular curve
CS	Junction of circular curve and spiral
ST	Junction of spiral and tangent

p shift;   approx. equals $\dfrac{L^2}{24\,R}$

k   " $\dfrac{L}{2}$

x_c "   L

y_c "   4p

T tangent length   equals $k + (R+p)\tan\dfrac{\Delta}{2}$

E external distance   equals $(R+p)\sec\dfrac{\Delta}{2} - R$

θ Angle subtended
by spiral   equals $\dfrac{L}{2R}$ radians

Length of circular
curve   equals $R\,(\Delta_{rads} - 2\theta_{rads})$

FIG. 6.25. Circular and transition curves.

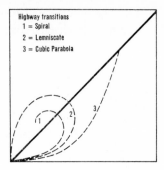

FIG. 6.25 (*continued*).

Several methods have been used to determine the length of transitions, mainly arising from railway practices such as that of Short. If a vehicle travelling with a velocity v m/s takes time t s to travel the length l of the spiral, then $t = l/v$. On the circular curve, at the end of the spiral, the vehicle will have a radial acceleration of v^2/R and the rate of gain of radial acceleration, C, is given by:

$$C = \frac{v^3}{Rl} \quad \text{m/s}^3.$$

Early railway practice used a value of $C = 0\cdot31$ m/s³, but values of up to $0\cdot61$ m/s³ and greater are used in road design. The modified Short formula takes the superelevation into account and the expression reduces to the traditional Short relationship for zero superelevation:

$$l = \frac{v}{C} \left(\frac{v^2}{R} - gi. \right)$$

Leeming and Black investigated the path followed by a large number of drivers during the transition movement from straight to circular arc. They found that the path followed depended on the unbalanced sideways force a driver was willing to accept. The magnitude of this force is dependent on the vehicle's speed and on the radius/superelevation combination. Drivers proportioned the amount of the curve spent in transition and in a constant circular arc according to speed, the radius/ superelevation combination, sideways force and the total length of curve to be negotiated. A set of nomograms was published (*Jn. Inst. of Municipal Engrs.*, vol. LXXXVI, No. 8, 1950) enabling transition lengths to be selected, which satisfy the majority of drivers, e.g. for a design speed of 96 km/h ($R = 366$ m) transition lengths of 79 m and 94 m are required for deviation angles of 25° and 45° respectively as compared to Short's method which gives lengths of 173 m and 115 m ($C = 0{\cdot}30$ and $0{\cdot}46$ m/s³) and modified Short lengths of 114 m and 76 m for the same values of C.

Generally curves in excess of 1200 m do not require transitions because the shift is minimal (less than 25 mm) and the vehicle can be adequately accommodated in the lane with little deviation. However, for visual reasons, transitions are usually inserted for curves of less than about 1750 m.

Application of superelevation. The rate of application of superelevation is important, both in terms of vehicle control and the appearance of the curve. Values for the gradient of the carriageway edge profile, with respect to the centre line, should not normally exceed 1 in 200 and the length of a transition determined by this rule depends on carriageway width.

Methods of applying superelevation are shown in Fig. 6.26 for a two-way road. Drainage, topography, aesthetics and other factors determine

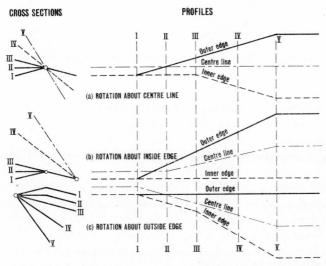

FIG. 6.26. Methods of application of superelevation to single carriageways.

which method should be selected in a particular situation, although method (1) is commonly used as it leads to minimum displacement of the carriageway edges. Method (2) is preferable where drainage problems may arise and method (3) leaves the outer edge free. However, drivers position their vehicles by following the eye through the inner edge of a curve or the centre line markings. In practice the intersecting gradients are suitably rounded at points I, III and V. Figure 6.27 indicates methods

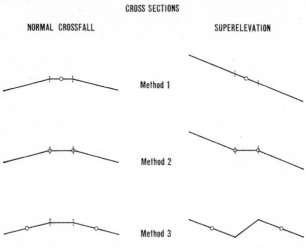

Fig. 6.27. Methods of application of superelevation to dual carriageways.

of superelevating dual carriageways and centres of rotation. An additional factor to be considered in this case is the difference in levels between the median edges.

Due to the effects of off-tracking, vehicle overhang and positional control on curves, it is recommended that curves on sharp radii in substandard conditions should be widened. For standard width lanes, with radii less than 150 m, 0·3 m per lane should be used. On less than standard width carriageways widening, up to the standard width, should be provided at the following rates: radius less than 150 m—0·6 m per lane, radius between 150 m and 300 m—0·5 m per lane; radius between 300 m and 400 m—0·3 m per lane.

Vertical Alignment

The vertical alignment consists of a series of gradients connected by vertical curves. Gradients are normally expressed as a percentage, i.e. the vertical rise for each 100 m of horizontal distance. By convention gradients are considered to be positive when ascending from left to right and negative when descending. Maximum gradients are established by reference to vehicle performance and the functional purpose of the route. While passenger cars can maintain their performance on gradients as steep as 10%, grade limits are normally based on truck performance and, on important routes, are limited to 4% or less.

Critical gradient length. When a vehicle reaches a balance between power input and output, the resulting stabilised speed is called the crawling speed. Vehicles at the crawling speed cause marked impedance to the traffic stream. This is a critical factor in design and a commonly accepted criterion allows a reduction of 25 km/h from the entry speed to the gradient. The distance up the gradient at which this speed reduction is reached is known as the critical length. Where the critical length is exceeded it is advisable to construct an additional up-gradient lane, for slower moving vehicles. The benefits from these truck climbing lanes can be assessed against the additional construction costs. On long steep down gradients, where brake failures may occur, it is often necessary to provide escape roads which imbed the vehicle without danger to the occupants.

Vertical curvature. A change from one gradient to another is effected by the use of vertical curves. The design is based on the type of curve, sight distances, riding comfort, drainage and aesthetic considerations. Several types of curve are used, such as the cubic parabola, simple parabola and the circular arc, as shown in Fig. 6.28. The circular arc provides

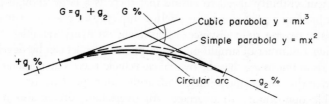

$G = g_1 + g_2$ G %

Cubic parabola $y = mx^3$

Simple parabola $y = mx^2$

$+g_1$ %

Circular arc $-g_2$ %

FIG. 6.28. Vertical curves.

constant visibility and for most practical highway applications the simple parabola is virtually identical. In designing vertical curves, it is usual to work with the mathematical properties of either, depending on which gives the simpler calculations.

Sight Distance

The necessity for a driver to see sufficiently far ahead to enable him to assess developing situations and to take appropriate action is obvious. The most frequent occasions that arise are those (a) calling upon him to stop when approaching an obstacle, (b) requiring a decision regarding over-taking, and (c) requiring an assessment of the course of action to be taken at an intersection. The sight distances needed in the circumstances are discussed below under the headings of stopping sight distance, passing sight distance and intersection sight distance.

Stopping sight distance. The distance is made up of three components: (a) the distance travelled during the perception time, (b) the distance travelled during the brake reaction time and (c) the distance travelled during braking. Values of 1·5 and 1·0 s are normally accepted for the perception and brake reaction time respectively in most road conditions encountered. The minimum braking distance is given by $d = v^2/2gf$ where d = braking distance (m), v = speed (m/s) and g = 9·807 m/s^2. In practice, due to brake fade and the decrease in f inversely with speed, the braking distance is more likely to be proportional to the cube rather than the square of the speed. The value of f is also affected by the type of road surface, tyre condition and tread, and whether the surface is wet or dry.

Passing sight distance. An overtaking driver on a two-way road requires sufficient visibility ahead to ensure that there is a large enough gap in the opposing traffic stream to safely complete the passing manoeuvre. This safe passing sight distance is dependent on many variables, but by making a number of simplifying assumptions a model can be developed. The assumptions are that the overtaken vehicle travels at constant speed and that the overtaking vehicle trails at the same speed whilst awaiting a suitable opportunity to overtake. An overtaking driver also requires a perception time before commencing a manoeuvre and during the manoeuvre accelerates to a speed which is, on average, 16 km/h faster than the overtaken vehicle. The overtaking vehicle returns to its own lane with a safe clearance distance between it and the oncoming vehicle which is assumed to be travelling at the same average speed as that of the overtaking vehicle. As shown in Fig. 6.29, the safe passing sight distance is comprised of four separate distances:

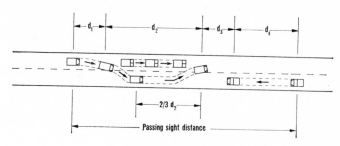

FIG. 6.29. Passing sight distance.

The preliminary delay distance d_1, in metres, is given by:

$$d_1 = v_1 t_1 + \frac{a t_1^2}{2}$$

where v_1 = average speed of overtaken vehicle (m/s),
       t_1 = preliminary delay time (s),
       a = average acceleration of overtaking vehicle (m/s^2).
Overtaking distance d_2 (m) is as follows:

$$d_2 = v_2 t_2$$

where t_2 = time vehicle occupies opposing lane (s),
       v_2 = average speed of overtaking vehicle (m/s).
The safety distance d_3 has been found in the U.S.A. to range from about 35 m to 90 m with the larger distances for higher speeds. It is usual in American practice to make d_4 two-thirds of the overtaking distance d_2 on the basis that the overtaking vehicle can decelerate and return to its own lane during the first part of the overtaking manoeuvre. Values are shown in Table 6.14, derived by A.A.S.H.O. from observations made in the U.S.A. (C. W. Prisk, *Passing Practices on Rural Highways*, Highway Research Board Proceedings, 1941).

TABLE 6.14.   ELEMENTS OF SAFE PASSING SIGHT DISTANCES,
TWO-LANE ROAD

Speed group, km/h	48 – 64	64 – 80	80 – 96
Preliminary delay time, t (s)	3·6	4·0	4·3
Average speed of passed vehicle V_1 (km/h)	40·0	54·3	68·4
Average acceleration of passing vehicle, a (m/s²)	0·63	0·64	0·66
Average speed of overtaking vehicle, vehicle, V_2 (km/h)	56·1	70·5	84·5
Time vehicle occupies opposing land, t_2 (s)	9·3	10·0	10·7
Safety distance, d_3 (m)	30·0	55·0	76·0
Distance travelled by opposing vehicle $d_4 = \frac{2}{3}d_2$ (m)	96·0	130·0	168·0

For three-lane roads, A.A.S.H.O. recommend that the three distances d_1, d_2 and d_3 be used omitting d_4, the distance travelled by the opposing vehicle.

Table 6.15 gives the minimum sight distances for standard road widths as generally adopted in Britain. The distances are based on the distance travelled during the following phases of perception, braking and reaction plus the distance travelled when decelerating to a stop. Minimum overtaking sight distances are required in the operation of two-way flow roads and are based on the time an overtaking vehicle occupies a counterflow lane. Practical safe distances will vary according to circumstances, e.g. the speeds of overtaking and overtaken vehicle, approach vehicle speeds in the counterflow lane, the number and size of overtaken vehicles and also alignment characteristics. To ensure adequate standards of comfort and appearance, vertical curves should not be shorter than $L = KA$, where L = vertical curve length (m), A = algebraic difference in gradients (%), and K = the value selected from Table 6.16. The values in Table 6.16 for minimum curve length will only be used if they are greater than the length obtained by using the formula $L = KA$.

TABLE 6.15. MINIMUM SIGHT DISTANCES (STANDARD WIDTH ROADS)

Design speed, km/h	Urban sight distance (m)		Rural sight distance (m)	
	Overtaking	Stopping	Overtaking	Stopping
120	—	—	—	300
100	—	—	450	210
80	360	140	360	140
60	270	90	270	90
50	225	70	—	—
30	135	30	—	—

TABLE 6.16. *K* VALUES FOR DETERMINATION OF MINIMUM VERTICAL CURVE LENGTHS

Design speed km/h	Rural K values			Urban K values		
	Stopping sights distance (crests)	Stopping sight distance (sags)	Overtaking sight	Stopping sight	Overtaking sight	Absolute min. curve (m)
120	105	75	—	—	—	—
100	50	50	240	—	—	—
80	25	30	150	25	—	50
60	10	20	90	10	—	40
50	—	—	—	6	60	30
30	—	—	—	1	20	20

Safe passing distances are considerably greater than safe stopping sight distances and situations will arise where topographical conditions make it uneconomical to provide them and the effective capacity of the road is reduced. The reductions are greatest with higher operating speeds and for an increasing proportion of the road with sub-standard conditions and range from about 10%, with a 50% length restriction at 60 km/h, to more than 80% with all the highway restricted at 85 km/h.

Eye and object heights. The sight distance available is dependent on the eye height of the observer, which in U.K. practice is taken as 1·05 m. This inevitably represents a compromise as anthropometric measurements and vehicle dimensions will vary considerably. The minimum height selected for the object is also important and ideally should be the minimum detail discernible by, at least, the average visual acuity, for the given speed and viewing conditions. A.A.S.H.O. recommends 6 in. (152 mm), since the saving in distance is considerable up to this figure, but there are diminishing returns beyond this level. Generally, such hazards can just be overrun without the consequences being too severe. Somewhat illogically the British standard recommends an object height of 1·05 m, which is partly compensated for in a comparison with U.S. standards by the adoption here of a lower eye height standard.

The principal control in the design of summit curves is the sight distance requirement. Two conditions arise which depend on whether the vertical curve is longer or shorter than the specified sight distance, as shown in Fig. 6.30. Because large earthwork cuttings may be needed for the establishment of safe passing sight distances it is frequently the case that the shorter safe stopping sight distances are adopted for economic reasons. Figure 6.31 shows a plot of vertical curve length against the gradient intersection angle for various sight distance standards.

Riding comfort. The effect of travelling over a summit curve is to give an apparent loss of weight and, on a sag curve, an apparent increase due to the centripetal acceleration. It is desirable that this centripetal acceleration, C, is limited to a value of $0·3 - 0·75$ m/s^2. The selection of a value enables the length of vertical curve (L) to be established from the following relationship:

$$L = \frac{1}{100} \frac{v^2 G}{C}$$

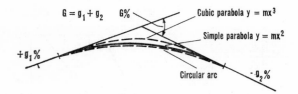

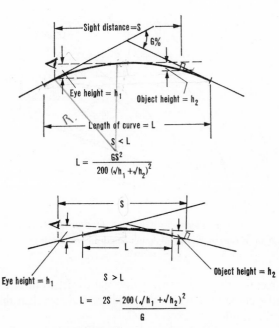

Fig. 6.30. Sight distances in vertical curves.

where v = vehicle speed (m/s),

G = algebraic difference in gradient (%).

Lengths of curves for values of C are shown in Fig. 6.31 and it can be seen that centripetal acceleration is more often a controlling factor with sags rather than summit curves. It is important to check the night-time headlamp visibility distance on vertical curves. Also shown in the figure are minimum drainage conditions. The absolute minimum of 1 in 300

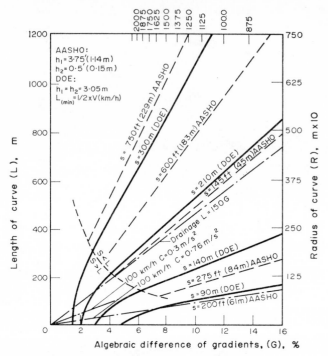

Fig. 6.31. Length of vertical curves, minimum length in two-thirds the speed in km/h, in metres.

requires exceptionally high construction standards; to limit to 30 m the length of the curve over which the gradient is flatter than this the total curve length, *L*, must not exceed 46G.

Sight distances at junctions. The operation of junctions is affected by the sight distances allowed for approaching drivers and the relative and absolute speeds of the vehicle manoeuvres. Priority junctions are the simplest form of mandatory control and are either of the Give Way (or yield) type and those requiring the side road vehicle to stop at the major road.

In the case of Give Way junctions it is necessary for a driver approaching on the minor road to have a sufficiently long length of the intersecting road in view to enable him to assess the major road traffic situation and to make a decision whether to cross or not. A view far enough back along the approach is needed to enable a stop to be made at the junction, if required, and this gives rise to the concept of a sight triangle as illustrated in Fig. 6.32. Inside the sight triangle *XYZ* there must be no

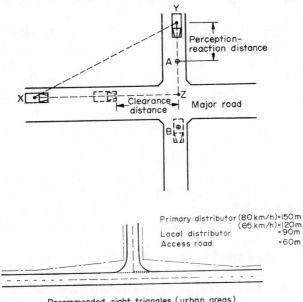

Recommended sight triangles (urban areas)

FIG. 6.32. Sight triangles.

obstruction to the visibility between the approaching vehicles. The side *YZ* of the triangle is the distance travelled by the approaching vehicle whilst the driver perceives and reacts to the situation, and the required braking distance to bring the vehicle to rest. It is determined from:

$$YZ = ut_1 + \frac{u^2}{2d}$$

where u =   approach speed (m/s),
t_1 =   perception–reaction time (s),
d =   allowable deceleration (m/s²),
YZ =   distance in metres.

Assuming that the approach speed after the junction sign is 20 km/h (5·556 m/s), a 2 s perception–reaction time, and a braking deceleration of 3·50 m/s^2, the distance YZ will equal, approximately, 15·5 m.

The length XZ is the distance travelled by the major road vehicle during the perception–reaction time t_1 of the other vehicle, the time t_2 for the minor road vehicle to accelerate from point A to reach point B clear of the junction, and a safety clearance time t_3. Hence $XZ = v(t_1 + t_2 + t_3)$, where v = speed of major road vehicle (m/s). The time, t_2, is dependent on the length AB and this includes the braking distance $(u^2/2d)$, the width of the major road and the length of the minor road vehicle. If the rate of acceleration of the minor road vehicle is a m/s^2, then

$$t_2 = \frac{(u^2 + 2\,as)^{\frac{1}{2}} - u}{a}$$

where s = distance AB (m),
          u = approach speed of minor road vehicle (m/s).
If $T = t_1 + t_2 + t_3$, the length $XZ = vT$.

Assuming the following typical values u = 20 km/h, t_1 = 2 s, d = 3·50 m/s^2, width of major road s = 7·30 m, passenger car length = 4·50 m, commercial vehicle length = 9·00 m, a = 1·25 m/s^2 (car), 0·60 m/s^2 (commercial vehicle), design speed of major road v = 100 km/h, and a safety time margin t_3 = 2 s, the distance XZ, by substitution, is approximately 175 m. If the minor road traffic contains a high proportion of commercial vehicles (say over 10%) the commercial vehicle length and acceleration values should be used, and this gives a design length XZ of 200 m.

Where there is a stop control on the side road of the junction a halted driver must have time to perceive the traffic situation, decide to cross (perception–reaction time, t_1, s) and accelerate from the stopped position to clear the junction (acceleration time, t_2, s). The required sight distance (S.D. m) is given by:

$$\text{S.D.} = v(t_1 + t_2)$$

where v = major road design speed (m/s),
          t_2 = acceleration time to move distance S (m) from stop line to clearance point at an acceleration rate of a (m/s^2),
          = $(2S/a)^{\frac{1}{2}}$.

Using the previous values the sight distance required for cars is 175 m and 260 m for lorries. Sight distances are shown in Table 6.17.

TABLE 6.17.   INTERSECTION SIGHT DISTANCES—GIVE WAY AND STOP AT
THE MAJOR ROAD

Control	Car				Lorry			
	Give way		Stop		Give way		Stop	
Carriageway width (m)	7·5	10	7·5	10	7·5	10	7·5	10
Design speed of major road (km/h)								
50	89	95	95	101	101	107	134	144
65	117	123	123	131	136	143	175	187
80	135	150	152	162	168	177	219	231
100	179	188	190	204	201	213	275	289
120	214	225	228	243	250	264	330	346

Where intersecting roads are skewed it is necessary to allow for the extra distance to be travelled across the major road by the minor road vehicle. If there are approach gradients allowance should be made in the braking distances and also to acceleration times on uphill gradients, e.g. YZ should be increased for cars by 20% for a gradient of 3% and by 50% where the commercial vehicle type is used in design.

FURTHER READING

AITKEN, J. and BOYD, J. (1945/6) A consolidation of vertical curve design. *Inst. Civ. Engrs.* **23**(2).

AMERICAN ASSOCIATION OF STATE HIGHWAY OFFICIALS (1957) *A Policy on Arterial Highways in Urban Areas.* Washington.

AMERICAN ASSOCIATION OF STATE HIGHWAY OFFICIALS (1968) *Design of Rural Highways.* Washington.

ANON (1967, 1969) Computers and highway design. *Rds. & Rd. Constr.* **45**(538), and **47**(553).

APPLEYARD, D., LYNCH, K. and MYER, J. R. (1963) *The View from the Road*. M.I.T. Press.

BROADBENT, D. E. (1958) *Perception and Communication*. Pergamon.

COLBORNE, H. V. (1971) Road safety and pre-school children. *Safety Education*, 123.

COOPER, L. (1970) A bibliography with abstracts of research into the use of polarised headlights. RRL Report 343. *The Road Research Laboratory*.

COUNTY SURVEYORS SOCIETY (1969) *Highway Transition Curve Tables (Metric)*. Carriers Publishing Co. Ltd., London.

COWLING, H. (1968) Highway design. *J. Inst. Highway Engrs.* **xv** (7).

CRAM, I. (1969) Standards for the design of rural roads. *J. Inst. Highway Engrs.* **xvi**(10), October.

CRISWELL, H. (1967) *Highway Spirals, Superelevation and Vertical Curves*. Carriers Publishing Co. Ltd.

CROWE, SYLVIA (1960) *The Landscape of Roads*. The Architectural Press, London.

DENTON, G. G. (1971) The influence of visual pattern on perceived speed. RRL Report LR 409. The Road Research Laboratory.

DEPARTMENT OF SCIENTIFIC AND INDUSTRIAL RESEARCH (1963) *Research on Road Safety*. Road Research Laboratory, H.M.S.O.

DREW, G. C., COLQUHOUN, W. P. and LONG, H. A. (1959) Effect of small doses of alcohol on a skill resembling driving. M.R.C. Memorandum No. 38, H.M.S.O.

EVANS, L. (1970) Speed estimation from a moving automobile. *Ergonomics*, **13**(2).

GALLAGHER, W. E. and CORNICK, P. C. (1969) Programming for horizontal alignment. *J. Inst. Highway Engrs.* **xvi**(4).

GILES, J. G. (Ed.) (1968) *Steering, Suspension and Tyres*. Iliffe, London.

GUIGNARD, J. C. and GUIGNARD, E. (1970) Human response to vibration: a critical survey of published work. Univ. of Southampton, Inst. of Sound & Vibration, Research Memorandum No. 373.

HADFIELD, W. (1971) Designing for deliveries — design standards for service and off-street loading areas. The Freight Transp. Assoc.

HALL, H. C. (1968) Sight distance on rural trunk roads. *Highways and Public Works*, **36**(1705), September.

HARRIS, A. J. (1963) On the analysis of the possible motions of a vehicle. Symp. Control of Vehicles during Cornering and Braking, Inst. Mech. Engrs.

HEIMSTRA, N. W. (1970) The effects of stress fatigue on performance in a simulated driving situation. *Ergonomics*, **13**(2).

HIGHWAY RESEARCH BOARD. *Driving and Drivers*, H.R. Record 292 (1969); *Night Visibility and Driving Behaviour*, H.R. Record 336 (1970); *Vehicle Characteristics*, H.R. Record 344 (1970).

HIGHWAY RESEARCH BOARD (1970) *Methods of Determining Optimum Vertical Alignment under Specified Conditions*, H.R. Record 306; *Application of Aerial Surveys to Highway Engineering*, H.R. Record 315; *Design of Traffic Safety Barriers*, H.R. Record 343. National Academy Sciences, Washington.

HIGHWAY RESEARCH BOARD (1971) *Improvement of Visibility for Night Driving*. H.R. Record 368, Washington.

HIGNETT, H. J. (1970) Vehicle loading and headlamp aim. R.R.L. Report LR 329. The Road Research Laboratory.

HOSKING, J. R. (1970) The role of aggregates in providing skid-resistant roads; and LUPTON, G. N. The field testing of skidding. The Influence of the Road Surface on Skidding. Symposium, 1968, University of Salford.

HUNT, T. J., DIX, B. and MAY, P. I. (1968) A preliminary investigation into a physiological assessment of driving stress. Metropolitan Police, Accident Research Unit.

JOHANSSON, G. A. and RUMAR, K. (1968) Visible distance and safe approach speeds for night driving. *Ergonomics*, **11**(3).

KAO, H. S. R. (1969) Feedback concepts of driver behaviour and the highway information system. *Acc. Analysis and Prevention*, **1**(1).

KISHTO, B. N. and SAUNDERS, R. (1970) Variations of the visual threshold with retinal location, Pts. 1 and 2. *Vision Research, London*, **10**.

LEEMING, J. J. and BLACK (1950) Road curvature and superelevation. *J. Inst. Munic. Engrs.* **76**(8).

LOWE, A. F. (1969) Engineer participation in the highway design integrated program system. *J. Inst. Highway Engrs.* **vi**(8), Aug.

MILNER, G. (1972) *Drugs and Driving*. Basle, Karger.

MINISTRY OF TRANSPORT (1968) *Roads in Urban Areas*. H.M.S.O., London.

MINISTRY OF TRANSPORT (1967) *Roads in the Landscape*. Symposium, M.O.T.

MINISTRY OF TRANSPORT (1968) *Layout of Roads in Rural Areas*, H.M.S.O., London.

MOORE, R. L. and JEHN, V. J. (1968) Recent developments in barrier design. Ninth Int. Study Wk. in Tr. and Saf. Engng. W.T.A.O.

MOORE, R. L. (1969) Some human factors affecting the design of vehicles and roads. *J. Inst. Highway Engrs.* **xvi**(8).

NEWLAND, R. M. (1963) Driver eye height and highway design. *Roads and Road Construction*, **41**(484),(485).

NEWLAND, R. M. (1964) The design vehicle. *Traff. Engng. and Control*, **6**(2).

PAISLEY, J. L. (1965) Design standards for roads in urban areas. *Traff. Engng. and Control*, **7**(2).

PEARSON, R. G. and BYARS, G. E. (1956) Development and validation of a check list for measuring subjective fatigue. USAF School of Aerospace Medicine, Report No. TR-56-115.

QUENAULT, S. W. (1968) Driver behaviour—safe and unsafe drivers, RRL Report LR 145; Task capability while driving, RRL Report LR 166; and Dissociation and driver behaviour, RRL Report LR 212. The Road Research Laboratory.

ROBERTS, H. E. and STOTHARD, J. N. (1969) Use of computer for road design. *J. Inst. Civ. Engrs.*

SABEY, B. E., WILLIAMS, T. and LUPTON, G. N. (1970) Factors affecting the friction of tyres on wet roads. 1970 Internat. Auto. Safety Conference Compendium. Soc. of Auto. Engrs. Inc., New York.

SHEPPARD, D. (1969) The 1967 drink and driving campaign; a survey among drivers. RRL Report LR 230. The Road Research Laboratory.

SPENCER, W. H. (1948) The co-ordination of horizontal and vertical alignment of high speed routes. Inst. Civ. Engrs. Road Paper No. 27.

STARKS, H. J. H. (1953) *The Braking Performance of Cars and Brake Testing.* Road Research Tech. Paper No. 26, H.M.S.O.

STOCKLEY, N. H. (1972) Aesthetics of urban motorways. *J. Inst. Highway Engrs.* **xix**(9).

SYMPOSIUM PSYCHOLOGICAL ASPECTS OF DRIVER BEHAVIOUR (1971) *The Driver* (Vol. 1) and *Applied Research* (Vol. 2). Inst. for Rd. Saf. Res., Netherlands.

TAGGART, P. (1969) Some effect of motor-car driving on the normal and abnormal heart. *Brit. Med. J.*

TAYLOR, D. M. (1964) Drivers' galvanic skin response and risk of accident. *Ergonomics*, **7**.

VALLIS, J. (1969) The effect of metrication on highway engineering. *J. Inst. Highway Engrs.* **xvi**(2).

VARIOUS (1972) Digital terrain models. Proc. P.T.R.C. Seminar, Planning and Transportation Research & Computation Co. Ltd.

WELFORD, A. T. (1960) Measurement of sensory-motor performance. *Ergonomics*, **3**.

WHITE, R. (1958) The three-dimensional design of roads. *J. Inst. Highway Engrs.* **v**(3).

WILKINS, H. A. (1971) The instability of articulated vehicles. *J. Auto. Engng.* **2**(3).

YERRILL, J. S. (1971) Headlamp intensities in Europe and Britain. RRL Report LR 383. The Road Research Laboratory.

CHAPTER 7

The Traffic Stream and Capacity

THE TRAFFIC STREAM

There are many ways in which the traffic engineer can define a traffic stream, but the fundamental measures most commonly used are flow concentration and speed. Flow and volume are often used synonymously, although the former is more appropriate when considering the traffic stream and implies a quantity of vehicles in space measured in an interval of time, whereas the latter is more often limited to a count of the number of vehicles passing a point in space during an interval of time. Concentration is expressed as the number of vehicles in a given length of road, but is also sometimes referred to as the density. Speed is determined from the distance covered by a vehicle in unit time or, for a number of observations, the mean is computed from the time-distribution of speeds (time mean speed) or the mean of the space distribution of speeds (space mean speed).

If a traffic flow (Q) has a speed (V) then the mean time interval between vehicles is evidently $1/Q$ and the mean distance between vehicles is V/Q. Hence, the instantaneous number of vehicles per unit length, the concentration (K), is Q/V and the mean space interval is given by its reciprocal ($1/K$). Thus the basic traffic equation relating flow, concentration and speed is $Q = KV$. Values used in the equation should be obtained in a dimensionally similar way, i.e. only spatial measurements can relate space mean speed and concentration to flow. Flow is taken here as the number of vehicles in space at an instant in time. These relationships have been demonstrated by Wardrop to show that a traffic stream moving along a length of road can be considered as a series of n subsidiary streams with flows q_i and a steady speed of v_i, where i has values $1, 2, \ldots, n$. The total flow Q is obtained by summing the flows in the n subsidiary streams:

$$Q = \sum_{i=1}^{n} q_i$$

The concentration of each subsidiary stream is $k_i = q_i/v_i$ and the total concentration

$$K = \sum_{i=1}^{n} \frac{q_i}{v_i}.$$

By definition, from the arithmetic mean of the speeds of vehicles occupying a given length of road:

$$\bar{V}_s = \frac{\sum_{i=1}^{n} k_i v_i.}{K}$$

By substitution,

$$\bar{V}_s = \frac{\sum_{i=1}^{n} \frac{q_i v_i}{v_i}}{K} = \frac{\sum_{i=1}^{n} q_i}{K} = \frac{Q}{K}$$

and it can be seen that it is the space mean speed that relates flow and concentration.

The traffic stream is constituted initially from spatially separated single vehicles, moving at a driver's desired speed, but unimpeded and travelling independently of other traffic. Because of speed differences faster vehicles will be continuously closing up to slower vehicles, but if traffic conditions prevent the faster vehicle overtaking then moving queues are formed. These gradually lengthen and separate groups (platoons) coalesce until all the vehicles form a single flow, albeit "loosely packed". For any further increase in flow the concentration must also increase causing some oscillations, due to a driver's inability to maintain a minimum spacing consistently and without a response time lag, which in turn creates instabilities and a throughput lower than the theoretical maximum. In this condition the maximum flow level cannot be recovered until the input volume is reduced. However, if the flow continues to increase it follows that concentration also increases and speeds fall to match the reduced spacings available, causing a further reduction in flow. As speed falls to zero, concentration rises to its maximum value known as the jam concentration (K_j), when vehicles are packed together as closely as possible. In practice, even when stationary, vehicles do not touch and the jam concentration, for cars only, ranges from about 190 to 210 veh/km. The size of each space between vehicles can be seen as a zone of influence ahead of each vehicle which is dependent on both vehicle and driver characteristics.

HEADWAYS

Spacing can be measured in terms of either distance or time respectively, known as a distance headway and a time headway. Headways are fundamental to all traffic operations and control, and to vehicle manoeuvres including those of overtaking, lane changing and intersection operation. As a faster moving vehicle approaches a slower one, the driver of the rear vehicle will, at some critical point, decide either to reduce speed, until the relative speeds are zero and trailing occurs, or to change lane and overtake if sufficient sized gaps are present in an adjacent lane. The headway at which the following driver is influenced by the preceding vehicle is known as the interference headway. The total number of vehicles so impeded in a stream can be used as a measure of capacity. A figure of 9 s has been found in American rural conditions, but from limited studies it appears to be at about 6 s in Great Britain. The charts in Fig. 7.1 show typical distributions of headways on various types of British roads.

On a two-lane, two-way road, queues of vehicles will start to form behind slower moving vehicles as soon as the headway in the opposing lane falls below a minimum requirement for overtaking. It can also be seen that as flow increases the proportion of suitable sized headways above the required limit falls. In other words, increasing flow on any lane requires more frequent overtaking to maintain individual speeds but there is a reduction in the availability of headway gaps to accommodate these. Restricted vertical and horizontal sight distances and the formation of short queues will further reduce the opportunities because even greater headways are required.

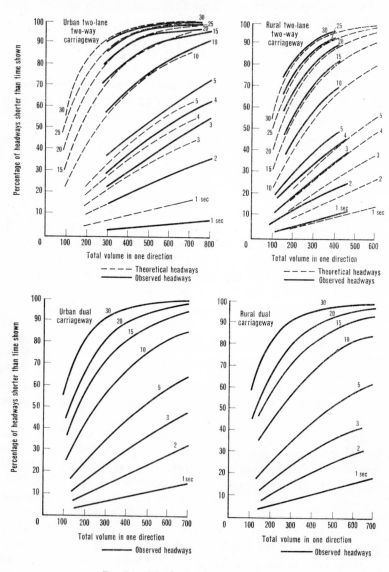

Fig. 7.1.   Distribution of stream headways.

If vehicles are not subject to interference each driver operates independently of all other drivers. Under these conditions equal intervals of time or space are equally likely to contain a given number of vehicles. The resulting distribution can then be defined as random.

Traffic considered in these terms can be shown to conform to the Poisson distribution where the probability of an event occurring can be determined theoretically:

$$p(x) = \frac{e^{-\mu}\,\mu^x}{x!}$$

where $p(x)$ = the probability that x vehicles will arrive in the given interval of time,

   μ = the mean number of vehicles arriving in the given interval of time, t,

i.e.

$$\mu = \frac{tV}{3600}$$

   (e = base of Naperian logarithms = 2·71828)

where t = given interval of time (s),

   V = traffic volume (veh/h).

Hence the probability that no vehicle will arrive in time t at a volume V,

$$p(o) = \frac{e^{-\mu}\,\mu^0}{0!} = e^{-\mu}$$

and this, in effect, is the probability of a headway of time t occurring.

Theoretical headway distributions are shown as dashed lines in Fig. 7.1. It is interesting to note that in the shorter headway ranges fewer drivers adopt the predicted values, due to varying individual assessments of safety, when trailing at short distances.

Headways can be measured under different lane conditions and speeds or they can be derived by selecting values for perception time, braking distance and vehicle length. Whereas braking distances and vehicle length are readily ascertainable for given conditions it is more difficult, due to variability in road conditions and human behaviour, to select values for perception time. A general expression for determining the distance headway (H_D) in metres is as follows:

$$H_D = L + pv + \frac{v^2}{2gf}$$

where L = length of vehicle in m,
  v = speed in m/s,
  p = perception time in s,
  f = coefficient of friction for selected conditions,
  g = 9·807 m/s^2.

The values of H_D show a wide variation, reflecting the arbitrary nature of selecting appropriate constants in the second and third terms of the expression. In practice drivers often travel at closer headways than circumstances warrant and they depend on their ability to perceive situations some way ahead of the vehicle they are following. The second and third terms of the expression can be used to determine the safe stopping distance giving, respectively, the distance travelled during the perception of an emergency situation, before the start of braking, and the actual braking distance.

TRAFFIC FLOW RELATIONSHIPS

Both theoretical and empirical derivations for the relationships between concentration, speed and flow have been a popular field of investigation by many researchers and practitioners over the years. They may be divided into microscopic and macroscopic models, the former based on fluid flow, wave theory and statistical methods and the latter on car following behavioural models expressing the performance of a vehicle in terms of its velocity and position with respect to the vehicle immediately preceding it. More recently, traffic flow has been synthesised by assuming traffic laws and programming rapidly repeated calculations in a computer, thus using a simulation model to assess the performance of intersections, road lengths and networks.

Congestion is caused by the flow demands of arrivals in a system requiring a service which has a restriction on its availability, and by irregularities in either the demand or service operation, or in both. This is a queuing system and traffic can be defined as queuing when a following driver must immediately react to a speed reduction made by a preceding vehicle. Figures 7.2 and 7.3 show the general relationships between flow, speed and concentration.

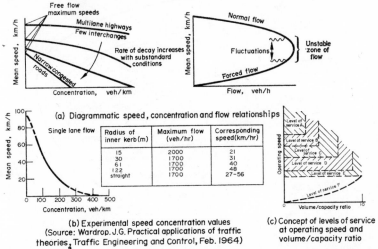

(a) Diagrammatic speed, concentration and flow relationships

Radius of inner kerb (m)	Maximum flow (veh/hr)	Corresponding speed (km/hr)
15	2000	21
30	1700	31
61	1700	40
122	1700	48
straight	1700	27–56

(b) Experimental speed concentration values
(Source: Wardrop. J.G. Practical applications of traffic theories, Traffic Engineering and Control, Feb. 1964)

(c) Concept of levels of service at operating speed and volume/capacity ratio

FIG. 7.2.   (a) Diagrammatic speed, concentration and flow relationships. (b) Experimental speed concentration values. (c) Level of service.

Observations of traffic flow, under different operating conditions, have established curves that are broadly similar, either wholly or in part, to those derived theoretically. The curves for flow with concentration or speed have been shown to be generally of parabolic form. At constant speed an increase in concentration results in an increased flow until a critical concentration is reached where speed and flow decrease even though the concentration continues to rise. The relationship between concentration and speed, as shown in Fig. 7.2, was determined in single lane conditions, mainly on a test track, by the Road Research Laboratory.

CAPACITY

The evaluation of capacity while fundamental to all traffic operations and design problems is also associated with the safe and economic operation of highways. Capacity as a measure of performance, under varying conditions, can be applied to individual locations or a complete network.

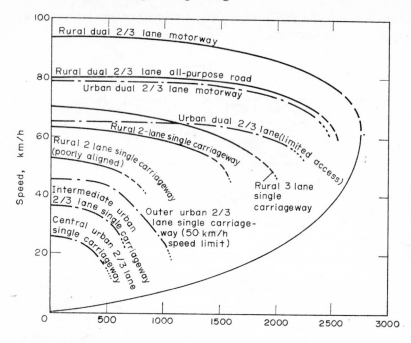

Flow (pcu/h per standard width lane 3·65m)

FIG. 7.3.   Upper values of speed flow relationships for selected types of rural and urban carriageways.

Because of the diversity of road geometry, vehicles, drivers and environmental conditions, and their interactive nature, capacity varies with the circumstances.

The total number of vehicles present in a traffic stream obviously affects a drivers journey time and costs, and his freedom to manoeuvre safely at a definable level of task comfort in the prevailing conditions and road layout. These concepts of performance have led to a definition of operating capacities in terms of a level of service criterion. The maximum flow attainable in an hour, under the most nearly ideal roadway condition, was referred to in the original *U.S. Highway Capacity Manual* as the basic capacity while the maximum flow attainable under prevailing conditions was defined as the possible capacity. These definitions in effect set an absolute and an upper boundary to the capacity of a roadway. In order to accommodate traffic fluctuations the design capacity, allowing practical operating conditions, had to be set well below these upper levels. Practical capacities were chosen by taking into account both concentration, speed and driver's freedom to manoeuvre. Similar absolute and upper capacities can be deduced from the following flow formula by substituting values for the safe headway (H_D):

$$C = \frac{1000 \times V}{H_D}$$

where
C = capacity of a single lane, veh/h, for selected conditions,
V = speed, km/h,
H_D = average minimum distance headway, m.

Smeed obtained a maximum lane flow value of 2750 cars/h at an optimum constant speed of 75 km/h. Maximum flows approaching this value have been measured on a few occasions on a commuter route motorway.

It is clear that many subdivisions of practical capacity can be made depending on the degree of restraint accepted for delay, safety and freedom of manoeuvre. The revised *U.S. Highway Capacity Manual*, published in 1965, uses a single definition of capacity for each type of highway synonymous with the former term possible capacity. Several service volumes replace the earlier practical capacities and relate to a group of desirable operating conditions known as the level of service. Thus the service volume is the maximum flow carried at a particular level of service, as shown in Tables 7.1 and 7.2 and depicted in Fig. 7.2(c). The manual sets out procedures for determining capacity and indicates appropriate levels of service and service flows for design purposes in urban and rural conditions. Advantages of this design procedure are that a constant level of service can be set throughout a route including intersections and that the engineer can choose a suitable level for the conditions. Generally it is suggested that the lower limits of L.O.S. B are appropriate with service flows used in designing rural highways and a L.O.S. C for urban conditions. The principal roadway factors which affect capacity are lane widths less than 12 ft (3·65 m), lateral clearances (walls, lamp standards, etc.) less than 6 ft (1·83 m), presence of shoulders, surface conditions, alignment, sight distances and grades. The proportions of medium and heavy vehicles, lane distributions, variations in peak hour

TABLE 7.1.   HIGHWAY CAPACITY — LEVELS OF SERVICE
(U.S.A. Standards)

Level of service	Freeway A.H.S. = 70 mph (113 km/h)					Multilane – undivided and/or little acess control			
	Operating speed		V/C			Operating speed		V/C	
			D2	D3	D4			AHS =	
	mph	km/h				mph	km/h	70 mph (113 km/h)	60 mph (97 km/h)
A	≥ 60	≥ 97	≤ 0·35	≤ 0·40	≤ 0·43	≥ 60	≥ 97	≤ 0·30	≤ —
B	55	88	0·50	0·58	0·63	55	88	0·50	0·20
C	50	80	0·75	0·80	0·83	45	72	0·75	0·50
D	40	64	0·90	0·90	0·90	35	56	0·90	0·85
E	approx. 30 – 35	48 – 56	1·0	1.0	1·0	approx. 30	48	1·0	1·0
F	<30	<48	–	–	–	<30	<48	–	–

A.H.S.	=	average highway speed (design speed).
S.D.	=	sight distance.
D2	=	dual 2-lane carriageways.
D4	=	dual 4-lane carriageways.
2L2W	=	2-lane 2-way road.
V/C	=	volume to capacity ratio.

factors and access control are some of the traffic factors which also affect capacity.

Practical capacities in Britain recognise "the variation" in expected conditions between rural and urban conditions. In urban conditions drivers expect fewer overtaking opportunities and lower speeds for the shorter journey distances, and practical capacities can be higher. Because of the differences in traffic characteristics, capacities for rural roads are based on the number of passenger car units for an average August day

TABLE 7.1 (*continued*)

2L2W A.H.S. = 70 m.p.h.				Remarks
Operating speed		V/C		
		S.D. < 1500 ft (457 m)		
mph	km/h	0%	100%	
≥ 60	≥ 97	≤ 0·20	≤ 0·04	Free flow
50	80	0·45	0·24	"Reasonable" freedom
40	64	0·70	0·54	Still stable, less freedom
35	56	0·85	0·80	Approaching instability
approx. 30	48	1·0	1·0	Unstable, at or near capacity
<30	<48	–	–	Forced flow, below capacity

while peak-hour traffic demands are used in the design capacities of urban roads. Table 7.3 sets out some of the more important rural capacity values currently recommended and allow for 60% of the total flow on dual carriageways to be carried on one carriageway.

Lane capacities vary according to the geometric layout and traffic operating conditions. The highest category types of urban motorway, with grade separation and no frontage access, have practical operating capacities of 1500 passenger car units (pcu) per lane per hour. All-purpose routes without frontage access and with full no-waiting controls, have capacities of about 1200 pcu per lane per hour, but this drops to 800 pcu per lane per hour with increasing frequency of major junctions. On other routes the capacity is more often restricted to that of the "bottleneck" junctions.

M

TABLE 7.2.   HIGHWAY CAPACITY

Facility	United States					
	Practical capacity				Possible capacity	
	Cars per hour		Cars per 16 hr day		Cars/hr	Cars/16 hr day
	Urban	Rural	Urban	Rural	Urban & rural	Urban & rural
2-lane 2 way**b**	1,500	900	(15,000)	(9,000)	2,000	(20,000)
3-lane 2 way**b**	2,000	1,500	(20,000)	(15,000)	4,000	(40,000)
Multi-lane (per lane)	1,500**o**	1,000**o**	(10,000)**o**	(6,700)**o**	2,000**o**	(13,400)**o**
Dual 2-lane	3,000**o**	2,000**o**	(50,000)**b**	(33,000)**b**	4,000**o**	(67,000)**b**
Dual 3-lane	4,500**o**	3,000**o**	(75,000)**b**	(50,000)**b**	6,000**o**	(100,000)**b**

NOTES:
1. **b** indicates both directions.
   o indicates one direction.
2. Figures in brackets derived on basis of (1) 60%/40% split between directions of travel in peak hours; (2) 10% of 16 hr flow passes in peak hour.

TABLE 7.3.   BRITISH CAPACITIES FOR RURAL ROADS

Carriageway width, m.		Design speed, km/h.	Design capacity, pcu/day
D4,	14·60	120	66,000
D3,	11·00	120	50,000
D2,	7·30	120	33,000
3L2W,	10·00	100	15,000
2L2W,	7·30	100	9,000
2L2W,	7·30	80	9,000

SPEED CHARACTERISTICS

A number of equations have been derived relating the mean speed of journeys, for particular categories of route, to such factors as average values of traffic flow, road widths and numbers of intersections.

In a study, based on observations in a number of areas, Freeman Fox and Associates have shown a linear relationship (1972, *Speed/Flow Relationships on Suburban Main Roads*) as follows:

$$V = V_o + S\left(\frac{Q-300}{1000}\right)$$

where
V = journey speed in km/h,
Q = one-way flow of all vehicles expressed in veh/h per standard lane (3·65 m); Q is found by dividing the one-way flow of that width, expressed in standard lanes,
V_o = free speed, i.e. when Q is 300 veh/h per lane (km/h),
S = the slope of the regression line, which is the change in speed observed for an increase in the value of Q of 1000 veh/h per lane.

The value of free speed may be measured for a site and corrected to a standard composition

$$\frac{V_o \text{ (standard)}}{V_o \text{ (measured)}} = \frac{100}{102 - \frac{2}{15}(P + P_B)}$$

where
P = percentage of heavy vehicles observed in stream,
P_B = percentages of buses observed in stream.

The following correction factors should also be used to adjust the observations to a standard weather and road condition by adding $0·84\,w$ to the observed free speed if measurements have been made in extreme conditions. A value for w, a composite factor, is obtained by adding three numerical values for visibility, weather and road surface from Table 7.4.

The value of free speed may be obtained from the following:

$$V_o = \left(50 + \frac{d}{10}\right) - 10\,(i - 0·8) - \frac{3}{20}\,(a - 27·5)$$

TABLE 7.4.   CORRECTION FACTORS FOR CONDITIONS

Conditions—w	0	1	2	3	4	5
Visibility	Light	Dark	Twilight			
Weather	Dry	Rain	Falling snow		Mist	Fog
Road surface	Dry	Wet	Slush	Snow	Ice	

where V_o =   free speed (km/h) with a composition 85% light veh, $13\frac{1}{2}\%$ heavy veh (greater than four tyres), and $1\frac{1}{2}\%$ buses, within range 38 to 71,

i =   number of major intersections/km where the road considered does not have priority, within range 0 to 2,

a =   accessibility/km, the sum of intersecting priority minor intersections and private driveways on both sides of all roads, within range 5 to 75,

d =   proportion of dual carriageway (%),

and the slope S from the equation:

$$S = -25 - 4/3 \left[V_o - \left(50 + \tfrac{d}{10} \right) \right] - 30 \, (i - 0 \cdot 8) - 2/5 \, (b - 65)$$

where b =   proportion of roadside developed taken as an average for both sides of the highway (%), range 20 to 100.

For suburban main roads, where there were no major intersections, a free speed of 63·5 km/h with a slope of –12 were obtained from the studies, while the speed dropped to 53·5 km/h and the slope to –28 with one major intersection per kilometre.

The above relationships are typical of the factors which are likely to affect the journey speed of traffic on all types of sites.

OVERTAKING

It has been previously explained that a restriction of overtaking opportunities affects the mean speed of traffic and leads to a reduction of capacity. A brief example will demonstrate the overtaking mechanism on a two-lane, two-way road.

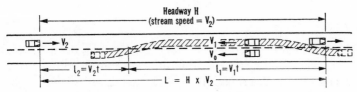

Fig. 7.4. Overtaking model.

This can be computed in terms of the length of time spent in a headway H in the overtaking lane where $l_1 + l_2 = L$, as shown in Fig. 7.4; l_1 is the distance travelled by an overtaking vehicle at speed V_1 (km/h) and l_2 is the distance travelled by an oncoming vehicle at speed V_2 (km/h) and t is the time taken to complete the overtaking manoeuvre.

$$\text{Hence} \quad L = H \times V_2$$
$$= t(V_2 + V_1)$$
$$\text{and} \quad H = \frac{t(V_2 + V_1)}{V_2} \,.$$

If a typical time to complete an overtaking manoeuvre by a vehicle travelling at 70 km/h is 10 s then the headway required in the opposing lane, if the oncoming vehicle is travelling at 50 km/h, is

$$H = 10 \; \frac{70 + 50}{50} = 24\cdot0 \text{ s.}$$

Multi-lane highways operate in a similar manner except that for changing lanes to overtake other vehicles the speed of the vehicles will be subtracted instead of added and hence smaller gaps are needed, e.g. in the above example

$$H = 10 \; \frac{70 - 50}{50} = 4\cdot0 \text{ s.}$$

For any given flow level the number of gaps in the traffic stream of the required size for overtaking can be estimated from the Poisson curves in Fig. 7.1, and the probability of having to wait for a suitably sized gap can be deduced in terms of the total time in an hour when gaps of less than the required size will block the manoeuvre.

JUNCTIONS

Operation

The operation of junctions is greatly influenced by the total volume, type of vehicle and turning movement present in the separate streams. Values for each are determined from traffic studies, as described in Chapter 2, but emphasis is placed on peak flows and there may be a requirement, for instance, to consider the highest 15-min flow, for instance, to prevent queues overlapping other junctions. If junction improvements are to be undertaken a design year will have to be chosen and traffic growth determined for that period. Generally, major junction improvements warrant an evaluation by preparing a programme of construction in stages commencing with an immediate period of 5 years ahead, then the next 5–10 years with a final stage of from 10–15 years. As each stage is progressively reached earlier construction and equipment is incorporated, wherever possible, in the new work but modifications can still be made to accommodate traffic and design changes. A typical programme for a major route with important cross streets could be as follows:

(i)   Channelisation at the principal junctions, road widening and improved signal control.

(ii)   Road widening between junctions.

(iii)   Completion of stage (i) signalisation at minor streets and introduction of progressive signal linking control.

(iv)   Over- or under-passing intersecting streets.

Maximum benefits usually arise by dividing the work between a number of junctions and streets rather than carrying out a single costly improvement, which may only transfer a bottleneck a few hundred metres along a street.

Because traffic intersections are critical to the total capacity of a network, and junctions expensive to construct, it is essential that designs are efficient. This applies not only to accommodating traffic but to safety as junctions are the most frequent sites of accidents.

Driver and Vehicle Characteristics

Drivers vary according to individual traits, habits and circumstances. Design standards need to be based on selecting the 85th percentile value of driver response or performance taken from a distribution, measured in the given circumstances, and raising or lowering the level to meet the likelihood of accident risk. The engineer's task is basically concerned with reducing the complexity of decision-taking by presenting to a driver a situation developed in stages. This means separating each task, in time or distance, into simple parts. Invariably an increase in situation complexity requires extended thinking time and not only reduces safety but often capacity.

The characteristics of the vehicle used in design, the design vehicle, are based on the proportions of the various categories present in the turning movements. It is suggested that the requirements for the largest vehicle are used where these comprise from 5 to 10%, or more, of the turning traffic.

Sight Distance Requirements

All of a driver's tasks are dependent on seeing, thinking and acting, and the provision of sight distance, by allowing thinking time, is tantamount to a reduction in situation complexity. If no approach sight distance is available, a driver must stop at the point of manoeuvre, expend perception and decision time and, because of the ensuing high relative speed condition, a greater gap is required in the main traffic stream and it is with these conflicts that the capacity, safety of operation and design are primarily concerned.

For new routes either the results of an origin destination survey or the traffic assignments from a transportation survey are used to derive the turning movements at the proposed traffic intersection. Classifications and distributions of vehicle types are necessary for the computation of economic benefits and the setting of design standards for turning radii, superelevation, gradients, median opening widths and acceleration and deceleration lanes. The presence of heavy pedestrian traffic, in conflict with vehicular flows, indicates the need for special treatment and control measures.

Factors which affect operation are:
(a)   Driver and vehicle characteristics.
(b)   Sight distance requirements.
(c)   Stream volume and pedestrian movement.

(d)   Angles and speeds of approaching and departing streams.
(e)   Vehicle movements and manoeuvres, which can be divided into the following basic categories: diverging, merging, weaving and crossing.

With the exception of diverging movements, all other manoeuvres require a driver decision for the acceptance of a suitable time or distance gap in the intersected or crossed traffic stream. The size of the gap required varies with the circumstances and between drivers, as discussed below.

Stream Volumes and Pedestrian Movement

The development of time gaps and their distribution in the traffic stream are dependent on the flow level, driver and vehicle characteristics and road layout, including the type and spacing of intersections. For free-flowing roads, where overtaking is not prevented and traffic is not halted or slowed at intersections, headway distributions can be computed theoretically from the Poisson distribution. In other cases, queues of vehicles are formed which move through the system in platoons before dispersing, at a rate dependent on the width of road and traffic volume, until they are reformed due to other road restrictions. The presence and size of these gaps determines whether a vehicle can merge or cross another stream at a given instant of time, or whether delay will occur whilst awaiting a suitable gap. A similar situation prevails for the pedestrian seeking to cross a road. Intersection control, either by layout or by using traffic devices, seeks to efficiently utilise these gaps for both vehicles and pedestrians.

Angles and Speeds of Approaching and Departing Streams

Small angles of approach and departure help position a driver and vehicle correctly for an easy move into or out of the traffic stream, enabling smaller gaps to be utilised on entering the stream or cause less interference to a stream when leaving it. Narrow angle opposed crossing movements are generally undesirable for safety reasons, particularly where pedestrians are present, due to the high relative speeds developed and their serious accident potential. They are acceptable on high standard urban dual carriageways with wide central reservations and low turning flows, at such sites as tee intersections.

To a large extent the angles of intersection and the geometric layout will determine speeds of approach and departure. Where speeds of the individual streams are similar, minimum gaps will be utilised and acceleration/deceleration losses will be reduced to a minimum.

At the points of convergence or divergence of intersecting vehicle paths it is necessary to consider the speeds of vehicles in one stream relative to those in another. The term relative speed is used to define this relationship between vehicles moving with individual speeds and directions at a point in time and space. Relative speed vectors can be drawn for intersecting streams as shown in Fig. 7.5. For the purposes of this discussion the terms low relative speed are used to indicate orders of speed differences between vehicles in different streams of $\pm$ 10 km/h at

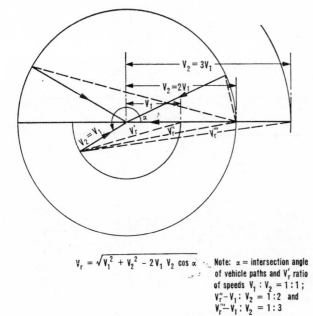

$$V_r = \sqrt{V_1{}^2 + V_2{}^2 - 2V_1 V_2 \cos \alpha}$$

Note: α = intersection angle of vehicle paths and V_r' ratio of speeds $V_1 : V_2 = 1:1$; $V_r'' - V_1 : V_2 = 1:2$ and $V_r''' - V_1 : V_2 = 1:3$

F ɪ ɢ. 7.5. Relative speed vectors.

small angles of intersection, say less than 5°; medium relative speed at ± 25 km/h < 15° and high relative speed ± 40 km/h > 25°.

VEHICLE MOVEMENTS AND MANOEUVRES

Conflicts

A typical four-legged cross-roads sign is shown in Fig. 7.6, with single lane and exits. The diagram indicates the points where vehicle paths conflict and collisions are most likely. The number of conflicts developed per hour can be ascertained directly for each type of intersection by

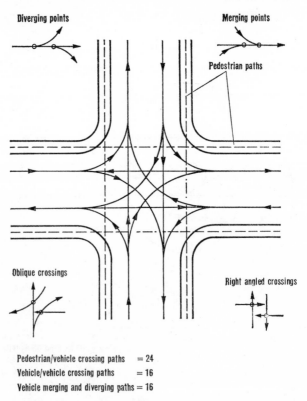

Pedestrian/vehicle crossing paths	= 24
Vehicle/vehicle crossing paths	= 16
Vehicle merging and diverging paths	= 16

FIG. 7.6. Pedestrian and vehicle crossing points at an intersection of cross-road flows.

separately measuring volumetric flows for all the movements. Each point contains a possible accident zone and the potential severity of an accident is linked to the relative speed involved. If pedestrians are crossing the legs of the intersection, direct vehicle/pedestrian conflicts also arise; the frequency is again dependent on the magnitude and direction of the individual vehicular and pedestrian flows. When the pedestrians cross an approach, within the bell mouth, 24 pedestrian/vehicle conflicts points are developed for the intersection, ignoring any diagonal movements by pedestrians.

The simplest operations involve only one merging, diverging or crossing manoeuvre and it is desirable, wherever possible, to avoid multiple or combined movements to preserve this operational simplicity. Usually there is a demarcation of preferential directional flows and then controlled movements are made to and from a secondary flow. The decision to accept or reject a gap is then placed on the driver from the non-preferential flow.

Diverging

This movement is the simplest to perform as the driver's decision is limited to choosing a suitable departure point from the path of his present stream, and thus does not involve the time selection of a suitable gap. Adequate pre-warning of departure points must be given to enable the driver to gradually adjust his speed to that required for a correct exit. The amount of speed reduction will affect the size of the collision area which develops as soon as speed reduction commences. Designs which allow a departure without speed reduction do not develop conflict points or potential collision areas. With a left-hand rule of the road divergence to the left is associated with rear-end collisions but is normally safer than divergence to the right, where both end and side collisions may occur from following vehicles or side and front collisions from approaching vehicles. Right divergences usually develop opposed crossing movements dependent on gap selection unless one-way streets or grade separation are used. Vehicles are invariably stopped, or moving slowly in the collision zone, so inducing impact potential and reducing capacity due to lane space occupancy. The basic movements and collision areas are shown in Fig. 7.7.

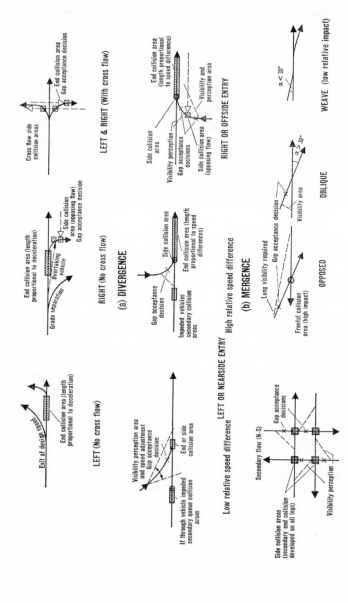

Fig. 7.7.   Vehicle manoeuvres at intersection of streams.

Merging

A driver merging his vehicle into a preferential traffic stream is compelled to select a suitable gap. The critical requirement is that the time or distance interval, between his arrival at the point of mergence, is matched in relation to his own vehicle's speed and to the speed of the next approaching unit in the main stream. The decisions and conditions imposed by merging from the nearside are easier than those made from the offside position. The latter movement, in the case of at-grade intersections, is normally made immediately after a previous stream crossing and, hence, is carried out from a stop or at a low speed, i.e. (high relative speed condition). Collision areas are developed behind the merging vehicle and ahead of the oncoming vehicle as shown in Fig. 7.7(b). The gap size for merging largely depends on the relative speeds involved; high relative speed conditions require greater gaps for safe movement and correspondingly shorter ones at low relative speed. Where this is zero, and absolute speeds are not too great, many of the small gaps developed in a stream are utilised by the majority of drivers. For very high operating speeds, manoeuvre areas must be designed for merging to take place over a longer distance.

Crossing

Crossing movements without control (i.e. where no preferential flow is established) are particularly dangerous as both drivers must make a decision which allows one or other the right of way. More often crossing a preferential flow will require, like merging, the selection of a suitably sized gap. While short gaps can be utilised, even where speeds of approaching crossing vehicles are not reduced, they create situations of likely human error and require excessive sight distances. Opposed crossings, from a stopped or low speed condition, are usually of shorter duration (though of more severe accident potential) than right-angled crossings. The first crossing of a two-lane, two-way flow (from the near side) is easier to judge, provided that visibility is adequate, than the crossing of the far flow. Collision zones, shown in Fig. 7.7(c), are developed at all speed reduction points. Although the primary collision zone is very small in this case, it is severe because of the high relative speed condition.

Weaving

Weaving might be considered to be a special case of crossing but the actual point where it occurs is flexible and, as it can only take place at small intersecting angles (less than 30°), it should be treated separately from oblique directional crossings. As the word weaving implies, it takes place by threading individual vehicles, from different streams, continually through a section although usually at reduced speed, without stopping. Gap size is again important but, by implication, continuous movement imposes, even at high volumes, the acceptance of small gaps.

Typical examples of weaving occur on roundabouts and between exit and entry ramps of grade separated interchanges. A special type arises on urban routes where the local roads flank either side of a major road. Entry and exit, between the routes, is across a gap in the dividers at an oblique angle sometimes referred to as a scissors movement. Former British practice did not lay down a priority at roundabouts and two mutually compatible decisions were required, one driver taking precedence over the other. However, drivers entering roundabouts must now give precedence to vehicles from the right. Because weaving is carried out at low relative speed, vehicle accidents are generally less severe than those for crossing movements but careful attention must be paid to the design needs of pedestrians and cyclists. They may be obscured from view by windscreen pillars and remain masked for long periods due to the turning paths and speeds relative to each other. Mini-roundabouts operate more on the principle of oblique crossing manoeuvres than weaving and undoubtedly create more hazardous conditions with poorer directional control than either traditionally channelised or roundabout junctions.

It can be seen, from the preceding explanation of collision areas, that the vehicle should not be looked upon as being solely confined within physical boundaries but rather as an object with zones of influence projecting outwards from its edges. The size of the zone depends on both the performance characteristics of the vehicle (e.g. braking, speed, visibility) and the inherent characteristics of the driver, and is also influenced by the nature of the operating conditions. If all the variables are correctly evaluated then influence zones can be plotted using various values of contour interval, dependent on the situation, vehicle type and speed.

DELAYS

It will have been seen that in most circumstances of intersection operation time will be lost due to the following causes:

(a) Stopped time, e.g. vehicles waiting for a suitable gap.

(b) Deceleration time, e.g. vehicles slowing from the approach stream speed to a suitable intersection speed, or to a stop.

(c) Acceleration time, e.g. acceleration time after completing a movement for vehicles to raise their speed from the exit road stream speed, to that of the through road.

Stopped Time

The computation of stopped time and delay can be made for intersections with traffic signals as explained later. For other forms of control approximations of vehicle stopped time, while awaiting a suitable gap size for a particular manoeuvre, can be made by summing all the time gaps of insufficient length present in the stream to be crossing or intersected, similarly to the computation for overtaking. Adams showed in 1936 that the assumption that vehicle arrival times past a point on the road are randomly distributed is generally justified, except when traffic is heavy or has been subject to moving or static queuing by road or control conditions. He derived the following expression for stopped delay time:

$$D \ = \ \frac{1}{Ne^{-Nt}} \ - \ \frac{t}{1-e^{-Nt}}$$

where D = average delay per vehicle (s),

N = number of vehicles per second,

t = acceptable gap time for selected manoeuvre (s),

e = base of Napierian logarithms = 2·71828.

Similar conditions exist where pedestrians await an acceptable gap for crossing a traffic stream. The above relationship does not take queue time conditions into account, although empirical studies have shown that an allowance can be made for this condition. Figure 7.8 shows some typical performance data for a gap requirement manoeuvre.

Deceleration and acceleration times can be calculated by selecting appropriate rates measured from traffic studies. Typical average values for cars approaching a stop line are 2·4 m/s² and for leaving 1·2 m/s². In cases where vehicles are not queuing in the side road deceleration and acceleration delay time may well equal or exceed stopped time and is, therefore, important when assessing economic benefits.

TYPES OF JUNCTIONS

There are three general types of junction:

(a) At-grade junctions where intersecting roads meet at a common level.

(b) Grade separated junctions, with or without interchange facilities, where intersecting roads are carried over or under each other.

(c) Combinations of types (a) and (b).

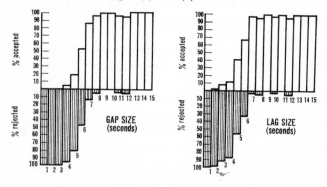

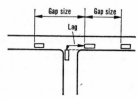

Fig. 7.8.   Gap and lag acceptance time for a left-turn merging manoeuvre at a T-junction (two 8 m roads).

The capacity of urban roads, and sometimes rural roads under peak conditions, is governed by its junctions and, therefore, the choice of appropriate types and their spacing is critical. The minimum spacing for urban motorway junctions is about 600 m and 100 m for local distributors. Individual designs will need to be prepared with alternatives for each site based on site conditions including topography, land costs, adjacent land uses, future widening and improvement potential. The principal traffic factors are based on the character of the route (motorways, principal roads, primary and district distributors and local roads) with special regard to design speeds, present and future traffic flows, composition and turning movements as distributed in time.

At-grade Junctions

Where the major road carries a low volume, and the side roads are also lightly trafficked, simple priority junctions are normally adequate.

At intersections where all turning movements are present it is desirable that the number of intersecting legs should not exceed four, both in the interests of design simplicity and operation. This limits the number of conflict points and assists the driver to appreciate a situation. A preferential flow should be established by Stop, Give Way, Yield or Slow signs and all direct unprotected crossing movements should take place at, or nearly at, right angles to the flow to be crossed. Where large volumes of right- and left-turning traffic must be accommodated additional lanes can be made available by flaring, which is a form of widening, both on the preferential flow approach and exit roadways.

As turning and crossing flows increase, more complete designs will be required, including channelisation, roundabouts, traffic signals and grade separation.

Channelisation

Larger pavement areas, to accommodate multi-channel turning movements, have to be correctly marked for drivers to move smoothly and safely through a junction. While carriageway markings by arrow and line assist the manoeuvres it is usually necessary to physically separate the areas by constructing raised islands and providing reservation space.

The application of such measures is known as channelisation and its chief purposes are:

(a) Separation of traffic stream by direction, turning movement and speed.

(b) Segregation of pedestrian waiting points from the vehicle stream by providing "stepping stones" across the vehicular flows.

(c) Control of approach angles and speeds by funnelling to assist the driver and provide easy vehicle operation.

(d) Time and distance separation of movements, particularly where complex turns require simplication or stage by stage application.

(e) The prevention of prohibited movements by siting barrier islands at entry to or exit from a street.

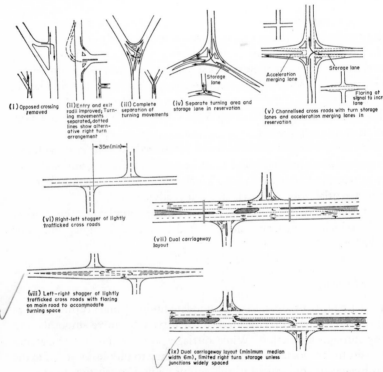

FIG. 7.9. Example of channelisation showing before and after layouts with alternatives.

Traffic islands also form a useful place to erect traffic control devices and signs. The carriageway areas allocated for specific functions can have surface treatment with distinctive colours or textures. Great care must be taken to avoid haphazardly placed islands with insufficient approach visibility or unsuitable radii for entry speeds and vehicle types. Adequate signing, including carriageway marking, is needed to avoid confusion, hazard and damage to street furniture. The main aim is to allow drivers a smooth transition from one direction to another with decisions suitably spaced in time and distance. Some examples of channelisation are shown in Figs. 7.9 and 7.10.

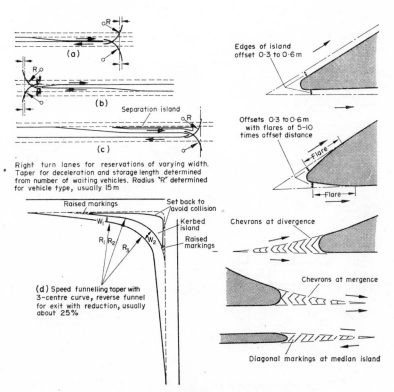

FIG. 7.10. Details of storage lanes, funnelling and noses.

ROUNDABOUTS

Roundabouts can be considered to be a special case of channelisation where the central island provides divisional and directional control for a one-way circulating system. In this way all crossing movements are eliminated and replaced by weaving. With a central island diameter of less than 15 m oblique crossing movements take place at a high relative speed and such a roundabout no longer provides orthodox weaving. With very large central island diameters, greater than 20 m, the weave is generally made up of an entry merge, lane movement and, finally, a divergence from the stream at the exit point.

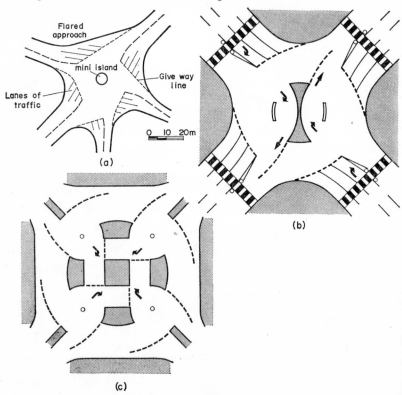

FIG. 7.11. Mini roundabouts: (a) Cardiff layout. (b) Welwyn Garden City "Hollow Island". (c) Track experimental layout. (Source: *Road Research* 1971, H.M.S.O. 1972.)

Since 1964 experiments have shown that roundabouts, with the offside priority rule, have a greater throughput of vehicles with a smaller central island than provided for hitherto. This has led to the introduction of mini-roundabouts with central island diameters between 5 and 15 m and heavily splayed approaches and exits. A guidance island is used to direct entering traffic on an approach, as shown in Fig. 7.11. More recently, "hollow island" designs have been constructed which effectively prevent straight crossing movements from entry to exit by increasing the diameter of the central island. However, the space within the central island is utilised for right-turning movements in association with heavy carriageway guidance and control marking. Mini-roundabouts function more closely to channelised junctions, but with some of the characteristics of traditional roundabouts, especially where traffic demands are similar on each of the legs.

Large roundabouts overcome the main disadvantage of the stop/start situation for crossing movements at channelised intersections. The principal aim is to provide continuous movement, but this is invariably at the expense of capacity and the land area required. It is also inconsistent with large pedestrian movements, which have to be accommodated on subways, if the junction is to operate effectively. Taking into account the greater travel distances, and the inevitable reduction in entry speed from the approach roads, the total vehicle delay may exceed that for a similar channelised intersection. However, their continuous movement with large turning movements on all legs will reduce accident potential and provide pleasanter driving conditions, particularly at medium volume suburban sites. While signals on roundabouts raise capacity they defeat the object of continuous movement. Signal controlled channelised intersections are generally preferable and the work can be developed in stages.

ELEMENTS OF DESIGN

The essential elements of junction design are resolving conflicts, providing manoeuvre areas, channelling and controlling traffic into clear paths and permitting entry and exit to and from streams safely at correct speeds and angles. Where visibility is not adequate, stop signs have to be used and at other hazards carriageway markings or warning strips are employed. Generally stopped vehicles, waiting to manoeuvre in movement areas, should be protected by raised kerbs.

Speed control measures are normally an important part of intersection design. The simplest forms, such as signs, are discussed in Chapter 9. Physical control by tapering approaches to narrow widths and the introduction of additional curvature, while often effective, must be used with caution as they can lead to dangerous conditions and driver error. The introduction of a false hazard should not be considered in the interests of safety; most difficulties can be overcome by warning devices and good design should always be conducive to appropriate performance.

Correct vehicle speeds and entry and exit angles are dependent on radii. Because of space limitation it is often impossible to provide sufficiently large radii to avoid speed reduction to the turning vehicle. It is particularly necessary on high volume roads, in the interests of capacity and safety, to avoid speed changes or stopped traffic on lanes accommodating through traffic. This can be overcome by providing special areas for storage and deceleration and acceleration manoeuvres. Acceleration and deceleration lanes are of several forms but the two principal types either offer a fixed single manoeuvre point or a length of lane in which to complete or commence the requisite manoeuvre. The additional areas may be provided on the junction approach or parallel to the through lanes. The latter case is more common on heavily developed sites where space requirements are a controlling factor. Figure 7.12 shows the general geometric arrangements of the alternatives.

Studies have shown that acceleration lane practice at merging areas varies with volume; more drivers are forced to accept shorter gaps in the through lane at higher flows, thus causing an increase in the number of vehicles utilising single gaps. Shorter vehicle paths are also adopted due to the pressure on drivers to accept the fewer available gaps and the lower running speeds present in the main stream. The critical decision point seems to occur in a position where the merging vehicle's wheels are separated transversely from the main stream vehicles by about 3 m. It is necessary, where little or no difference exist in the speeds of approaching streams, for additional manoeuvring space to be provided if high operating speeds and volumes are to be maintained without interruption.

It is both logical and preferable for entry ramps leading to acceleration areas to be on down gradients in order to improve visibility and give the

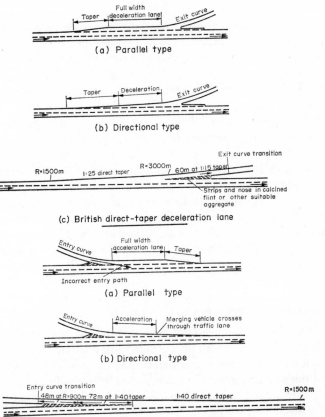

(a) Parallel type

(b) Directional type

(c) British direct-taper deceleration lane

(a) Parallel type

(b) Directional type

(c) British direct-taper acceleration lane

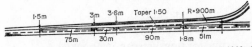

(d) Suggested U.S.A. standard (I. Fukutome and K. Moskowitz—
Traffic Behaviour and on Ramp
Design, H.R.B. Bulletin 235)

Fig. 7.12. Deceleration and acceleration lanes for speed change manoeuvres.

merging driver a clear view of the configuration and approaching traffic. Entry speeds, particularly for commercial vehicles, are also aided by the gradient; conversely, exits to the secondary roads should be on up-gradients although the approaches to the side road should be level, for some distance along the ramps, to improve visibility. Parallel acceleration lanes make merging more hazardous as the driver must either turn his head to look backwards or depend on a rear view from a mirror. Generally, direct alignments are preferred but with a minimum parallel lane for about 100 m, allowing final speed adjustment for merging with high-speed streams. The acceptable range of acceleration tapers appears to lie between the limits of 1:40 to 1:60. The main difficulty of deceleration lane operation is to make the approaching high-speed driver aware of the start to the exit lane and prevent sudden last-minute turns or braking. The use of high contrast, colour, markings and marker posts help in distinguishing a lane from the shoulder. All entry and exit terminals should be clear of structures and, where the through pavement is to be reduced by a lane after an exit, they should be tapered for at least 100 m beyond the exit nose.

ACCELERATION AND DECELERATION LENGTHS

As discussed in Chapter 6 vehicle performance varies according to vehicle type but, for design purposes, a value is selected for longitudinal acceleration to suit each particular case. As the vehicle must also move in and out of a lane gradually a rate for transverse movement must also be stipulated. An acceptable rate for general application is between 0·6 and 1·0 m/s of lane width.

The length of taper for a 3·5 m wide acceleration lane is calculated as follows:

$$S_t = V_D t$$

where
$$S_t = \text{length of taper (m)},$$
$$V_D = \text{design speed (m/s)},$$
$$t = \text{time for transverse movement (s)}.$$

For a design speed of 80 km/h for a lane width of 3·5 m, then

$$S_t = \left(80 \times \frac{1000}{3600}\right)\left(3\cdot5 \times \frac{1}{0\cdot6}\right) = 130\,\text{m}.$$

If the design speed for the entry curve to the acceleration lane in the above example is 40 km/h, then the required acceleration length will be based on raising the entering vehicle speed by 40 km/h at an acceptable rate, e.g. 1·25 m/s², and can be determined from

$$S_A = \frac{v_f^2 - u_i^2}{2f} = \frac{\left(80 \times \dfrac{1000}{3600}\right)^2 - \left(40 \times \dfrac{1000}{3600}\right)^2}{2 \times 1 \cdot 25} = 148 \text{ m,}$$

where
v_f = final speed (m/s),
u_i = initial speed (m/s)
f = acceptable rate of acceleration (m/s²).

The total length of taper and acceleration lane in this case is thus $130 + 148 = 278$ m. As most vehicles in the main stream will be at running speeds of less than the design speed it is normal practice to select the average value of running speed for design purposes. Care must be exercised in the selection of running speeds, acceleration rates, sight distances and proportion of heavy vehicles present in the minor flow. Acceleration lane lengths are also affected by gradients and this factor can be directly taken into account, or approximated, by adding to the normal lengths for uphill acceleration lanes 0·12G and deducting 0·089 on down grades, where G is the gradient expressed as a percentage. On heavily trafficked routes with a large proportion of trucks it may be necessary to construct an additional lane on an up-grade approach.

Deceleration lane requirements can be similarly calculated after determining the exit curve radius, deceleration design rates and the running speed of the main stream. They are usually shorter, because higher deceleration than acceleration rates can be used, but difficulty is usually experienced in making drivers aware of their commencement. Marking must be clear for both day and night operation. At points of heavy entry or exit two or more lanes may be required, but additional lanes must also be added for appropriate distances on the main highway after entry or before exit.

GRADE SEPARATED INTERCHANGES

Junctions of the more important roads are normally grade separated and, because of the need to provide turning movements without at-grade crossings, elaborate slip roads (turning roadways) and costly structures are required. Interchanges also occupy large land areas and their siting and layout is often strongly influenced by topography. All turning movements are normally provided at the junction of urban motorways and a balance achieved between entering and leaving lanes with those on the motorways. Interchanges with more than four legs are inadvisable both from considerations of cost and traffic. The terminal manoeuvre areas at entry and exit should follow a consistent pattern. Examples of the multiplicity of interchange types is shown in Fig. 7.13.

Spacing usually varies inversely with the local traffic density, but for weaving sections carrying 2000 to 3000 pcu/h the minimum distances between entry and exit noses will range from 550 m to 800 m at weaving speeds of about 50 km/h. In central and suburban areas the minimum desirable distances between interchanges should be not less than 1000 m and 2000 m respectively.

Slip roads are of three general types—direct, semi-direct and indirect (loop). Direct types permit the largest radius, for a given land area, as they only turn through 90° but necessitate a large number of structures and both entry and exit is made on and off high-speed lanes. Indirect loops are suitable for low-speed turning roadways and their area rises rapidly with design speed, e.g. at 30, 50 and 65 km/h the required areas for a single loop are 0·1, 0·5 and 1·5 ha respectively. Design speeds should normally lie between two-thirds and a half of that of the major road, with a minimum of 25 km/h for loops. Gradients should be limited to 5% and not exceed 8%, but where the flow contains a large volume of heavy vehicles the maximum should preferably not exceed 4%. Some typical design values are shown later in Tables 7.5 and 7.6.

CAPACITY

CAPACITY OF JUNCTIONS AND INTERCHANGES

General Factors

It is impossible to tabulate the capacity of junctions under all conditions and it is often the capacity of a comprehensive section of a route that is normally required rather than that of an isolated point. Junctions will,

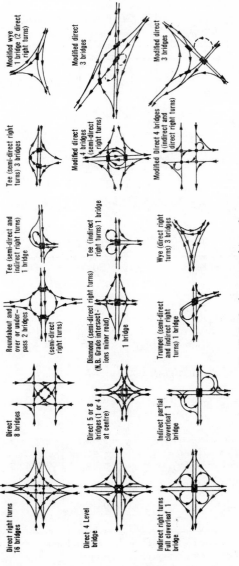

FIG. 7.13. Grade separated interchanges.

TABLE 7.5. RAMP GRADIENTS

	Operating speed, km/h	Percentage up-gradients (max.)		
		Cars only	10% trucks	25% trucks
Ramp gradients	70	5	4	3
	55	6	5	4
Up as shown	40	7	6	5 (110 m)*
Down + 1%	25	8	6	6 (75 m)*

Note: Gradients in excess of 5% should be heated.
*Maximum length.

TABLE 7.6. RAMP DESIGN ELEMENTS

Operating speed (km/h)	30	50	65
Radius (minimum) (m)	24	72	131
Friction coefficient (maximum)	0·28	0·20	0·16
Superelevation rate (maximum) (m/m)	0·02	0·06	0·09[a]
Rate of change of acceleration (m/s^3)	1·22	1·07	0·92
Maximum cross slope change (i.e. algebraic difference)	6%	5%	4%[b]
Lane width (m) (no provision for passing)	4·3 – 4·9	4·0 – 4·5	3·7 – 4·3[c]
Shoulder; additional width (m) (passing stalled vehicle)	2·0 – 2·5	2·0 – 2·5	2·0 – 2·5
2-lane, 2-way width	8·0 – 9·0	8·0 – 8·5	7·5 – 8·0

Notes: [a] Can be increased if run-off length is available.
     [b] 2% preferable on high-speed interchanges.
     [c] Add 0·3 m if barrier kerb is used.

however, mainly determine capacity limits and overall route safety. The problem is to decide how many units, whether pedestrian or vehicular, may use a facility, and with what degree of safety and comfort. From a social point of view the traffic engineer must, for a given expenditure, be prepared to accept greater traffic delays for improvements in safety. However, most measures that improve traffic flow also reduce accident potential.

Factors that have been shown to influence capacity are:

(1) Sufficient numbers of lanes must be provided to prevent high volumes reducing speed below an optimum for the design conditions, and large flows should be directionally separated.

(2) High capacities require uniformity of vehicle speeds and low relative speed differences at exit and entry.

(3) Heavy turning movements need such features as separated storage lanes.

(4) Radii must be sufficient for the types of vehicle present to prevent encroachment on adjacent lanes, and pavement edges should be free from obstructions.

(5) Gradients must be suitable for the types and numbers of vehicles present, or special provision made for specific classes.

At-grade Junctions

The capacity of uncontrolled junctions is very low and, for reasons of safety, it is usual to install Stop or Give Way signs long before delays to traffic become serious. Where main stream volumes are relatively large, compared to the entering and crossing traffic, channelisation improves operation, safety and capacity, and aggregate delay for the whole junction is minimised because the main flow is unimpeded. Particular peak turning movements can usually be adequately handled by channelised junctions and, as demand builds up, signalisation will extend the junction's useful life before resorting to expensive interchanges, as shown later. Where all turning movements are present at junctions of two or more roads carrying similar volumes, roundabouts operate safely and satisfactorily, provided that the central island diameter is large enough to allow adequate weaving lengths. Their useful life can also be extended by traffic signal control at peak hours. However, in the more confined areas of city streets, traffic signals are to be preferred to roundabouts, with separate phases accommodating heavy turning movements. Mini-roundabouts may also be considered.

The capacity of priority junctions depends on the ratio of flows on the major and minor roads, the gap acceptance criterion for the turning movements, and the maximum acceptable delay to the minor road traffic. Tanner has shown that the maximum flow (q_m) which can pass on the minor road is given by:

$$q_m \text{ (max)} \; = \; \frac{q_M\left(1-\beta_M q_M\right)}{e^{q_M\left(a - \beta_M\right)}\left(1-e^{-\beta_m q_M}\right)}$$

where q_M, q_m = major and minor flows respectively,

$\qquad \beta_M, \beta_m$ = minimum headways of major and minor roads respectively,

$\qquad\qquad a$ = minimum acceptable gap in major stream.

The sum of q_m(max) and q_M is a value for the ultimate capacity for a particular flow ratio, with 90% a suitable practical capacity. If it is assumed that an entering side road vehicle requires a gap of 8 s, and that the minimum headway is assumed to be 3 s, this is equivalent to a saturation flow of 1200 veh/h for non-stopping conditions. A value of 5 s or 720 veh/h is a suitable value for stopping conditions, again with a single entry lane. A typical comparison of capacity is shown in Fig. 7.14, for three cases of one-way saturation flows on the major road. There is a wide range of acceptable gaps for different drivers at junction turns; the smallest gaps required are left turns into the stream and for crossings while the longest are for right turns into the major flow. Right turns out of the major flow are usually also short. Typical median values range from 4 to 8 s.

Roundabouts

The capacity and delay to vehicles in single and multiple weaving sections has been the subject of both theoretical and practical studies. Theoretically, by assuming a vehicle length, angle of converging stream and inter-vehicular headways, a minimum clearance time can be determined for the common occupancy point of the crossing paths. It can be

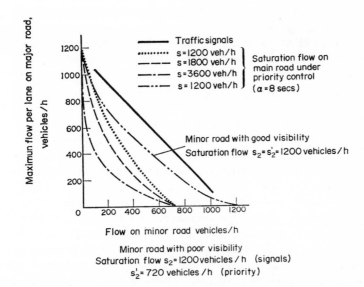

Fig. 7.14. Comparison of traffic signal capacity with that of priority control. (Source: F. U. Webster and J. G. Wardrop, Capacity of urban intersections, *Sixth International Study Week in Traffic Engineering*, 1962.)

shown that the common area is never wholly clear of vehicles below a certain minimum critical speed. Hence, stop–go conditions will prevail below the critical speed with weaving only occurring above this speed. Refinements can be introduced into the calculation of headways by allowing for the approaching stream to decelerate on the approach to the weaving point and accelerate on completion of the manoeuvre. Clayton developed a graphical method for determining weaving capacity, based on the capacity of a single one-way lane as equivalent to a 0° weave (1200 veh/h) and a 90° weave as equivalent to the capacity of a signal controlled intersection (3200 veh/h) with saturated approach flows. In this case equally distributed turning movements will allow 1600 vehicles on each segment, i.e. 533, 400 and 320 veh/h/lane for 3, 4 or 5 lanes. Other values are based on the assumption that capacity is inversely proportional to the weaving angle. Working capacity is normally assumed to be 75% of the calculated value.

A controlled experiment at Northolt Airport included a study of the following variables: traffic composition, percentage of approaching vehicles weaving, entry width, exit width, weaving width and length of weaving section. The maximum flow of vehicles per hour (Q) through an individual weaving section is computed from the formula:

$$Q = \frac{16 (w + e) (4l-3w) (3 - p)}{l (0 \cdot 56 + h)}$$

where w = weaving width (m), values between 6 and 18 m,
e = entry width (m), ratios e/w between 0·4 and 1·0,
l = weaving length (m), ratios w/l between 0·12 and 0·4,
p = proportion of vehicles weaving, values between 0·4 and 1·0,
h = proportion of medium and heavy vehicles, including buses, values between 0 and 0·25.

Working capacities, where adjacent weaving sections on roundabouts are heavily trafficked, should be taken as 80% of the maximum flow. Journey times rapidly increase at flows of 90% of the maximum value and suitable traffic control measures will increase capacity by between 10 and 20%. A typical capacity value for a 3 m weaving width is 800 veh/h. For a practical capacity, Q_p, in pcu, where the equivalent values for cars, medium and heavy vehicles, and motor cycles and cycles are respectively 1·0, 2·8 and 0·5, becomes:

$$Q_p = \frac{282w (1 + e/w) (1 - p/3)}{1 + w/e}.$$

Mini-roundabouts are usually designed with an entry taper of 1:6 and exit taper of 1:12, with a central island diameter of about one-third of the circle within the outer kerb line. The distance between the Give Way line and conflict point should not be less than 25 m. A tentative formula for the maximum capacity (Q_m) was given in *Road Research* 1968, as follows:

$$Q_m = K (\Sigma w + \sqrt{A}) \text{ pcu}$$

where Σw = the sum of all the basic road widths carrying traffic into and out of the junction (m),
A = area added to junction by flared approaches (m), i.e. additional to standard road widths,

K = factor to account for site conditions, e.g. values for K under ideal conditions 100, for junctions under practical operating conditions, 3, 4 and 5 ways; 80, 70 and 65 respectively.

The capacity of a traditional roundabout replaced by mini-islands has shown marked increases, ranging from 25% to more than 50% with flared approaches.

The capacity of channelised junctions is determined by the presence and numbers of priority and non-priority flows and the methods of achieving these controls (e.g. merging area design, flaring, traffic signal control, numbers and directions of streams to be crossed, etc.). Thus, the total capacity is determined by separately summing individual capacities of the parts. Generally, junctions are designed for the design year turning volumes, after selecting design speeds (e.g. for a roundabout the value might range from 0·5 to 0·67 of the approach road speed), priority flows, minimum radii, based on design speeds and vehicle types, tapers, refuges and carriageway areas and numbers of lanes and separators.

Grade Separated Interchanges

The capacity of grade separated interchanges is affected by the individual components of the design layout and depends primarily on the standards adopted for points of mergence with the main through flows, weaving areas and the capacity of the connecting roadways linking these terminal areas.

At points of entry the maximum capacity that can be handled approaches the capacity of a through lane and depends on the composition of traffic, speeds at point of mergence, the length of joint pavement available, and numbers of vehicles present in the intersected lane of flow. In general, as entering traffic increases, the normal occupancy by through vehicles of the intersected lane decreases. However, increasing volume in the other lanes decreases available headways, compelling more vehicles to remain in the nearside lane because of insufficient gaps to permit a lane change. Figure 7.15 shows typical capacities for merging areas. Similar considerations apply to diverging traffic streams and the maximum

N

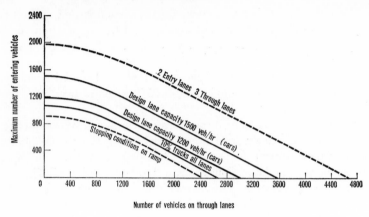

FIG. 7.15. Ramp terminal capacities.

number of vehicles that can leave a lane also depends on geometric layout and the number and types of through vehicles occupying the departure lane. The capacity of interchange (ramp) roadways depends primarily on the percentage of trucks in the stream, gradient, width and operating speed. The latter, in turn, determines minimum radius superelevation and side friction factors. Some typical design values were shown in Tables 7.5 and 7.6 (see p. 338).

Single lane operation, both for the interchange roadway and its terminals, is desirable but high volumes at major interchanges often require multiple merging and diverging facilities. The presence, at some types of intersection, of large numbers of entering and leaving traffic weaving on through lanes, both reduces capacity and increases the danger of accidents, besides presenting difficulties in the design and location of suitable signs. The problems posed can be overcome, to some extent, by suitably spaced entrances and exits, one-way streets and the use of special collector roads free from through traffic flow, as shown in Fig. 7.16. Designs should be checked to ensure adequate weaving lengths and widths between successive points of entry and exit; suitable values are given in Table 7.7.

If weaving takes place on slip roads, weaving lengths can be reduced directly in relation to the operating speeds. The number of lanes required

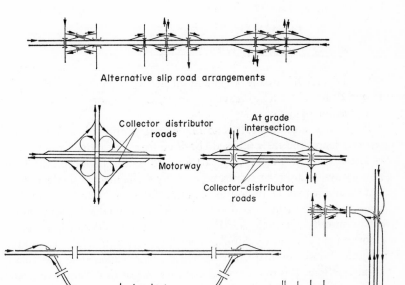

Alternative slip road arrangements

FIG. 7.16. Collector and distributor road arrangements.

TABLE 7.7

Weaving volume (pcu/h)	Minimum weaving length (m)
1000	75
1500	120
2000	200
2500	300
3000	425
3500	575

for weaving sections (N) is based on American practice, with hourly volumes inserted, in pcu, as follows:

$$N = \frac{W_1 + 3W_2 + F_1 + F_2}{C}$$

where W_1 and W_2 are the larger and smaller weaving flows respectively, F_1 and F_2 are outer non–weaving streams, C is the normal lane capacity of the major road.

For higher outer flows, it is normal practice to provide additional and separate lanes, and their flows are omitted from the above formula.

The continuous movement of traffic onto and off high capacity urban motorways, and similar routes, poses many difficulties for the local street system and it may be impossible or undesirable to widen many of these roads to handle the increased volumes. Without suitable feeder routes to urban motorways such facilities will either be underused, or create environmental damage. Similar considerations also apply to normal growth of traffic on major streets, which become congested, particularly at intersections. It is thus essential that these major routes are investigated on a comprehensive basis, not only considering their traffic impact but their environmental intrusion, community severance and role in the total transport plan. The siting of interchanges is particularly critical, and their effects on the traffic movement pattern within an area must be carefully scrutinised.

FURTHER READING

ADAMS, W. F. (1936) Road traffic considered as a random series. *J. Instn. Civ. Engrs.*, November.

AMERICAN ASSOCIATION OF STATE HIGHWAY OFFICIALS. A policy on arterial highways in urban areas, 1957; A policy on geometric design of rural highways, 1965; A policy on design of urban highways and arterial streets, 1973. Washington.

ASHTON, W. D. (1966) *The Theory of Road Traffic Flow.* Methuen, London.

ASHWORTH, R. (1968) A note on the selection of gap acceptance criteria for traffic simulation studies. *Transportation Research*, 2.

ASHWORTH, R. (1970) Traffic delays at priority-type intersections. *Proc. Instn. Civ. Engrs.*, 47.

ASHWORTH, R. (1973) The capacity of rotary intersections. *J. Instn. Highway Engrs.*, **xx**(3).

BENNETT, R. F. (1970) The design of roundabouts since the priority rule. *J. Instn· Highway Engrs.*, **xvii.**

BERRESFORD, M. R. and SEDDON, P. A. (1972) The capacity of merging areas on urban roads. *Traff. Engng. & Control*, **14**(2).

BLACKMORE, F. C. (1970) *Capacity of Single-level Intersections.* Tenth Int. Study Wk. in Tr. & Saf. Engng. W.T.A.O., London.

DREW, D. R. (1967) Taking the scourge out of the merge. *Traff. Engng.* **37**(11) and **38**(1).

ELLE, B. L. (1967) Gap utilization, *Traff. Engng.* **38**(1).

GRANT, E. (1969) Traffic capacity of small roundabouts. *Traff. Engng. & Control*, **10**(12).

GREENBERG, H. (1959) An analysis of traffic flow. *Opn. Res.* **7**(1).

GREENSHIELDS, B. D. (1974) A study of highway capacity. *Highway Research Bd. Proc.* 14.

HAIGHT, F. A. (1963) *Mathematical Theories of Traffic Flow.* Academic Press Inc., New York.

HENDERSON, A. and COLE, M. (1968) Design vehicle criteria and geometric design. *Traff. Engng. & Control*, **9**(9).

HIGHWAY RESEARCH BOARD. *Freeway Operation*, H.R. Record 244; *Freeway Traffic Characteristics and Control*, H.R. Record 279; N.C.H.R.P. Report 68, *Application of Vehicle Operating Characteristics to Geometric Design and Traffic Conditions*; *Traffic Flow, Capacity and Quality of Service*, H.R. Record 349; *Operational Improvements for Freeways*, H.R. Record 363; N.C.H.R.P. Report 113, *Optimising Flow on Existing Street Networks*; *Freeway Operations and Control*, H.R. Record 388; *Highway Capacity and Quality of Service*, H.R. Record 398. Washington.

HIGHWAY RESEARCH BOARD. *Highway Capacity Manual*, 1965. Special Report, 87, Washington, 1965.

HONG, H. (1966) Some aspects of interchange design. *Traff. Engng.* **36**(10).

JACOBS, G. D., OLDER, S. J. and WILSON, D. G. (1968) A comparison of X-way and other pedestrian crossings. RRL Report LR.145. The Road Research Laboratory.

LIGHTHILL, M. J. and WHITHAM, F. B. (1955) On kinematic waves, II. A theory of traffic flow on long crowded roads. *Proc. Roy. Soc. (Series A)*, 229.

MARLOW, M. and BLACKMORE, F. C. (1973) Experiment at Brook Hill roundabout, Sheffield, Yorkshire. TRRL. Report LR.562. The Transport & Road Research Laboratory.

MINISTRY OF TRANSPORT. *Roads in Urban Areas*, H.M.S.O., 1966; *Layout of Roads in Rural Areas*, H.M.S.O., 1968; *Urban Traffic Engineering Techniques*, H.M.S.O., 1965.

MURGATROID, B. (1973) An investigation into the practical capacity of roundabout weaving sections. *J. Instn. Highway Engrs.*, **xx**(3).

NEWELL, G. F. (1971) *Applications of Queueing Theory.* Chapman & Hall, London.

NEWLAND, R. M. (1964) Vehicle turning paths for road junction layout. *Rds. & Rd. Constr.* **42**(499).

NEWMAN, L. *et al.* (1969) Freeway ramp control — what it can and cannot do. *Traff. Engng.*, **19**(7).

PRIGOGINE, I. and HERMAN, R. (1971) *Kinetic Theory of Vehicular Traffic.* Elsevier Pub. Co., New York.

SALTER, R. J. (1970) Some effect of lag and gap acceptance distribution on average delay at priority intersections. *Traff. Engng. & Control*, **12**(4).

SEDDON, P. A. (1972) Another look at platoon dispersion. *Traff. Engng. & Control*, **13**(8–10).

SMEED, R. J. and BENNETT, G. T. (1949) Research on road safety and traffic flow, Road Paper No. 29. *Proc. Instn. Civ. Engrs.*, Part 11.

TANNER, J. C. (1962) (1967) A theoretical analysis of delays at an uncontrolled intersection. *Biometrika*, **49**(1), (2); The capacity of an uncontrolled interse ction. *Biometrika*, **54**(3), (4).

VARIOUS. Papers and Proceedings Int. Symp. on the Theory of Rd. Tr. Flow, 1st Symp., Herman, R. (Ed.), Elsevier, 1961; 2nd Symp., Almond, J. (Ed.), O.E.C.D., 1965; 3rd Symp., Edie, L. C. (Ed.), Elsevier, 1967; 4th Symp., Leutzbach, W. and P. Baron (Eds.), *Strassenbau und Strassenverkehrstechnik*, 1969.

VARIOUS (1972) *Junction Design; From Assignment to Design; Urban Road Design.* Proc. Symp. P.T.R.C.

WARDROP, J. G. (1957) Some theoretical aspects of road traffic research. Road Paper No. 36. *Proc. Instn. Civ. Engrs.*, Part 11.

WARDROP, J. G. (1968) Journey speed and flow in central urban areas. *Traff. Engng. & Control*, **9**(11).

WEINER, S. and TSONGOR, N. G. (1969) Day and night gap acceptance probabilities. *Pub. Rds.*, **35**(7).

CHAPTER 8

Traffic Control Systems

THERE have been many different forms of traffic control developed to reduce the number of conflicts and improve safety at intersections, but doubtless the most important is traffic signal control. While they prevent continuous flow, by allowing the right of way in some set sequence to the conflicting traffic streams, they have the advantage over other forms of intersection control, such as roundabouts and grade separation, in that they occupy less space. The main types of traffic signal control are designed to operate at isolated junctions or, in some interactive way, in an area control of a road network.

A traffic signal is a manually, mechanically or electrically operated device which, by means of its indications, directs traffic to stop or to proceed. Those which operate to a predetermined programme by allocating the right of way according to a schedule are known as fixed time signals. However, the majority of signals in the United Kingdom are vehicle actuated, responding to demands, by varying the allocated time intervals, in accordance with detected traffic impulses registered through suitably sited vehicle detectors. European countries and the U.S.A. have generally preferred fixed time signals and these two different approaches have meant that there are characteristic differences in signal control development between these countries.

DEFINITIONS AND NOTATION

The indication shown by a signal face is an aspect which follows a sequence in Britain of red, red-and-amber together, green, and amber. Amber periods are standardised at 3 s, and the red-and-amber, shown together, at 2 s (older controllers display 3 s). Each repetition of this complete coloured light sequence is called a signal cycle and its duration the cycle time. The roadway leading to a junction is said to form an approach, which may contain a number of approach lanes. If traffic is designated particular lanes, for a directional movement, at a junction, it can be considered to have a separate approach.

The term phase is applied to one or more streams of traffic which receive, during a cycle, simultaneous signal indications, i.e. those approaches with common directional movements subject to the same signal indications. An approach may thus have one or more lanes for a specific directional movement. A more precise definition than that of phase has been used by Alsopp, and overcomes the problem of split phases. It is termed a stage and refers to that part of a signal cycle that is green for every approach concurrently offering right of way.

Lost Time

Figure 8.1 shows what happens when a queue of vehicles, held back

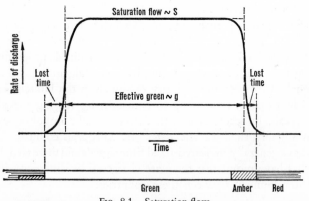

FIG. 8.1.   Saturation flow.

by a red signal on an approach, is given the right of way. Initially, the vehicles accelerate to a normal running speed when the rate of discharge remains more or less constant at what may be called the saturation flow, i.e. the maximum rate of discharge which can be sustained. Assuming there are sufficient vehicles in the queue to utilise the available green time (i.e. the green period is fully saturated), vehicles will continue to discharge at the saturation flow until the green time terminates. Some vehicles will pass through in the succeeding amber, but the rate of discharge will fall to zero in the manner shown. The area under the curve will then represent the number of vehicles discharged during the period and, if this number is divided by the saturation flow, the resulting value is the effective green time. This is sensibly less than the green time plus amber time, i.e. the area under the curve has been replaced by a rectangle of equal area, assuming that the total passage of vehicles remains the same but that they flow at a constant rate during the effective green period. The difference, during a phase, between the sum of green time (k) and amber time (a), less the effective green time (g), is known as lost time (l) since it is mostly not available to another phase for the passage of vehicles. It is expressed as follows:

$$l = k + a - g.$$

If b represents the average number of vehicles discharged during a saturated phase, with saturation flow s, then g, the effective green time, is equal to b/s.

The lost time value will vary, depending on site conditions and other factors; under typical conditions it will have a value around 2 s, but ranges from almost 0 to 7 or 8 s on difficult sites with steep gradients. As it arises at each change of phase, the total time lost per cycle, due to starting delays and the falling off in the discharge rate, will be nl if there are n phases.

Additionally, in certain circumstances, there is another element of lost time. For various reasons, discussed later, it may be necessary to have the signals on all phases showing red, or red and red/amber simultaneously. This time is also lost to the intersection since no vehicles may be moved. If this latter element of lost time is R, then the total lost time per cycle is

$$L = nl + R = \Sigma(I-a) + \Sigma l$$

where n = number of phases,
   l = average lost time per phase, due to the inertia of the queue,
   R = lost time per cycle, due to the simultaneous showing of red, or red and red/amber on all phases,
   I = inter-green period,
   a = amber period.

Examples of inter-green periods are shown in Fig. 8.2.

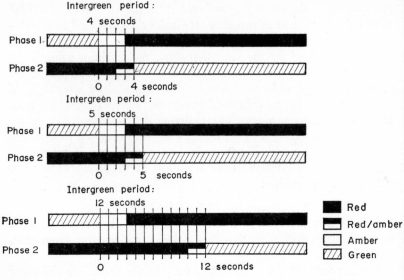

FIG. 8.2. Examples of signal settings—two-phase (stage) controller.

Saturation Flow

It can be seen that the signal sequence for each junction approach is divided up into an effective red period, during which no traffic departs, and an effective green period when traffic passes steadily at the saturation flow rate. Saturation flow is generally measured in vehicles per hour of green time, i.e. the flow, if a continuous queue of vehicles were discharged given 100% green time. The capacity of an approach can be expressed as gs/c veh/h where c is the cycle time.

Both saturation flow and lost time can either be measured directly, by methods described in R.R.L. Road Note No. 34, or calculated from relationships derived from field studies and simulation. The saturation flow (s), expressed in passenger car units per hour and without turning traffic or parked vehicles, has been given by the Road Research Laboratory, for an approach width (w), measured between kerbs or to the centre line, as follows:

$$s = 525w \text{ pcu/h (for values of } w \text{ between } 5.50 \text{ and } 18.00 \text{ m)}.$$

For narrower approaches, saturation flow has a stepped effect, which is influenced by the proportion of heavy vehicles in the stream and stream speeds, and can be adjusted as follows:

$$w \text{ (m)} = 3{\cdot}00 \quad 3{\cdot}50 \quad 4{\cdot}00 \quad 4{\cdot}50 \quad 5{\cdot}00$$
$$s \text{ (pcu/h)} = 1840 \quad 1885 \quad 1960 \quad 2210 \quad 2575$$

Saturation flows are strongly influenced by traffic composition and by the time of day; in the less hurried off-peak periods saturation flows may be 5% less than at peak periods. Whereas uphill gradients increasingly reduce saturation flow with greater slopes, there is a tendency on downhill grades for an increased flow. Vehicle manoeuvre paths also affect flow rates, particularly as the radius of the curve is reduced. The saturation flow (s_t), measured by Webster, for a single stream turning through a 90° angle of curve with radius r, in metres, is:

$$s_t = \frac{1800}{1 + 1{\cdot}524/r} \text{ pcu/h.}$$

However, unless additional approach lanes are constructed for right-turning traffic, straight through vehicles will be impeded while they await suitable crossing gaps in the opposing flow. Special account has to be taken in the design for turning traffic, both in geometric layout of the junction and signal control arrangement, as shown in Fig. 8.3. Other influential factors to be considered are pedestrian movements, parked vehicles and bus stops and other adjacent junctions (both upstream and downstream), which may increase or reduce the flow.

CAPACITY OF JUNCTIONS WITH SIGNALS

Circle time is divided into effective green time, when traffic can flow at the respective saturation rate, and lost time, which is generally unavailable for traffic flow. Each phase will handle one, two or, possibly, three approaches to a junction and each will carry its own flow of vehicles and be capable of a maximum flow, its saturation flow. It is usual for the traffic flow to be higher in one direction than another, particularly in the peak hour, and it will also vary in magnitude throughout the day. Therefore, individual approaches, within a phase, will have a separate value of the ratio of approach flow to saturation flow, and this will vary by the

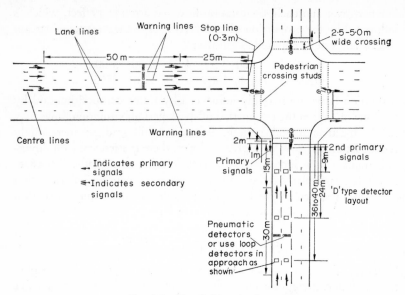

FIG. 8.3. Signalled junction layout.

hour. Webster has shown that the phase may be represented by the directional arm with the highest ratio of approach flow to saturation flow, the predominant arm, and this is termed the y valve for the particular phase, i.e. $y = q/s$, where q and s are the approach and saturation flows respectively, for the approach in the selected phase having the highest ratio. If Y is the sum of y values over all the phases and L is the total lost time in the cycle, then the minimum cycle time (c_m) required to just pass all the traffic through the junction is:

$$c_m = \frac{L}{1-Y}.$$

For practical reasons, it is not possible to have cycle times normally in excess of 120 s and, because of statistical variations in flow, it is usual to select a value of Y less than unity, e.g. 90%. The practical maximum value of Y is then found by substitution in the above equation and for the given values:

$$Y_{\text{pract.}} = 0{\cdot}9(1-L/c_m) = 0{\cdot}9-0{\cdot}0075L.$$

CYCLE TIME CHOICE

The selection of a cycle time is a compromise between a number of conflicting factors. Optimum cycle lengths can be based on minimising delay or queue lengths, either for the whole junction or for particular approaches, or for maximising capacity. Similarly, the probability of a particular movement, receiving an immediate green phase, can be maximised. In the interests of safety and convenience, it is also necessary to set arbitrary minima and maxima lengths for cycle times, and to accommodate the traffic variations in time (short—by the hour, or long —by the day) with a compromise cycle, unless special control facilities are available to adjust the settings automatically.

Equations, derived from theory and a simulation study, have been developed by Webster at the Road Research Laboratory, and these determine the average delay per vehicle computed as a function of cycle time length, the proportion of the cycle length which is green, the approach volumes and the flow ratios, as follows:

$$d = \frac{c(1-\lambda)^2}{2(1-\lambda x)} + \frac{x^2}{2q(1-x)} - 0.65 \left(\frac{c}{q^2}\right)^{\frac{1}{3}} x^{(2+5\lambda)}$$

where d = average delay per vehicle on the particular arm (s),

c = cycle time,

q = flow (veh/s),

λ = proportion of the cycle which is effectively green for the phase under consideration (i.e. g/c if g = effective green time),

x = the degree of saturation; this is the ratio of the flow to the maximum possible flow under the given signal settings (i.e. $q/\lambda s$).

The equation, which has been extensively compared and checked against field studies, is used to obtain the optimum settings of signals to minimise overall junction delay. An optimum cycle time (c_o), minimising the total delay with respect to cycle time (c), is found by differentiating the above equation:

$$c_o = \frac{KL + 5}{1 - \gamma_1 - \gamma_2 - \cdots \gamma_n} = \frac{1.5L + 5}{1 - Y}$$

where K is a constant, a value of 1.5 being suitable for typical junctions, and other terms are as defined previously.

Because of the shape and slope of the delay curve, values of cycle time c are usually taken in excess of c_o.

While early work was based on regular arrival and departure patterns, subsequent methods have assumed random arrivals and used probability theory to derive signal settings. Some models are based on the criterion that the queue has a set probability of being discharged in the next green phase. The higher this probability level is set, the greater is the level of service implied, i.e. the less frequently a queue is likely not to be discharged. For example, with a probability level of

$$0{\cdot}95 \; = \; \sum_{x=0}^{N} f(x),$$

where $f(x)$ is the Poisson probability for x arrivals. If the mean arrival rate $\mu = VT/3600$ (V veh/h and T is the cycle time), s, then

$$0{\cdot}95 \; = \; \sum_{x=0}^{N} \frac{e^{-\mu}\mu^x}{x!}$$

Miller, who assumes an arrival rate and the degree of bunching (I), derives the following expression for the average delay per pcu:

$$d \; = \; \frac{1-\lambda}{2\,(1-\lambda x)}\left[c(1-\lambda) + \frac{(2x-1)I}{q(1-x)} + \frac{I+\lambda x - 1}{s} \right]$$

where $I = \dfrac{\text{the variance of the vehicle arrivals (pcu) in one signal cycle}}{\text{mean of the vehicle arrivals (pcu) in one signal cycle}}$

and other terms as defined previously. This expression is similar, in the limiting case as x approaches the value 1, to that of Webster's equation above, since $I = 1$ for Poisson arrivals.

Calculation of Optimum Cycle Time

Consider the four-arm junction controlled by two-phase fixed time traffic signals carrying the traffic, shown in Fig. 8.4. If the intergreen period I is to be 8 s between each phase, when red or red/amber show simultaneously, and the lost time delay to starting on each phase is 2 s, determine the optimum cycle time of the signal settings.

$$L \; = \; \Sigma(I{-}a) + \Sigma L = (8{-}3) + (8{-}3) + 2 + 2 = 14 \text{ s}.$$

$I = 8\,sec$

$l = 2\,sec$

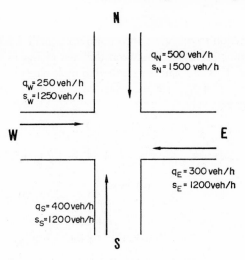

FIG. 8.4. Data for cycle time calculation.

	N	S	E	W
q	500	400	300	250
s	1,500	1200	1200	1250
q/s	0·33	0·33	0·25	0·20
γ	0·33		0·25	
Y	0·58			

$$C_o = \frac{1 \cdot 5\,L + 5}{1 - Y} = \frac{1 \cdot 5 \times 14 + 5}{1 - 0 \cdot 58} = 62\,\text{s}.$$

The optimum cycle time for these conditions is 62 s, and the overall delay (i.e. the total delays to all vehicles) will be at a minimum when this cycle time is used.

Within the optimum cycle time of 62 s there will be 14 s lost time. Accordingly, the total effective green time in the cycle is 62 – 14 = 48 s.

Green Times

For the junction to operate with minimum overall delay the effective green time must be divided between the two phases in proportion to their y values. This rule can be extended to multiphase operation. In this case, where g_{NS} and g_{EW} are the effective green times of the NS and EW phases respectively,

$$g_{NS} : g_{EW} = y_{NS} : y_{EW} = 0.33 : 0.25.$$

Hence,

$$g_{NS} = \frac{0.33}{0.33 + 0.25} \times 48 = 27.4 \text{ (say 27 s)},$$

and

$$g_{EW} = \frac{0.25}{0.33 + 0.25} \times 48 = 20.6 \text{ (say 21 s)}.$$

Thus, the proportion of green time for each phase, if $C_o\text{-}L$ is the total effective green time in the cycle, is given by the formulae:

$$g_1 = \frac{y_1}{Y}(C_o\text{-}L); \quad g_2 = \frac{y_2}{Y}(C_o\text{-}L); \quad \text{etc.}$$

To convert these effective green times into actual green times, it is necessary to add the portion of the lost time and deduct the amber time, i.e. $k = g + l - a$; i.e. $k_{NS} = 27 + 2 - 3 = 26$ s, and $k_{EW} = 21 + 2 - 3 = 20$ s.

Compromise Cycle Time

Under practical conditions, the volume of traffic approaching an intersection will vary during the course of the day and so, also, will the proportionate distribution of the volume between the different phases. With vehicle actuated signals the action of the traffic on the detectors is made to vary the cycle time, and to allocate the green time between the phases to suit the circumstances prevailing, as discussed later. However, with fixed time signals, it is often necessary that compromise signal settings be made so that the varying demands of the traffic can be satisfied with one programme without undue delay being caused at extremes of flow.

In most practical cases it has been found that by using a cycle time within the range of $\frac{3}{4}$ to $1\frac{1}{2}$ times that of the optimum then the average delay to vehicles is not increased by more than 10–20%. A compromise cycle time can be calculated for variable demands from: (a) the optimum cycle times for each hour of the day when traffic volumes are at heavy or medium levels, and taking the mean; (b) determining the optimum cycle time for the heaviest peak hour, and taking three-quarters of its value; (c) by choosing the largest of the values deduced from (a) and (b). Since the y values will also vary throughout the day the green times, for maximum efficiency, should be allocated in proportion to the average of the y values for the peak periods.

In the example shown in Table 8.1, hourly counts of traffic approaching a junction, controlled by a two-phase fixed time signal, are indicated.

The saturation flow was measured by averaging, over a representative time, the number of vehicles discharged in each fully saturated green period and dividing the number by the effective green time, assumed to be 2 s less than the green plus amber time. To accommodate pedestrian movements, a 4 s all-red period has been incorporated on each change of phase making the intergreen period 9 s.

$$L = (9 - 3) + (9 - 3) + 2 + 2 = 16 \text{ s.}$$

(a) *By substitution in the cycle time* formula for the lost time and appropriate Y value for each of the 12 h gives an average cycle time of $662 \cdot 5/12 \simeq 55$ s and comparing this with three-quarters of the optimum cycle time for the peak hour, i.e. $\frac{3}{4} \times 86 \simeq 64$ s. As this value is the larger, it is used as the compromise cycle time.

(b) *Green times.* Using the cycle time of 64 s, and lost time of 16 s, gives a total effective green time of 48 s.

Peak periods occur at:

(i) 8 to 9 a.m. when

$$y_{NS} = 0 \cdot 283 \text{ and } y_{EW} = 0 \cdot 356.$$

$$\text{thus} \quad y_{NS} = \frac{0 \cdot 283 + 0 \cdot 319}{2} = 0 \cdot 31;$$

and

(ii) 5 to 6 p.m. when

$$y_{NS} = 0 \cdot 319 \text{ and } y_{EW} = 0 \cdot 344,$$

$$\text{thus} \quad y_{EW} = \frac{0 \cdot 356 + 0 \cdot 344}{2} = 0 \cdot 350.$$

TABLE 8.1.   CALCULATION OF COMPROMISE CYCLE TIME

Time of day	South-bound		North-bound			West-bound		East-bound			$y(\Sigma Y)$	$1-Y$	$C_o = \dfrac{(1.5L-5)}{1-Y}$ (s)
	q_S veh/h	$\dfrac{q_S}{s_S}$	q_N veh/h	$\dfrac{q_N}{s}$	y_{NS}	q_w veh/h	$\dfrac{q_w}{s_w}$	q_E veh/h	$\dfrac{q_E}{s_E}$	y_{EW}			
7 to 8	395	0·152	585	0·195	0·195	435	0·193	465	0·258	0·258	0·453	0·547	53
8 to 9	475	0·183	850	0·283	0·283	800	0·356	585	0·325	0·356	0·639	0·361	80
9 to 10	510	0·196	710	0·237	0·237	585	0·260	410	0·228	0·260	0·497	0·503	57·5
10 to 11	500	0·192	540	0·180	0·192	425	0·189	310	0·172	0·189	0·381	0·619	47
11 to 12	560	0·215	530	0·177	0·215	290	0·129	260	0·144	0·144	0·359	0·641	45
12 to 1	520	0·200	550	0·183	0·200	385	0·171	310	0·172	0·172	0·372	0·628	46·5
1 to 2	420	0·162	540	0·180	0·180	300	0·133	340	0·189	0·189	0·189	0·369	46
2 to 3	440	0·169	620	0·207	0·207	360	0·160	300	0·167	0·167	0·374	0·626	46·5
3 to 4	635	0·244	650	0·217	0·244	400	0·178	350	0·194	0·194	0·438	0·562	51·5
4 to 5	670	0·258	670	0·223	0·258	425	0·189	385	0·214	0·214	0·472	0·528	55
5 to 6	830	0·319	790	0·263	0·319	520	0·231	620	0·344	0·344	0·663	0·337	86
6 to 7	595	0·229	500	0·167	0·229	340	0·151	310	0·172	0·172		0·599	48·5
Saturation flows veh/h	2600		3000			2250		1800					662·5

Effective green times for NS phase (see p. 358) are thus 22 s, and for EW phase 26 s; actual green times are 21 s and 25 s respectively.

An alternative to using compromise times is to set up two separate programmes in the controller and arrange for the appropriate programme to be brought into operation at a suitable time by means of a time switch. In the example above, one "peak hour" programme, using a cycle time of 80 s, could be made to operate from 8 a.m. to 9 a.m. and from 5 p.m. to 6 p.m., and a second programme with a cycle time equal to the average optimum cycle for the remaining hours would be used at off-peak times each programme having green times suitable for the separate conditions. This system makes for more efficient use of the intersection, providing the volume patterns remain consistent.

Delay at Fixed Time Signals

The relationship for delay, derived by Webster, was shown earlier. A tabulation method has been developed to simplify the computation from the delay equation, shown in the following form:

$$d = \left[cA + \frac{B}{q} \right] C$$

where $A = \dfrac{(1-\lambda)^2}{2(1-\lambda x)}$, $B = \dfrac{x^2}{2(1-x)}$ and C = empirical correction term,

all other terms as defined earlier.

The first term arises from the assumption that vehicle arrivals at the signals are regular but seriously underestimates delay at higher flows. Used with a second term, obtained from queueing theory for random arrivals to account for their irregularity, it overestimates and is adjusted by the application of a correction factor. Values for the terms A and B have been tabulated in Road Research Technical Paper No. 39 for a wide range of variables together with values of C, expressed as a percentage correction.

In the following example, the flow on one leg of a signal controlled intersection is 700 veh/h. The effective green time is 30 s, the cycle time 60 s, and the saturation flow 2000 veh/h. Determine the average delay per vehicle.

$$\lambda = \frac{g}{c} = \frac{30}{60} = 0 \cdot 5$$

$$x = \frac{q}{\lambda s} = \frac{700}{0 \cdot 5 \times 2000} = 0 \cdot 7.$$

$$\text{Term } A = \frac{(1-\lambda)^2}{2(1-\lambda x)} = 0 \cdot 192 \left.\vphantom{\frac{x^2}{2(1-\lambda x)}}\right\}$$

$$\text{Term } B = \frac{x^2}{2(1-\lambda x)} = 0 \cdot 817 \left.\vphantom{\frac{x^2}{2(1-\lambda x)}}\right\} \quad \text{(from Technical Paper No. 39)}$$

Term C as percentage correction $= 10\%$.

$$d = \left[60 \times 0 \cdot 192 + \frac{0 \cdot 817 \times 3600}{700} \right] \frac{9}{10} = 14 \cdot 1 \, \text{s}.$$

The empirical percentage correction term ranges in value for normal conditions from 5% to 15% and a reasonably close approximation to delay is obtained if it is taken as 10%.

VEHICLE ACTUATED SIGNALS

The neccessity to adopt compromise signal settings with fixed time signals handling fluctuating volumes immediately reveals their major disadvantage. They are unable to adjust themselves to changing traffic conditions. Vehicle actuated signals, within certain limits, do not suffer from this drawback. Vehicles approaching an intersection register their presence by actuating a demand signal through a detector, which is a sensing device, linked to a controller. Basically, the controller is an electronic timer which governs the cycle time and changes the signal aspects in response to traffic demands. The level of sophistication is dependent upon the complexity of the controller and the amount and nature of the detector information.

Basic Operation

Consider a simple four-legged intersection with two-phase operation, phase A being given to the east/west traffic and phase B to the north/ south traffic.

If phase A has the right of way it will retain the right of way until a vehicle approaching from the north or south actuates one of the phase B detectors and registers a demand for the right of way. If there is no traffic on phase A, the right of way will transfer and under no conditions will the right of way be lost to phase B until the expiry of the minimum green time, called the minimum running period. When a group of vehicles are halted between the detector and the stop line they need, upon receipt of the right of way, a sufficient length of green time to permit them to get into motion and for the last vehicle to reach a safe clearance point on the intersection, from where a vehicle can completely clear the intersection under the cover provided by the amber signal which must always follow green. The minimum running period, during which time the right of way cannot be terminated on a phase, is thus composed of two elements. The first is the time required to overcome the starting-up inertia of the queue. This is dependent on the number of vehicles between the stop line and the detector, and also on the distance of the detector from the stop line. Acceleration is affected by the proportion of heavy vechicles in the queue and the approach gradients. For a level site, operating under typical conditions, with a detector sited 30 m back, the required time is approximately 5 s but has to be increased for uphill gradients, and the proportion of heavy vehicles.

The second element of the minimum running period is the safe clearance distance, often considered to be the centre of the junction, and if the distance from the detector to this point is 35 m, a vehicle requires about 6 s starting from rest. Under average conditions the total time is about 11s, but controllers can automatically vary the time, depending on the number of waiting vehicles, from 7 to 13 s.

If during the period of timing of the minimum green a demand is registered on phase A, the controller will "store" the demand until the end of the minimum running period and only then will it transfer the right of way (Fig. 8.5(a)). Figure 8.5(b) shows the situation when further demands are made on phase B. The arrivals of the second and third vehicles extend the green time beyond the minimum and only when the last vehicle to arrive has received its vehicle extension time will the stored demand on phase A be answered.

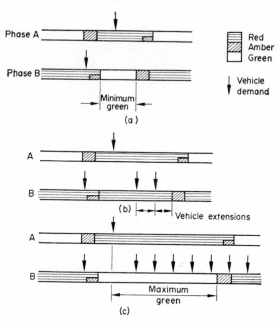

FIG. 8.5. Vehicle actuated signals.

Vehicle Extension Periods

This extension of the minimum running period by each vehicle passing the detector is known as the vehicle extension period. Vehicles crossing the detectors require sufficient clearance time to travel from the detector to the safe point (usually 3 – 6 m beyond the stop line), and this depends upon their approach speed together with detector and site layout. If, for instance, these are 35 m and 30 km/h respectively then a vehicle extension of 4 s is needed. Lengthening this time will make the signal operation appear sluggish, i.e. there will be a slow response to demands for a change in the right of way. Conversely a shorter extension may interfere too much with the traffic stream since a vehicle with a headway longer than the extension time would lose the right of way. Controllers automatically speed-time vehicles varying the extension time to permit each vehicle to travel a preset distance within the range 25 to 50 m from the detector. An additional extension time is only granted if the extension demanded exceeds the unexpired time of the previous extension.

However, there is a limit to the amount the green time may be extended and, if there is a continuous succession of demands on phase B, the total extension will not go beyond a maximum green time (a preset maximum period) measured from the time of the demand on phase A (Fig. 8.5(c)) or, where vehicles are waiting on the halted phase, from the beginning of the green period. It follows from this that if there is a continuous demand on both phases the green time on each will run to their respective maxima and then the signals will, in effect, be operating as fixed time signals.

Delay at Vehicle Actuated Signals

The above relationships for delay at fixed time signals can be applied directly to vehicle actuated signals when these are running to a maximum because of high traffic flows. However, lower flows will contain gaps exceeding the vehicle extension period and this allows the right of way to be transferred to meet waiting demands on any other phase. In order to minimise delay the vehicle extension period should just allow the queues to clear, usually about 4 s being as short as safety considerations permit. If the vehicle extension is considerably longer, say 10 s, the signals will run to maximum in all but the lightest flows and delay may be calculated using the formula, as with fixed time signals. Vehicle extension periods of between 4 and 10 s will cause delays varying *pro rata* with the extension. Extensions shorter than 4 s will theoretically give less average delay, but due to the effect of breaking up the traffic stream, discussed earlier, are not usually practical.

Correctly set vehicle actuated signals are able to accommodate traffic variations between cycles, for long-term flow variations and for changes in the flow ratios of the phases. Where controllers are equipped with a variable maximum period facility the pre-set maximum can be automatically extended when the traffic flow on a terminating phase continues to exceed a critical, but rising, value with which it is continuously compared.

ADDITIONAL SIGNAL CONTROL FACILITIES

Control facilities can be extended by the use of additional equipment. While earlier controllers provided concurrent ambers, present practice is to indicate a minimum intergreen period of 4 s. This can be extended for wide junctions, or to accommodate particular turning movements likely to remain at the end of a running phase, by consecutive ambers.

All-red periods. Additional clearance time can be provided, for instance to meet the needs of pedestrians crossing the junction, by inserting an all-red period between the ambers of opposing phases. If the elapsed time between the last demand on a phase and the receipt of a demand on an opposing phase is greater than the all-red period, provided for vehicle clearance purposes, then the controller can be made to suppress all or part of this period and so reduce lost time. This variable all-red feature is shown in Fig. 8.2.

An alternative situation is in circumstances similar to a long narrow bridge where one-way traffic flow, in alternate directions, is controlled by signals. Where traffic is light and no demand on the opposing phase terminates the right of way, a vehicle crossing the bridge does so under the protection of the green. When, however, the right of way terminates due to a demand on the stopped phase, while a vehicle is still on the bridge it is necessary for it to be protected by an all-red period until it is clear. This can be achieved by the use of intermediate detectors spaced along the bridge so that the passage of the vehicle, over successive detectors, provides and extends all-red cover until it has reached the far end.

Late release. A further device which may be used to facilitate the movement of right-turning traffic is the late release. In the example illustrated in Fig. 8.6(a) the green aspect of the northern approach is delayed on phase B so that right-turners from the south are not hindered by the opposing traffic.

Early cut-off. An alternative shown in Fig. 8.6(b) is to provide an early cut-off. Here the green aspect on the northern approach is terminated before that on the southern approach so providing right-turning facilities towards the end of the phase.

Combined release. A late release operated on one approach with an early cut-off on the opposing one is used to prevent right-turning vehicles from pre-empting the two-way running period. It is usual for late releases to be of a fixed duration whereas early cut-offs can be extended by specially located detectors activated by the right-turning vehicles.

The choice between "late start" and "early cut-off" depends mainly upon the geometric layout of the southern approach. If there is sufficient width to permit the storage of right-turning vehicles in a separate traffic lane, then an "early cut-off" is preferable. This is because vehicles intending to turn right can be marshalled together ready to make maximum use of the time, at the end of the phase, when the opposing traffic on the northern approach is stopped. On the other hand, a narrow southern approach calls for a late start to clear as many right-turners as early as possible, before they start to hinder the straight through vehicles. In the United Kingdom no indication is given to the right-turning vehicles, on the southern approach, advising them when the opposing vehicles are halted. In Canada and some other countries the position is signalled by the use of a flashing green during the period when right-turners have priority.

Pedestrian phase. The use of an all-red period for the purpose of permitting pedestrians to cross an intersection is time wasted on those cycles when there are no pedestrians to use the facility. In order to limit its use to appropriate times a pedestrian phase may be introduced which operates on demand, by the actuation of a detector. This takes the form of a push-button which can be operated by pedestrians wishing to cross. If the button is pressed a pedestrian phase is introduced and red is shown to all vehicles; otherwise no provision is made for pedestrians, thus avoiding delay to vehicles. Pedestrian phases can also be timed to run concurrently with non-conflicting vehicle movements, particularly at tee junctions.

The Pelican type signals for pedestrians have replaced the earlier X-way types (which in West London had reduced pedestrian accidents on, or near, crossings by over 40% in their second year of operation) because of driver confusion over the meaning of the white X. Pelican signals are push-button operated with a flashing symbolic green man set in the 300 mm diameter optical unit, warning pedestrians not to start to cross. For

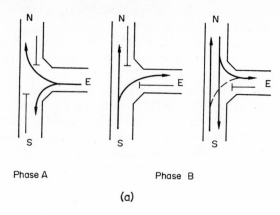

Phase A   Phase B

(a)

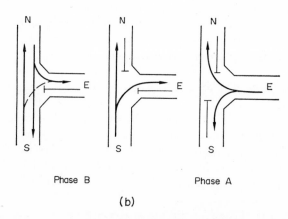

Phase B   Phase A

(b)

FIG. 8.6.   (a) Late release. (b) Early cut-off.

the driver, the red and green indications are standard, while the steady amber means stop unless unsafe to do so. The flashing amber is a cautionary proceed but only if the crossing is clear of pedestrians.

COORDINATED SIGNAL SYSTEMS

The effect of the stop aspect at a signal controlled intersection is to marshal vehicles in a queue behind the stop line. When this queue is released, upon receipt of the green, it travels on its way initially in the form of a platoon. If, as this platoon approaches another signal controlled intersection, its arrival is made to coincide with the receipt of the green right of way, the vehicles will experience no delay. In urban areas, where two or more signalled junctions are adjacent, it is thus profitable to consider each junction not separately, but in conjunction with its neighbours and to coordinate the signal timings so that maximum benefit is gained from the platooned flow.

A simple form, known as the simultaneous system, is sometimes used on a street where all signals display the same indication at the same time. It is only suitable for short signal spacings on streets with a predominant proportion of green time, and it has the unfortunate side effect of encouraging drivers to speed in order to beat a change of phase. The alternative system, best suited for equal signal spacing at about 300 m intervals, gives an opposite indication at the same time on alternate streets or the double alternate system uses a quarter-cycle offset. Systems for which time/distance diagrams are drawn, permitting a vehicle to progress through at a predetermined speed, are called Progressive Systems.

A very simple example of a progressive system of coordination is illustrated in the space-time diagram of Fig. 8.7(a). The slope of the diagonal lines represents the chosen speed of progression and the green phases of successive junctions along the road are offset in time. Vehicles travelling at the progressive speed, and having passed one intersection will then receive the right of way without impediment. Where the flow of traffic, on that street, is two-way and the junctions are unevenly spaced, the situation is more complex and, in order to accommodate traffic in both directions, it is necessary to compromise as illustrated in Fig. 8.7(b). With a flexible progressive system the cycle time at each intersection is fixed but the green indication is displaced to suit the selected road speed and is a compromise based on the directional flows, signal spacing and the needs of cross-street traffic. Local controllers are kept in a time relationship by the master controller, but with a vehicle actuated system some

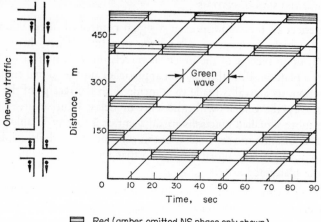

Red (amber omitted NS phase only shown)
Green

♀ Traffic light

(a) One-way Traffic

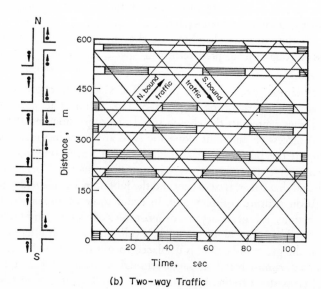

(b) Two-way Traffic

Fig. 8.7. Coordinated signals: (a) One-way traffic. (b) Two-way traffic.

allowance can be made for side-street traffic if no demand exists on the progression street. Time switches may be used to vary the basic plan on a predetermined basis for different periods throughout the day.

In practice certain control difficulties occur with signal coordination and these are particularly difficult to eradicate. Most important are the performance differences between classes of vehicle, parked vehicles, movement of pedestrians and turning vehicles. Other factors include the maintenance of stable platoons, and the entry and egress of vehicles within controlled sections. Disparity of performance is generally associated with buses and commercial vehicles and, as in future transportation plans, special attention must be paid to public transport journey times, segregation of lanes for reserved use may well yield more consistent flows. Parked vehicles on main streets in any case must be prohibited, certainly during selected hours of the day, and ensuing problems can be overcome by planning new development for shops, entertainment and other activities. These can be regrouped into pedestrian precincts, served by special parking areas. The mixed uses of existing streets tends to increase pedestrian movement and a more rigorous approach is necessary to pedestrian control, besides the construction of more pedestrianised areas.

Right-turning movements are a feature of at-grade junctions. The choice facing the engineer is, either to make special provision for them by constructing additional lanes or allocating part of a cycle time for their use (at the expense of through traffic time). Alternatively, G, T and Q block circuit techniques can be used to reroute traffic but these often only tend to disguise the effects of delay. Not only is this inconvenient to the individual motorist but it increases traffic flows on three other links in the system, and the movement still occupies signal time, as a straight through vehicle on the final link. These diversions probably also increase accidents for a given journey and may entail widespread use of residential streets.

Green Waves

Developments in system control techniques, particularly in Germany, have been directed towards eliminating lost time to vehicles accelerating from rest at the stop line and to increase capacity by the use of pre-signals. These permit a flying start and their siting, ahead of the main signal, is based on suitable acceleration rates. By erecting pre-signals before public transit vehicle stops, only the transit vehicle is allowed to move forward (into a so-called "time island") for passenger loading, at the termination of the running green phase; other traffic is held at the pre-signals.

One of the difficult problems of coordinated signal systems has been to control the platoon speed to arrive at the next signal precisely at the beginning of the green phase. This is not easy for a driver to achieve without some physical aid and the technique of bending vehicle traces (i.e. to reduce the speed of lead vehicles, and raise the speed of the trailing vehicles, in order that the group move through the signals as a closely packed platoon) has been developed in the so-called signal funnel. Here speed signals, usually displaying three values, are used together with pre-signals, as shown in Fig. 8.8. Theoretically capacity should be improved and although practice indicates some success, experiments by the Road Research Laboratory and General Motors tend to suggest little real improvement in capacity over standard control methods. It may be that drivers moving in lower gears from a stop can achieve denser packing for the short distance through an intersection than those moving at higher speed in top gear. However, the saving of unnecessary stops reduces fuel consumptions and vehicle wear, and almost always creates a favourable driver response. All are worthwhile factors, as important in benefits as small capacity increases.

Optimisation Plans for Coordinated Signal Systems

It has been shown in recent years that substantial improvements can be made to traffic operations, in coordinating groups of signals, by optimisation of fixed time plans. The Combination and Transyt methods are commonly used, and require, for the calculation of cycle times, specific traffic data for the selected network. Operational efficiency is assessed by minimising a performance index based on such criteria as total delay, or the number of stops on the route.

Road networks are divided into one-way links between intersection

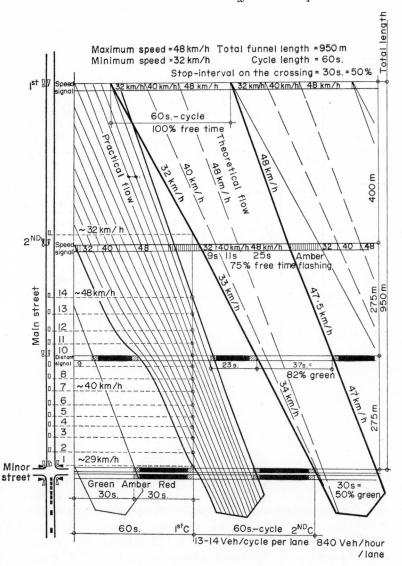

FIG. 8.8. Time–space diagram of a signal funnel in an urban street with two speed signals and one pre-signal. (Source: W. Von Stein, Traffic flow with pre-signals and the signal funnel, *Theory of Traffic Flow*, Elsevier, 1961.)

nodes. A number of operating plans are selected to suit major changes in traffic flows. Switching times are usually made for morning and evening peaks together with one or two off-peak period plans. Traffic data, either measured or estimated, is inserted on a network plan as shown in Fig. 8.9 and cycle times and green splits are calculated, for insertion

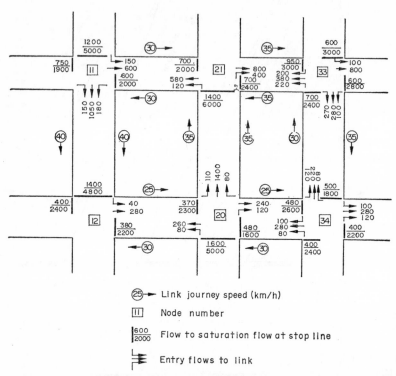

FIG. 8.9.   Diagrammatic network coded with link flows and journey speeds.

on the plan, based on a maximum degree of saturation on all approaches of 90% (i.e. $x = 0.9 = q/\lambda_s$ where $\lambda = q/c$).   A single cycle time (or double and single cycle times, e.g. 60 and 120 s) is chosen for the area or sub-areas and the distribution of the green times is recalculated to give splits an equal degree of saturation on opposing phases. Iterative procedures are used to attain the specified minimisation.

AREA TRAFFIC CONTROL

It is clear that where traffic is controlled at junctions in a street network that the outputs at one junction are related in some way to the inputs at adjacent junctions. The interaction between individual components of the system affects the overall network performance. Linked and co-ordinated signal plans are mainly applicable to the principal linear routes. Methods of controlling traffic in networks is referred to as area traffic control and may also include a control mode which is traffic responsive. Area traffic control first became feasible with the introduction of the electronic computer. However, the whole basis of dynamic control is dependent on information, which must be detected from the street, and the level of local and central control. The level and detail of information also varies with the type of control; for instance, different control strategies may be tried for a range of traffic conditions and the results analysed. The best can be stored and subsequently used, from a library of plan programmes, for similar traffic conditions. Information from detectors, sited at critical points, enables the most appropriate programme to be chosen for each situation by a supervisory programme. Further analysis can be carried out and modifications introduced which further refine the choices, and improve sensitivity and performance. In dynamic control systems the greatest difficulty lies in describing, in a logical and mathematical way, the behaviour of traffic and the rapid computation of optimum control policies. If control policies are changed too frequently dis-benefits arise and it is usual to use a weighted moving average, as control, before effecting plan changes.

An important part of the communication system is the link between the detectors and the central computer and the return link conveying instructions to the signals. The data transmission system usually operates through out-stations, connected to the traffic signal controllers, and collecting data from the individual detectors. This information before or after local processing is relayed over cables, usually rented telephone pairs, to the central controller. Control instructions are transmitted in a reverse direction to the local controller via the outstation. Each part of the system has a unique address which can be interrogated by the central controller either for data retrieval and resetting or for instruction and control operation. It is usually necessary to monitor those keypoints which have

o

a critical effect on the control of the whole system and closed-circuit television is often provided for this purpose.

The two major projects in A.T.C. in Britain are in West London and Glasgow, and detailed descriptions of their equipment and performance have been extensively reported elsewhere.

Entry Control to Major Routes

In order to maintain stable high flows on major urban routes it is important to prevent the concentration of vehicles exceeding a critical level. This is achieved by controlling entry ramps with traffic signals by a process of ramp metering. The two forms in general use are capacity demand and gap acceptance. In the first type the control system compares the actual highway volume with the maximum volume, i.e. the maximum capacity, and when spaces are detected waiting vehicles on a ramp are released to select their own gaps in the manoeuvre area. Gap acceptance control is a closer control system monitoring through lanes and releasing the correct number of vehicles at the appropriate time to arrive at the merging area, opposite the identified gaps. If a vehicle stops in the merging area, detectors immediately turn the ramp signal to red and similarly for vehicles moving too slowly on the approach ramp. Some systems release vehicles at a fixed rate when high flows are prevailing on the through pavements, requiring drivers to create their own opportunities.

TRAFFIC SIGNAL EQUIPMENT

Controllers

The controller is basically a timing apparatus carrying out switching operations on a set of signal lamps, to a definite programme. A typical vehicle actuated controller carries out its timing sequence electronically. In some forms an electrostatic condenser is charged by means of a nominal 50 V d.c. supply and while in a charged condition prevents the flow of current through the anode circuit of a simple triode valve. The charge is permitted to leak from the condenser at a rate determined by a timing resistance and, after a period, is sufficiently modified to allow current to flow through the valve and actuate an anode relay. This indicates the completion of a timed period, causing a sequence switch to operate one step; and the condenser to be recharged to time the next period.

Other types of controller use a synchrononous electric motor which responds to the frequency of the electricity supply. A change gear between the motor spindle and a timing dial permits the latter to rotate at a selected speed. It rotates once each completed cycle and through advance keys, solenoids, camshafts and contact breakers acts as a sequence switch. The motors are controlled by the supply frequency permitting controllers at a series of successive intersections to be coordinated to allow progressive signalling.

Modern solid state controllers are of modular construction and additional stages and phases can be simply plugged into the initial equipment.

Detectors

Vehicle detectors are needed to indicate the presence of a vehicle and they may be pneumatic, magnetic, electronic or mechanical and mounted below, on or above the road surface. In Britain pneumatic detectors have been widely used and operate uni-directionally with provision for speed timing. They have, however, been prone to breakdown and are now being replaced by the more reliable loop detectors, installed in a slot about 50 mm below the road surface. Unlike pneumatic detectors they do not give point detection and are usually installed, at greater cost, in sets of three. The loop furthest from the stop line gives the demand extension while the other two grant extensions if the preceding extension has expired, thus catering for a range of speeds from about 20 to 50 km/h. Long loops are used in special circumstances to indicate the number of vehicles occupying a length of carriageway.

Signal Lamps

The effectiveness of control by traffic signals will depend to a large extent on the visual attraction of the signal lamps and the clarity of their instructions. Accordingly, signals should be standardised, well situated and regularly maintained. Signal lamps are arranged in groups of three aspects, the top aspect being red, the centre amber and the bottom green. They are usually pole mounted but may be fixed to a wall or suspended from overhead wires. New 50W and 100W tungsten halogen lamps are of high intensity for use on restricted and unrestricted roads respectively, permitting secondary signals to be located on the far side of the junction, over the centre of the approach carriageways. These units can be dimmed at night by solar switches. The word stop has now been removed from the red lens and optical units, with green arrows, increased from 200 to 300 mm diameter.

Signs and Surveillance

The effectiveness of overall control is primarily dependent on the flow of precise and suitable information at a convenient rate from the street system to the controller, man or computer. In order to regulate speeds, close lanes, meter ramp flows, re-route and divert traffic requires a comprehensive system of signs and signals to be designed and installed for operation in all weathers. Control is usually by computer with inbuilt program checks to prevent incompatible displays and to ensure correct sequencing as new control modes are initiated. The consequences of control need monitoring by comprehensive surveillance systems installed in the control centre. These usually include closed-circuit television and mimic display diagrams of the control area which indicate a current state of the system, i.e. signal settings, signs lit, etc., and also feed data from the detectors to digital displays or warning lights of flows, speeds, densities and stoppages.

FURTHER READING

ALLSOP, R. E. (1971) Sigset. *Traff. Engng. & Control*, **13**(2); and Delay-minimising settings for fixed-time traffic signals at a single road junction. *J. Inst. Maths. Applications*, **7**.

ALLSOP, R. E. (1972) Delay at a fixed time traffic signal, Part I, Theoretical analysis; HUTCHINSON, T. P., Part II, Numerical comparisons of some theoretical expressions. *Trans. Sci.* **6**.

BRIERLEY, R. L. and PARKINSON, J. (1962) *The Traffic Pacer System*. General Motor Corp.

CLAYTON, A. J. H. (1940) Road traffic calculations. *J. Instn. Civ. Engrs.* **16**.

DEPARTMENT OF SCIENTIFIC AND INDUSTRIAL RESEARCH (1965) *Research on Road Traffic*. The Road Research Laboratory, H.M.S.O.

DUFF, J. T. (1969) M4 Motorway surveillance system. *Traff. Engng. & Control*, **10**(12), **11**(1), (2), and CANDY, P. J. H., Part 4, *ibid*. **11**(3).

ELLSON, P. B. (1964, 1965) Traffic funnels. *Traff. Engng. & Control*, **5**(12), and The pre-signal. *Traff. Engng. & Control*, **6**(9).

FUEHRER, H. H. (1970) Area traffic control Madrid. 1er Symposium International sur la Regulation du Traffic (IFAC/IFIP), Versailles.

GAZIS, D. C. and POTTS, R. B. (1965) *The Oversaturated Intersection*. Proc. of 2nd Int. Symp. on Theory of Traffic Flow, London.

HABERMANN, G. and SCHONLEITER, J. (1972) Lane-direction traffic signal control. *Traff. Engng. & Control*, **14**(1).

HOLROYD, J. and HILLIER, J. A. (1971) The Glasgow Experiment: Plident and after, RRL Report LR 384; and HOLROYD, J. and D. OWENS, Measuring the effectiveness of area traffic control systems, RRL Report LR 420. The Road Research Laboratory.

HUDDART, K. W. and CHANDLER, M. J. H. (1970) Area traffic control for central London. *Traff. Engng. & Control*, **12**(5).

HUDDART, K. W. and TURNER, E. D. (1969) Traffic signal progressions, G.L.C. combination method. *Traff. Engng. & Control*, **11**(7).

MAY, A. D. (1971) The effectiveness of motorway control signals. *Traff. Engng. & Control*, **13**(4).

MILLER, A. J. (1963/4) Settings for fixed-cycle traffic signals. *Proc. Aust. Rd. Res. Bd.* **2**, and *Opnal. Res. Quart.* **14**.

MILLER, A. J. (1968) The capacity of signalised intersections in Australia. *Aust. Rd. Res. Bd. Bulletin* No. 3.

ROBERTSON, D. I. (1969) Transyt method for area traffic control. *Traff. Engng. & Control*, **11**(6).

VARIOUS (1967) Area control of road traffic. Proc. Joint Symposium, Instn. Civ. Engrs.

VARIOUS (1968) *Optimum Settings of Traffic Control Signals in Networks*, Proc. P.T.R.C. Seminar, Planning & Transport Res. & Comp. Co. Ltd.

VARIOUS (1971) Focus on area traffic control. *Traff. Engng. & Control*, **13**(5).

VON STEIN, W. (1961) *Traffic Flow with Pre-signals and the Signal Funnel*. 1st Int. Symp. on Theory of Traffic Flow, Elsevier.

WALL, J. S. and BURR, M. A. (1972) Aston expressway signing and signal system. *Traff. Engng. & Control*, **14**(8).

WEBSTER, F. V. (1958) *Traffic-signal Settings*. Road Research Technical Paper No. 39, H.M.S.O.

WEBSTER, F. V. (1967) Effect of right-turning vehicles at traffic signals. RRL Report LR 86. The Road Research Laboratory.

WEBSTER, F. V. and COBBE, B. M. (1960) *Traffic Signals*. Road Research Technical Paper No. 56, H.M.S.O.

WEBSTER, F. V. and ELLSON, P. B. (1968) *Traffic Signals for High-speed Roads*. Road Research Technical Paper No. 74, H.M.S.O.

CHAPTER 9

Street Lighting, Signs and Road Markings

STREET LIGHTING

Street lighting, in common with other traffic engineering studies, is concerned not only with the well-being of the driver but that of the community generally. While the scope of the subject is wide and of a specialist nature, it is necessary that the broad principles are understood by the traffic engineer if he is to play his correct part in the lighting of the road system. A general application of established principles can be ensured by setting national or regional standards, but these serve only as a guide to uniformity of practice and have to be interpreted according to site conditions. It is impracticable to cover every individual case and, therefore, this section is concerned with the basic principles needed to correctly appraise the relevant general standards.

GENERAL PRINCIPLES

Considered simply, light is a form of energy travelling at a constant speed and radiated in a wave from a light source. The frequency of the radiation, impinging on the sensitive retinal area of the eye, determines the appreciation of colour. Wavelengths can vary from the single line spectrum, exhibited by some monochromatic sources, to a continuous spectrum such as daylight where radiations cover the range of all visible wavelengths (see Fig. 9.1). The light-sensitive cells in the human retina are of two types, rods and cones. The rods are sensitive to the low levels of illumination, such as those found under street lighting conditions, and

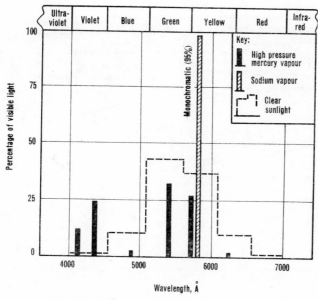

Fig. 9.1.   Comparative light distribution.

the cones to the higher illumination levels. The latter, more numerous around the area of the optic nerve, discriminate fine detail and colour. The whole process of seeing is dependent on the reflection properties of the object viewed in relation to its background, glare, the time factor in response, movement and disabilities.

LIGHT TERMS AND UNITS

Figure 9.2 illustrates the important quantitative terms needed for describing light and its measurement. A light source with luminous intensity (I), measured in candelas (cd), radiates luminous flux (F) which is measured in lumens (lm). These quantities, defining the emission of light from a source, can be broadly considered as referring to the "density of light" emitted in a particular direction and its rate of flow. Illumination (E) is measured in terms of the luminous flux received by a surface per unit area and is known as the metre candle (lux), i.e. lumens per square

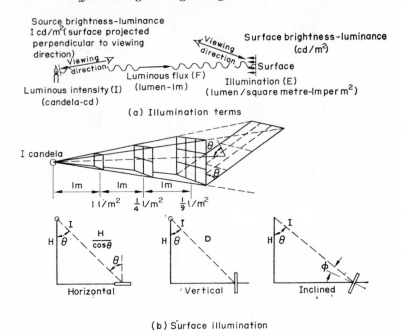

(b) Surface illumination

Fig. 9.2.   Illumination measurement.

metre (lm/m²). It can readily be seen from the diagram in Fig. 9.2(b) that the light from a source received in a plane, normal to the incident light, will be inversely proportional to the square of the distance of the plane from the source. If the plane is rotated at an angle θ to the normal the amount of light received is proportional to the cosine of the angle and is 0 where $\theta = 90°$. These two laws, known respectively as the Inverse Square Law and the Cosine Law, can be expressed mathematically as follows:

$$E = \frac{I \cos \theta}{d^2}$$

One further basic term which links sources and surfaces is known as brightness (B) or, as measured photometrically, luminance (L). It may be considered as the intensity of light emerging from a given area in a viewer's direction. Sources will obviously vary in brightness according to their size and intensity and furthermore illuminated surfaces which reflect light will themselves act, in a secondary sense, as light sources. Their performance in this respect is determined by the characteristics of the surface material and the amount of incident illumination. Clearly a distinction must be made between these two types of source and surface brightness. Measurements in the first case are related to sources in terms of luminous intensity per unit area (cd/cm^2) and in the second to reflected luminous flux per unit area. The latter is defined with respect to a perfect diffusing surface which emits 1 lm/m^2 and this unit of brightness (previously known as a foot-lambert (ft-L)), in $candela/m^2$, is sometimes referred to as the metre-lambert $\left(\dfrac{1}{\pi} \, cd/m^2\right)$. Because of variation of incident light over a surface, measurements are usually taken and averaged for an area. The brightness of a surface which emits 1 lm/m^2 is taken to be equivalent to 1 cd/m^2. Two identical surfaces, simultaneously observed with the same colour of light, will have the same luminosity when their luminance is the same. Other units are the nit (cd/m^2) and stilb (cd/cm^2).

The characteristics of a light source are usefully and often described in the form of either polar or isocandle diagrams, and examples are shown in Figs. 9.5 and 9.6. The total luminous flux for a uniform source with a luminous intensity of 1 cd is 4π lumens. From the polar diagram the length of the radius vector is directly proportional to the luminous intensity in that direction and hence can be used for calculating approximately the total flux. The area of the diagram is not a guide to the source's light output. More normal practice is for points of equal luminous intensity to be contoured and plotted on a sinusoidal isocandle diagram drawn so that equal solid angles surrounding the source are shown by equal areas of the diagram. Two diagrams representing both sides of the source are required for a non-uniform source. The total flux, or that directed to any part of the street, can be readily calculated in a tabular manner by using a planimeter to evaluate the contoured areas:

Total flux $F = \Sigma$ area within contour $\times$ mean intensity $\times$ constant
$\quad\quad\quad = $ mean spherical candlepower $\times 4\pi$ (mscp)
and the downward flux or lower hemispherical flux
$\quad\quad\quad = $ mscp (lower hemisphere) $\times 2\pi$ measured in candelas.

Illumination of vertical and horizontal surfaces is dependent on the flux, the distance from the source and the inclination of the plane. For a street lighting source at height H (see Fig. 9.2) the illumination on horizontal (E_H) and vertical (E_V) planes will be:

$$E_H = \frac{I \cos \theta}{D^2}$$

but $D = H/\cos \theta$,

$$E_H = \frac{I \cos \theta \cos^2 \theta}{H^2} = \frac{I \cos^3 \theta}{H^2};$$

$$E_V = \frac{I \sin \theta}{D^2} = \frac{I \sin \theta \cos^2 \theta}{H^2},$$

and for the inclined plane E_I

$$E_I = \frac{I \cos^2 \theta \cos \phi}{H^2}.$$

Calculations can be made for selected points surrounding a single source and contours of equal illumination plotted. These drawings are known as isolux diagrams. The illumination effects of further lanterns in the system can then be added to the values of the contours obtained for the single source. This can be most readily achieved by overlaying the single isolux diagram with the lantern centres in their respective positions and compounding the values.

Whereas the amount of light being received by a surface is important, this does not represent "seeing" conditions, particularly under street lighting, as this is dependent on the general luminance. It is necessary to consider this point further because of the mechanism of vision under varying levels of illumination. For the higher levels of surface luminance detail and colour can be distinguished, and this type of vision is required for correct appreciation of traffic signs at night. However, under the illumination levels normally found with street lighting, vision is generally achieved by distinction between surface luminances. This is detection by contrast where an object is perceived because it is sufficiently lighter or darker than its surroundings giving the familiar silhouette and shadow vision. This only happens if the general background street luminance is bright relative to the luminance of other surfaces, such as the clothes worn by pedestrians. Kerb lines will usually be distinguished by their dark shadow cast against the general background brightness. Where a gap occurs in the kerb line, such as at an intersection, the driver is aware of this fact because of the absence of shadow. As object size decreases so the relative contrast must increase for night detection and night accidents can often be attributed to insufficient stimulus at or below contrast thresholds.

In other cases, for instance where the light from vehicle headlamps falls on an object, the surface luminance of that object, if it is close to the source, will be higher than its background and discernment in this case is said to be by reverse silhouette. As the reflection characteristics of most road surfaces and their backgrounds vary considerably, overall levels of illumination are not an adequate guide to the resulting surface luminance which solely determines the "revealing power" of a particular installation. The understanding of these factors must now be considered in greater detail by studying light sources, lanterns, and road surfaces under differing weather conditions and layout.

STREET LIGHTING SOURCES

Street lighting sources are of two main types, incandescent or discharge tubes. The incandescent lamps normally use tungsten filaments in gas-filled tubes. They are cheap to produce and require no auxiliary control equipment but suffer the disadvantages that they have a short life and low efficiency. Relatively inert gases, such as nitrogen and argon, are employed and the evaporation rate of the filament is decreased by a rise in pressure. The use of coiled filaments reduces heat loss by presenting a small surface area to the gas. Because of their relatively poor performance, incandescent sources are only suitable for the lighting of residential areas where large capital expenditure is not justified. For higher intensity lighting purposes quartz-iodine lamps have been developed which yield 20% more light and almost maintain this output over twice the life of equivalent gas-filled lamps.

Discharge lamps fall into those with radiations within the visible spectrum, such as mercury vapour (high and medium pressure types) and sodium vapour, while the others are of the fluorescent type with radiations in the ultraviolet region. Changes of pressure and temperature will affect light output, wavelength distribution and arc. The discharge in a gas is dependent on the ionisation of atoms and, for the arc to strike, a voltage must be applied to the circuit. This initial process is assisted by using starter gases, argon (mercury vapour sources) and neon (sodium sources), thermionically activated electrodes, and subsidiary electrodes. The type of gas used controls the light colour, e.g. neon – red; nitrogen – buff; sodium – yellow; mercury – blue. In addition to the necessity of external methods of impressing the necessary starting voltages on the circuit, special methods must be used to limit and stabilise the current, otherwise the source would be self-destructive.

Fluorescent lamps are, in effect, low-pressure mercury vapour discharge tubes radiating mainly in the ultraviolet region. By suitably coating the discharge tube with a fluorescent material, calcium halophosphate, ultraviolet radiations are simultaneously irradiated over continuous wavelengths within the visible spectrum. This property can also be made use of in mercury lamps to improve the colour rendering of the light emissions. While discharge sources are more efficient and have a longer life than incandescent types, extra costs are involved in their manufacture, besides the necessity of providing auxiliary equipment and circuitry.

LANTERNS

The selection of a lamp determines the characteristics of light generation but, in addition, the output must be directed into the right directions by a correctly designed lantern. Light control is easier with the smaller lamps of the incandescent and high-pressure discharge types than with the low-pressure discharge sources, more than a metre in length. However, low-pressure, such as sodium (medium size) and fluorescent (large size), types have the disadvantage of lantern size mitigated by much lower surface brightness (source brightness being measured per unit area). The principal types of lighting control are reflectors or refractors, shown in Figs. 9.3 and 9.4, either used singly or in combined forms.

The reflection of light from a surface ranges from that known as specular, where an observer sited at the angle of reflection will see a

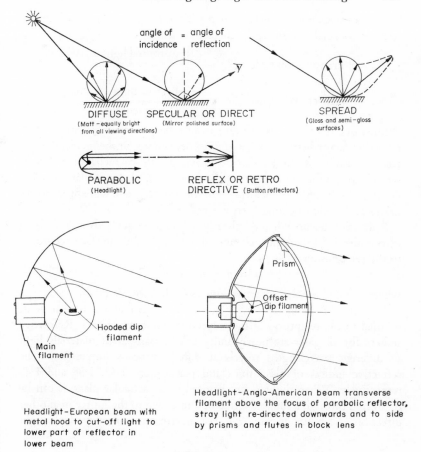

FIG. 9.3. Reflection characteristics.

mirror image of the source, to diffuse, where a surface is equally bright viewed from any direction. These types are illustrated in Fig. 9.3, together with that called spread reflection which has characteristics of a combined nature. Most surfaces exhibit increasing reflection factors as angles of incidence increase. This phenomenon is made use of in street lighting by emitting light at high angles of incidence to graze the road surface at some considerable distance from the source. When light is incident upon a surface, or passing through another medium, all will be absorbed, transmitted, reflected or scattered.

$$\text{Transmission factor (\%)} = \frac{\text{transmitted light} \times 100}{\text{incident light}}.$$

$$\text{Reflection factor (\%)} = \frac{\text{reflected light} \times 100}{\text{incident light}}.$$

Most dry road surfaces exhibit spread reflection characteristics with a reflection factor between 3% and 25% depending on the incident angle, colour, cleanliness, surface texture and aggregate characteristics. If these surfaces are immersed in water, then almost complete specular reflection occurs at high angles of incidence and the source image will appear to the driver at the end of a long narrow streak of light.

Refraction occurs when a light ray, passing obliquely from a medium of one density to another, changes direction at the interface according to the relationship:

$$n \sin \theta = n' \sin \theta'$$

where n and n' are the refractive indices of the two materials.

The ratio of the light velocity in a transparent material to that in air is equal to the reciprocal of the respective refractive indices. Refractive indices for all gases are nearly unity but in transparent materials light of different wavelengths travels at different speeds (dispersion). The refractive indices of glass, mica and perspex are 1·52, 1·58 and 1·49 respectively. Where light is not wanted in a particular plane it can be redirected through a suitable refractor and added to the source in another direction, as shown in Fig. 9.4. For maximum efficiency, little light

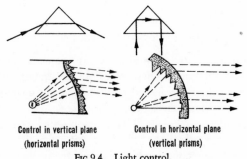

Control in vertical plane   Control in horizontal plane
(horizontal prisms)   (vertical prisms)

Fig. 9.4.   Light control.

should be absorbed by the refracting medium and glass or acrylic plastics are normally used. The latter are particularly suited to street lighting lanterns as they are lighter and tougher than glass but can only be used for low-temperature sources.

VERTICAL AND HORIZONTAL DISTRIBUTIONS

The principal street lighting vertical distributions are known as:

(a) High-angle-beam non-cut-off.
(b) Semi-cut-off or Medium-angle-beam non-cut-off.
(c) Cut-off.

Each type is illustrated in Fig. 9.5 and intensity distribution requirements are set down in B.S.1788, 1964. The three classes describe, in general terms, the output of light at angles near the horizontal. High-angle-beam lanterns have a main beam at about 80° from the vertical and a considerable output of light near the horizontal plane. Cut-off lanterns allow no light above the horizontal and have a main beam at about 70°. Semi-cut-off lanterns have characteristics between the two types with a main beam at about 75°. The current British Code of Practice has discontinued recommending the use of high-angle-beam non-cut-off lighting. It retains semi-cut-off lighting, most appropriately used for the smoother and light coloured surfaces, together with cut-off systems, preferable for lighting motorways, difficult sites and dark matt road surfaces. Lanterns are required to conform to B.S. 1788.

Horizontal distributions vary according to purpose and site conditions, but three main types can be distinguished, as shown in Fig. 9.5. The symmetrical distribution is most useful for large areas, such as at the ends of cul-de-sacs or pedestrian precincts. Axial distributions are most suitable for centrally mounted lanterns and non-axial types where the main beams are to be directed down the road rather than allowing too much light to fall behind the column line onto the adjacent footpaths. Costs of installation and maintenance have largely governed the past design of street lighting rather than the increased safety achieved with well-lit roads. Designers have sought to employ lanterns with light directed into two relatively narrow long beams, in plan, at high angles of incidence in the vertical plane, thus reducing the number of units required.

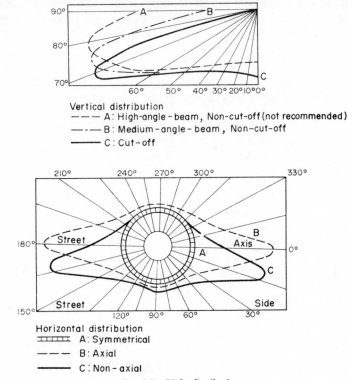

Vertical distribution
— — — A: High-angle-beam, Non-cut-off (not recommended)
— ·— · — B: Medium-angle-beam, Non-cut-off
——— C: Cut-off

Horizontal distribution
⊥⊥⊥⊥⊥ A: Symmetrical
— — — B: Axial
——— C: Non-axial

FIG. 9.5.   Light distributions.

GLARE

While visual acuity improves with increase in the brightness contrast between an object and its background once the source brightness becomes too large, in relation to its background brightness, glare will result. Darkness thus gives rise to conditions where glare is likely. The duration of the glare disturbance to the eye depends upon the magnitude and time interval of exposure, source size and angular separation (θ) of the source from the line of sight. The effect is that of superimposing a luminous veil on the visual field of magnitude $Lv = KE/\theta^n$, where

E is the illumination from the light sources, and K and n are constants. Often the glare will only be sufficient to cause background annoyance to the driver, of which he may not be consciously aware, but constant irritation has a serious effect on performance. This, coupled with the deterioration in normal vision at night, leads to a further reduction in night safety. Glare is most likely to be present where high-angle-beam lanterns are used to light dark and rugged surfaces. Lantern characteristics, mounting positions and heights, the road environment and the road surface are all factors which influence the type and extent of glare.

The Bright Patch

The shape, area and appearance of the brightened road surface, called the "bright patch", is the result not only of lantern and road characteristics but the observer's position. A symmetrical lantern output has a circular patch in plan but viewed in perspective is an ellipse. The patch is extended into a T-shape when light is concentrated directionally. Because of the small viewing angles, a tail of light is propagated between the lantern and observer caused by increasing specular reflection from the road surface. The length of bright tail depends on road surface smoothness and the light intensities emitted above angles of 70°. Rougher road surfaces widen the tail and lower its luminances. Patches are thus elongated T-shapes formed from a combination of diffuse reflection at the head and specular reflection in the tail. The tail is reduced as the cut-off angle is increased.

The aim of the lighting engineer is to produce a long broad tail which will coalesce with the bright patches of other lanterns to give uniform brightness at maximum spacings for economy, as shown in Fig. 9.7.

The shape and luminance is affected by the nature and colour of the materials in the road surface; aggregates with a large number of surface projections tend to dissipate the light locally in various planes producing a more uniform brightness but with a smaller tail. Smooth textured aggregates reflect light towards the observer, inducing high brightness along the main beams. The effects of wet weather are important and surfaces with insufficient depth of texture in the aggregate may become

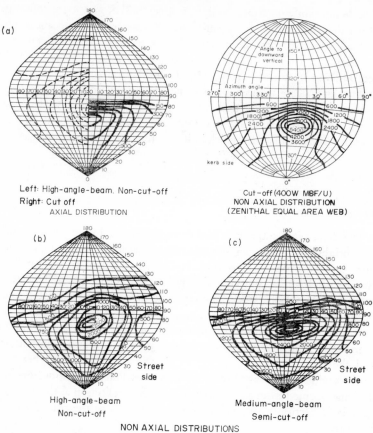

(a)

Left: High-angle-beam. Non-cut-off
Right: Cut off
AXIAL DISTRIBUTION

Cut-off (400W MBF/U)
NON AXIAL DISTRIBUTION
(ZENITHAL EQUAL AREA WEB)

(b)

High-angle-beam
Non-cut-off

(c)

Medium-angle-beam
Semi-cut-off

NON AXIAL DISTRIBUTIONS
(SINUSOIDAL WEBS)

Fig. 9.6.   Isocandle diagrams.

flooded, resulting in specular reflection. Smooth and even aggregates are now generally avoided because of skidding dangers but where unavoidable or in high rainfall areas surface crossfalls should be increased.

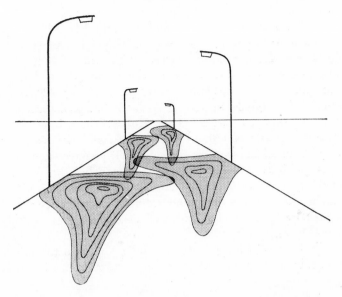

FIG. 9.7.   T-shaped patches coalesce in "semi–cut–off" lighting installation.

LAYOUT

Street lighting is installed for the convenience and safety of road users and residents, and is also necessary for policing purposes. Civic and commercial areas for shopping and entertainment may require special purpose lighting. The relative importance of these items, in a particular situation, determines the type of lighting installation used. For traffic routes where higher speeds prevail, special provision must be made to enable the driver to see both persons and objects in, or adjacent to, the carriageway necessitating high uniform surface brightness but without source glare. Such standards cannot be economically met where lighting is provided mainly for amenity purposes in residential areas and in such circumstances drivers must depend for road visibility on the use of lower beam headlamps. It is now illegal to drive without them at night, unless the street lighting is good.

British practice has been steadily improved since the first recommendations of a Departmental Committee in 1938 laid down a 25 ft (7·6 m) mounting height with an average spacing of not more than 150 ft (45 m) between lanterns. This distance was reduced to 120 ft (36 m) in 1952. The nine parts which comprise the British Standard Code of Practice C.P. 1004 are listed at the end of the chapter (p. 429) and their recommendations should be studied by the reader, particularly Part 1: General Principles and Part 2: Traffic Routes. These, issued in 1963, defined three groups of traffic routes, and established basic formulae for use with cut-off and semi-cut-off lanterns. Typical requirements were based on empirical formulae to achieve an average of 0·7 cd/m² luminance, with nowhere less than 0·2 cd/m², illustrated by ten design tables in the Code. This has tended to create minor differences in practice and alternative, but simplified, tables have been developed, using cut-off and semi-cut-off lanterns with standard lamps of 1200 lm and 20,000 lm output to allow a good A2 standard. The number of alternative mounting heights has been reduced in the Code and conforms to metric standards.

International Practice

Whereas the British system recommends tables of spacing and mounting heights for lantern light distributions the U.S. Code advises on the choice of light distribution for different road types and recommends illuminance levels. The International recommendations, C.I.E. Publication No. 12, are based principally on the European practice of using cut-off systems but other types are required and the means of achieving these without glare are indicated in Table 9.1.

Siting

The light distribution characteristics of the lantern and the street background condition are taken into account when deciding mounting position, spacing and height of the source above the carriageway. For traffic routes, mounting heights varying between 8 m and 12 m and for other streets between 3 m and 8 m are required. Cut-off lanterns are mounted centrally while semi-cut-off and high angle beam lanterns, because of their glare intensity, are mounted at the edge of the road. The

TABLE 9.1. INTERNATIONAL RECOMMENDATIONS AND GUIDANCE

(a) Requirements

Class of lighting installation	Types of road		Luminance of dry road surface		Glare	Types of luminaire	
			Mean cd/m²	Uniformity		Preferred	Permitted
A1	Motorways (when lit)		2	Very good			
A1	Rural roads	Heavy traffic			Strictly reduced	Cut-off	Semi-cut-off
A2		Considerable traffic	1	Good			
—		Light traffic		Unlit			
A1	Urban roads	Through ways and by-passes	2	Very good	Reduced	Cut-off	Semi-cut-off
B1		Principal local traffic routes	1	Good	Moderate	Cut-off or semi-cut-off	Non-cut-off
B2		Secondary roads with local traffic	0·5	Satisfactory			

(b) Means of achieving the requirements

Type of light distribution	Angle of peak intensity to downward vertical	Maximum intensity, candelas per 1000 lm from lamp		Maximum spacing in terms of mounting height†	Light flux required, lux per cd/m²	
		At 90° to D.V.	At 80° to D.V.		Road surface	
					Light	Dark
Cut-off	0° to 65°	10*	30	3	12	24
Semi-cut-off	0° to 75°	50*	100	3·5	9	18
Non-cut-off	—	—*	—	4	7	15

* But never more than 1000 cd for any value of lamp output.
† Mounting height 8 m or 10 m, or 12 m for wide roads or high light output.

principal lantern arrangements are shown in Figs. 9.8. and 9.9, and Tables 9.2 and 9.3 give examples of British installation recommendations. The most economical form of spacing for straight roads is generally that

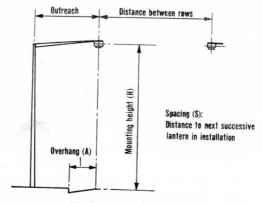

FIG. 9.8.   Street lighting terms.

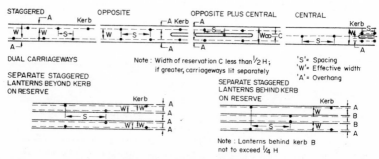

FIG. 9.9.   Street lighting arrangements.

of staggered bays except for widths greater than 20 m. Intersections, curves and pedestrian crossings determine control points for spacing; the intervening space is divided equally into appropriate distances selected from the design tables.

If dark patches are to be avoided on curves, except those of very large radius, it is necessary to take account of the angular separation of the

TABLE 9.2.   BASIC GEOMETRY AND LIGHT OUTPUT STAGGERED SYSTEMS

Lantern type	Lighting for group and type of traffic route	Maximum dimensions (m) where H is the mounting height (m)			Minimum light flux lower hemisphere (lumens)
		overhang A	spacing S	effective width W	
Cut-off	A1. Principal (important roads)	$0 \cdot 25H$	$3H$	$1 \cdot 5H$	$86H^2$
Semi-cut-off	A1. Principal (important roads)	$0 \cdot 25H$	$4H$	H	$108H^2$
Cut-off	A2. Normal (main roads)	$0 \cdot 25H$	$3 \cdot 2H$	$1 \cdot 6H$	$75H^2$
Semi-cut-off	A2. Normal (main roads)	$0 \cdot 25H$	$4 \cdot 4H$	$1 \cdot 1H$	$97H^2$
Cut-off	A3. Minor (less important through roads)	$0 \cdot 25H$	$3 \cdot 4H$	$1 \cdot 7H$	$65H^2$
Semi-cut-off	A.3 Minor (less important through roads)	$0 \cdot 25H$	$4 \cdot 8H$	$1 \cdot 2H$	$86H^2$

Code of Practice on Street Lighting: C.P.1004.

columns as viewed by the driver. Lanterns are therefore sited on the outside of curves for widths less than $1 \cdot 2 H$. It is usual with wider roads to include additional lanterns at alternate spacings on the inside of the curve. Table 9.4 indicates the optimum angular separation for any two lanterns, by adding together the angles for their respective distances from the observer (see Fig. 9.10) or a siting gauge can be constructed as explained in the Code of Practice. The critical spacing lies between 100 and 150 m and both directions need checking for two-way roads. The movement of pedestrians and vehicles is particularly important at intersections and light must be suitably directed to give a uniform background brightness when viewed from all approaches. Figure 9.10 illustrates the key lighting positions for various layouts.

Columns must be well set back in verges at roundabouts and on higher speed roads. The minimum desirable clearance between column and kerb is $1 \cdot 5$ m, but this may be reduced to 1 m to avoid obstructing a footway and where there is a speed limit to $0 \cdot 5$, but steep crossfalls

TABLE 9.3. INSTALLATION DESIGN RECOMMENDATIONS FOR CUT-OFF AND SEMI-CUT-OFF LIGHTING ON TRAFFIC ROUTES

Arrangement	Mounting height (H) (m)	Widths between kerbs (m)															
		Cut-off — Design spacing (m)								Semi-cut-off — Design spacing (m)							
		7	9	11	13	15	17	19	21	7	9	11	13	15	17	19	21
Single side	10	34								47							
	12	42	38								53						
Single central, single carriageway	10			35	35	32	28						47	44			
	12				42	42	41	36					47	44			
Staggered	10	32	30	25	21	18	16	14		44	44	44	37	32	28	25	
	12			36	30	26	23	21	19				53	46	41	37	33
Opposite, or off-set opposite	10					35	32	29					50	50	50	50	
	12						42	41	37					60	60	60	
Twin central, dual carriageway (width between kerbs is per carriageway)	10	34	27							47	37						
	12	42	38	31						56	53	43					

Code of Practice on Street Lighting: C.P.1004 (Appendix A) abstract.

must be avoided. Preferably, columns should be sited at the back of footpaths where they adjoin the carriageway. Only lightweight collapsible columns are suitable for mounting at minimum distances from the edge of the carriageway.

TABLE 9.4. ANGULAR SEPARATION OF LANTERNS OR LANES

		Mounting distance of lantern from observer (m)					
	Height (m)	60	90	120	150	180	210
Angular separation	7·5 – 9·0	2°52′	1°55′	1°26′	1°9′	0°57′	0°49′
	10·5 – 12·0	3°27′	2°18′	1°43′	1°23′	1°9′	0°59′

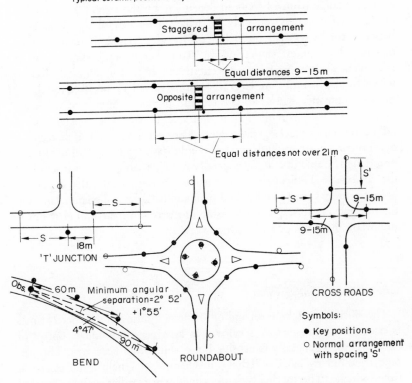

FIG. 9.10. Lighting installation at pedestrian crossings and at intersections.

Lighting for Grade Separated Interchanges

When the mounting height is below 12 m, columns have to be placed close to road edges, increasing both the risk of impact and the number of units as the larger lamp sizes of 1000 W cannot be utilised. Drivers are thus faced with a forest of lanterns creating irritating glare and adding complexity to direction finding. Intermediate height mounting, for lamps, in the range of 15–20 m is often suitable, particularly where roadways are well separated. Standard practice can be followed in siting columns along the edges of the link roads, but by utilising higher output lamps spacing can be increased.

High mast lighting has a minimum effective height of 18 m, but masts generally range from 24 to 45 m depending on the area and shape to be lit. Cost effectiveness can only be achieved by careful design as areas between roadways will often be equally illuminated. Difficulties arise on three-level interchanges where ramp height differences may be critical and shadowing from adjacent structures must be avoided. Because width-to-height ratios are large, directional specular reflection, to achieve surface luminance, is not so feasible and higher illumination levels are used. Good colour rendering is desirable because the mechanism of diffuse reflection places greater dependence on direct vision characteristics. Erection costs are high and soil conditions may be critical in foundation design. Cable ducting is generally installed with the construction of the structures. Difficulties have been experienced with the expensive hoisting devices used to clean and maintain lanterns and change lamps in the multiple clusters. The relationship of masts and structural elements is important in all bridge and viaduct work.

General Street Lighting Control

The efficient switching on and off of street lighting at the correct times is essential if a satisfactory service is to be given. Individual control of each lantern is generally expensive but is sometimes necessary. This can be carried out by hand switching, mechanical or synchronous electrical time switches. The mechanisms are sometimes guarded against electrical failure by a mechanical spring reserve. Photoelectric switches are also used sometimes but need an unobstructed north light. Small areas, with groups of lamps, can be controlled by a master timer or photoelectric switch. Larger schemes may use the cascade system where groups of lights are connected by loops with a separate cable connected to the supply through a contactor. An impulse is given to the first circuit which energises the contactor in the next loop circuit and so on until all the circuits are completed. A return circuit from the last group may be used for monitoring purposes in the event of a relay failure and alternative sections can include safeguard time switches set for 15 min later than the standard time. Other systems include the use of pilot wires and relays operating by a synchronous motor energising a switch to the main supply or relays at each column operated by high- or low-frequency signals impressed on the main supply.

Lighting Measurements

The measurement of light, either emitted by a source or received by a surface, is complex. Field measurement can be undertaken by photography or the use of photometers of the photoelectric or visual type. These measurements are useful, not so much for their accuracy but to provide a relative comparison of the efficiency of various sources and optimum mounting positions for a given site. The performance of a lighting unit assessed at the time of installation can also be used to compare its subsequent behaviour and provide a check on routine cleaning, orientation and to note deteriorating effects.

The simplest apparatus to use is a photoelectric photometer consisting of a sensitive, enclosed cell which energises a galvanometer when light falls on the surface of the cell. Resistances are included to vary the light measuring range of the instrument and it is usually calibrated directly in lumens/m². Colour correction factors must be applied to the standard reading for the various lamp types. Visual photometers, generally used for luminance (surface brightness) measurement, depend for their accuracy on observer judgement either in matching a particular surface against a number of graded silvered spots or a variable luminance spot controlled by the observer to match a surface. The latter instruments can be used both for measurements of road sign illumination and the reflective characteristics of road surfaces. Isolux and isocandle diagrams, mentioned previously, are used to illustrate surface and source characteristics respectively.

Running Costs

For the evaluation of street lighting schemes both capital and running costs must be assessed. Capital costs include the provision of the lantern control gear, brackets, columns and their erection and connection with suitable cabling. Running costs are divided into the supply of electricity, regular scouting (inspection) to check that lanterns are functioning correctly, cleaning and adjustment at suitable intervals of time and the replacement of lamps at the end of their useful life. Further items include repairs to switch gear, optical systems and painting. It is common British practice to negotiate all the above lamp running expenses under a service agreement with the electricity supplier.

Comparison of Installation and Running Costs

Assuming that a main road (12 m), in an urban area, requires replacement lighting, a comparative study can be undertaken as follows:

1. Tables 14 and 15 of Appendix B.C.P. 1004 indicate a staggered formation at a mounting height of 10 m or 12 m as being suitable with low-pressure, colour corrected mercury or high-pressure sodium lamps (mounting height 12 m) running throughout hours of darkness per annum, i.e. 4000 h.

2. From Fig. 9.11 the costs can be set down as in Table 9.5.

TRAFFIC SIGNS

Information is essential to the driving task and traffic signs, including road markings, are an important means of advising, warning and controlling drivers and other road users. They must be effective in their environment, both on and off the highway, by day and night, presenting continuity, standardisation and reliability in prevailing traffic and weather

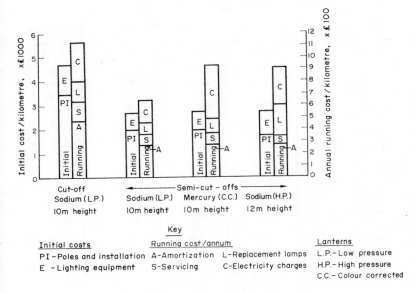

FIG. 9.11. Relative costs of street lighting installations.

conditions. The design and siting of signs must be considered in relation to their purpose and the performance capabilities of the road user in a specified situation.

The information presented on signs must be precise in meaning with messages displayed in words, symbols or in combined form. Their frequency should be such as to direct attention whenever required but not so indiscriminately as to cause disrespect. The main categories of sign can be considered as follows:

(i) Warning signs are required to identify actual or potential hazards of a permanent or temporary nature, e.g. junction, bend, hill, children, roadworks. They are normally equilateral triangles with apex uppermost; the principal exception is the use of an inverted triangle to warn of a Stop or Give Way sign ahead.

(ii) Regulatory signs define statutory regulations governing highway control and operation by giving notice of requirements, prohibitions or restrictions and, in Britain, are legally enforceable. There are two groups:

TABLE 9.5. INSTALLATION AND RUNNING COSTS

	Cut-off	Semi-cut-off	Semi-cut-off	Semi-cut-off
Lamp	140 W sodium	140 W sodium	400 W mercury	400 W HP sodium
Light output (K lan)	20	20	20	36
Mounting height (m)	10	10	10	12
Spacing (m)	21	37	37	53
Lanterns/km	48	27	27	19
Electricity consumption per lamp (kW)	0·175	0·175	0·425	0·430
Initial costs per km (£)				
Poles and installation	3300	1900	1900	1650
Lighting equipment:				
single unit	25	25	27	50
per km	1200	675	729	950
Initial installation costs	4500	2575	2629	2600
Running costs				
Amortisation (10%)	450	258	263	260
Power	324	183	444	315
Lamp replacement	166	93	118	251
Servicing	170	96	96	71
Total	1110	630	921	897

(a) Mandatory, which instruct drivers on what they must do, e.g. stop, slow, keep left, etc., and (b) Prohibitory, which instruct drivers on what they must not do, e.g. no entry, banned turns, no waiting, etc. With the exception of the inverted triangular Give Way sign, all regulatory signs are circular, although they are mounted in a rectangular sign on bus lanes.

(iii) Informatory signs are provided for the convenience of road users, and improve both the efficiency and safety of highway operations. The principal category in this group are the *direction signs* which provide information on destinations and distances, but others include information and advice on car parks, laybys, toilets and other types of service areas.

Most informatory signs are rectangular with a pointed end added to some direction signs.

Uniformity and standardisation are important both nationally and internationally, particularly with regulatory signs, and recommendations have laid down that the various groups should be recognisable by such features as shape and colour. Many countries, including Britain, have adopted, wholly or in part, the 1949 or 1953 revision of the United Nations Organisation Protocol on Road Signs and Signals and of the same title the 1968 U.N. Convention. While British practice is aligned with that of Western Europe, another system is followed by the U.S., and with modifications Japan and Australia. However, the gap between these international systems has been reduced by the issue in 1971 of a revised edition of the *U.S. Manual on Uniform Traffic Control Devices for Streets and Highways*. The new edition was issued as a National Standard Manual with provisions for all streets and highways applying for the first time to the Interstate system, state and local streets and National Park and Forestry Services.

Current British standards were based on the Final Report of the Advisory Committee, 1962 (*Traffic Signs for Motorways*. H.M.S.O., 1962) and the *Report of the Traffic Signs Committee*, 1963 (H.M.S.O., 1963). Highway authorities must prescribe to the types of sign authorised in Statutory Instruments or by special Orders. The approved signs and markings are fully detailed in the *M.O.T. Traffic Signs Manual* (H.M.S.O., 1965).

VISUAL ATTENTION

To be effective, a sign must attract the attention of the driver at a range greater than the reading distance requirement. The sign must be clearly distinguishable from its locational background and the message of the sign must, in turn, stand out from the ground colour and contrast to that of the sign board. Comprehension must also take place in sufficient time for the driver to act upon the sign's message without his attentions being unduly diverted from the road situation. Early recognition is assisted by standardisation of siting as well as the shape and colour of the sign. However, visibility is often impeded by curvature, hedges and trees, bridge abutments and street furniture, masking by other vehicles and mud splash. These are some of the factors to be taken account of in both a sign's design and location. It will be apparent from these few general considerations that different road conditions will affect the size, colour and location of road signs.

Size

The larger the sign, which in any case should be located within the driver's visual cone, the greater its impact on driver attention. However, there is a limit to size, not only from practical considerations of siting and lighting, but also for aesthetic reasons. In rural backgrounds a minimum of about 0·3 m² of white board area are required for each 30 m of viewing distance.

Colour and Contrast

Colour and contrast are important for the achievement of the two basic requirements that the sign stands out from its background and, furthermore, that the legend stands out from the sign board. These basic requirements can be effectively met by the use of different colours and differences of brightness. As viewing takes place by night as well as day, the effects of illumination on the sign must be considered together with the types of reflectorisation. For maximum contrast between the sign board and its markings one should be light coloured and the other dark. Generally, legibility is at its best where light coloured markings are made against a dark background as the legend appears more distinct.

The choice of colour for sign boards also depends on their detectability against their natural background; if that is dark, then boards must be light coloured and vice versa. The colours preferred for use against the darker backgrounds of vegetation and housing are yellow, white and then red, in that order. The minimum board area required for perception can be determined by viewing signs of varying size and colour from a standard observation point and, hence, an equivalent detectability can be obtained for each colour, as shown in Table 9.6.

TABLE 9.6.   COLOUR DETECTABILITY*
(area required for equivalent detectability for an
observation distance of 230 m)

Colour	Area (m^2)	Remarks
Yellow	1·3	Most conspicuous
White	1·5	
Red	1·7	Good for warning
Blue	1·9	For misty conditions, and against sky background, dark coloured signs are most conspicuous
Green	2·0	
Black	3·3	

*Based on P. Odescalchi, Conspicuity of signs in rural surroundings. *Traff. Engng. & Control,* **2**, Nov. 1960.

Dark lettering is normally used for yellow and white signs and light colours for the darker shades of blue, green and always black signs. The daylight degree of contrast can be measured by a comparative reflectance value of the colour against black expressed as a percentage, e.g. black–0, white on black–82, yellow on black–66, white on green–72, and blue on cream–71.

The choice of contrast is also affected by size; if a sign is large, it will be conspicuous in its own right, presenting a regular shaped area against a normally irregular background. However, the larger the sign the more expensive is the provision of external lighting, and particularly so for sign reflectorisation. It is obviously cheaper to reflectorise the smaller light coloured parts of a sign.

Colour coding can also be used to distinguish selected routes and is used extensively on the London Underground system for passenger direction and convenience in travel between important terminals. A similar objective can be achieved for road signing by colour coding routes; either the whole background or part of it, such as a stripe or disc, being of a selected colour. The following sections summarize the most important colour requirements for a sign:

P

(i) Large types, which are usually direction signs, are prominent by virtue of their size and should have light coloured markings (white or yellow) on a dark background colour of blue, green or black.

(ii) Small types of sign, used for warning and regulatory purposes, depend mainly on colour and shape for conspicuousness and have dark coloured markings (usually black) on a light background of either white or yellow.

(iii) Red can also be used in signs, but as this colour is inherently associated with danger, it should only be used in special cases to emphasise some particular hazard.

It has been suggested that sign colour is of greater significance than the use of shape or symbols and should have the same universality of meaning as traffic signal aspects, e.g. red for regulatory purposes, yellow/amber for warning and green for guidance, with blue reserved for services and brown for recreational activities.

Shape

In general, all signs should be of a single regular shape. Ideally, the shape of direction signs is rectangular with attention to arrows best focused by including them within the basic shape rather than in cut-out pattern form. Shape is also used in conjunction with colour to differentiate between categories of sign and, by standardising combinations, give added emphasis to recognition. European practice includes the use of circular signs for regulatory purposes and triangular shapes (apex upwards) for warning signs with inverted triangles for approaches to major roads. Most regulatory and warning signs have black legends set on white backgrounds; yellow backgrounds are used as an alternative in countries liable to snow. Examples of recommended British signs are shown in Fig. 9.12.

SIGN LETTERING AND LEGIBILITY

The size and style of lettering and their spacing influences legibility. Both basic types of lettering are used extensively:

Regulatory Signs

Stop

Give way

Turn left ahead or right if reversed

Turn left

Ahead

Keep left

Pass either side

Blue in white circle
White marking

No entry

No right turn

No left turn

No U turns

Goods vehicles prohibited

Buses and coaches prohibited

Except for access

Total weight limit

Width limit

Red circle with black legend on white ground

Informatory Signs

One way traffic

One way street

Priority over vehicles from opposite direction

No overtaking

No waiting

No stopping

Maximum speed limit

Maximum speed limit 70 mph

STOP 100 yds

GIVE WAY 50 yds

Signs used with road marking lines for waiting restrictions; with kerb marking for loading and unloading restrictions.

Mon-Sat 8am 6.30pm

No loading Mon-Fri 8.00-9.30am 4.30-6.30pm

Mon-Sat 8am-8pm Waiting Limited to 20 minutes Return prohibited within 1 hour

Times of limited waiting

Mon-Fri   4.00 -6.30 pm

Buses only

Bus Lane Sign

Warning Signs

Red triangle with black symbol on white ground

Cross roads

T - junction

Side road

Staggered junction

Bend to right (or left if symbol reversed)

Roundabout

Road narrows on off side (nearside if symbol reversed)

Road narrows on both sides

Dual carriageway ends

Series of bends

Double bend first to left (may be reversed)

Two-way traffic straight ahead

Steep hill

Children

Uneven road

Hump bridge

Wild animals

Slippery road

Motorway Signs

Advised maximum speed (variable)

Lane closed

Alternate amber signals

Change lane to left or right if reversed

Leave motorway at next exit

Lane clear

Alternate red signals comprise stop signal no legend shown

FIG. 9.12. Examples of British signs (*M.O.T. Traffic Signs Manual*, H.M.S.O.).

(a) Upper-case (capital letters) used throughout the sign or as starting letters to lower-case words as shown in Figs. 9.13 and 9.14.

(b) Lower-case (small letters) where the height of the letters with ascenders or descenders equals those of the upper-case letters shown in Fig. 9.13(a). The critical value for lower-case legibility determination is the x-height, as shown in Fig. 9.14(c).

Fig. 9.13. Examples show three signs (*Road Research* 1960, H.M.S.O.) using (a) block, (b) seriffed, and (c) lower-case scripts. Whilst little difference was shown in legibility, the upper-case seriffed alphabet was superior.

Experimental work has not shown conclusively any marked difference in legibility between the two types for comparable sized alphabets. It is generally thought that where a search is being made for a place-name that the word has a mental "shape", determined by the relative position of lower-case ascenders and descenders which cause the mental imprint to be recognised more quickly than complete upper-case words, i.e. at beyond reading distance no "clues" are given by the rectangular message form of upper case. Block style, rounded block style or seriffed scripts

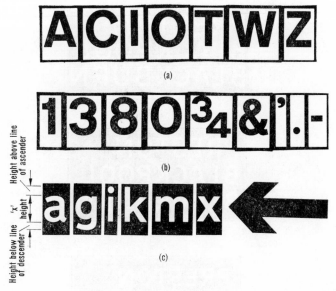

<figure>Fig. 9.14. Examples of (a) Transport heavy capital alphabet for use on white background. Each letter is placed on a tile to assist spacing and the narrowest (I) and widest (W) are shown with a parallel stroke letter A. (b) Transport heavy numerals and characters. (c) Transport medium lower-case alphabet for use on dark background showing narrowest (i) and widest (m). (*Traffic Signs* 1963, H.M.S.O.)</figure>

have been widely used. However, factors other than letter style have to be taken unto account and these are:

(a) Size of letter—height and width.

(b) Stroke width.

(c) Letter and word spacing, both horizontally and vertically.

(d) Size of margins.

Legibility is largely governed by the size and stroke thickness of individual letters. The smaller they are the longer the time required for interpretation. As reading time increases so does the observation angle θ (see Fig. 9.18) causing the driver to turn his head at close range. When this happens, forward vision is lost and further time is necessary for focus adjustment of the eye on its return gaze to the traffic stream. Not much purpose is served by an unnecessary increase in the height-to-width ratio of letters and ratios between 1:1 and 2:1 are usually suitable

FIG. 9.15. Effect on legibility of the width of space between lines and between legend and border. Spacing (a) one stroke width, (b) two stroke widths, (c) three stroke widths. (Source: *Road Research* 1959, H.M.S.O.).

for most letters. If more information has to be displayed on a given size of sign the narrower stroke widths can be used. Heavy stroke widths require greater spacing because of the eye's tendency to fuse together individual letters. Normal ratios for height to stroke width range between 9:1 and 5:1.

Visual acuity is a measure of eye performance revealed by a subject's ability to distinguish detail. Standard cards with different letter heights are read at a specified distance. British vision requirements are that a driver in daylight shall be able to read $3\frac{1}{2}$ in. letters at 25 yd, i.e. 13 m per 50 mm of letter height, and a declaration to this effect is signed in the application for a licence. This is, however, a very low standard and

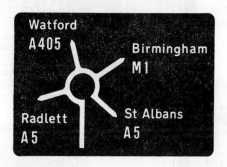

FIG. 9.16. Comparison of lower-case motorway sign and upper-case seriffed script sign (D. Kindersley, Motorway sign lettering, *Traffic Engineering and Control*, Dec. 1960). British motorway direction signs (lower example) have white legends on blue ground.

research work has indicated that a performance figure of 30 m per 50 mm of letter height would cover 98% of drivers. Using a standard block alphabet and height/stroke ratio of 6:1 in daylight, with a good contrast, then legibility for most conditions can be accepted at this value. Increased height/stroke ratios of 7:1 and 8:1 reduce this figure to about 24 m and 18 m per 50 mm respectively.

Spacing of individual letters must also be taken into account to achieve high legibility standards. For letters with parallel strokes, spacing should be between 1 and 2 times the stroke width. Opposing sloped letters like A, W and V will require a spacing from 0 to 0·5 times the stroke width. Numerals always require maximum spacing for good legibility.

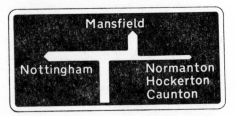

FIG. 9.17. Examples of informatory signs of the map type are shown at (a), (b) and (c), while (d) indicates the layout for a stack type sign. A route confirmatory sign (e) gives a driver confirmation that he is on the selected route after an intersection and the exit direction sign (f) repeats the advance direction sign names and route numbers. All these primary route signs have a green background with white lettering and yellow route numbers.

WORD SPACING

It is inadvisable to have words spread out across a sign due to the long horizontal scanning period required. Where this is unavoidable, adequate spacing between words must still be provided and this will range from $\frac{1}{4}$ to $1\frac{1}{4}$ times the letter height. On high volume urban roads and at major rural interchanges overlane mounting for long messages and place-names is preferable. In other cases it is more usual to stack word messages and place names and the requirements for spacing between lines again varies according to type. If upper-case letters are used throughout, an interlinear spacing between $\frac{1}{3}$ and 1 times the letter height is suitable. For lower-case letters the ascenders and descenders above and below the x-height (see Fig. 9.14) tend to merge into words in other lines unless adequately spaced. Hence, the need for greater between-line spacing distances, which normally range from $\frac{3}{4}$ to $1\frac{1}{2}$ times the x-height. Ascenders and descenders require about $\frac{1}{3}$ to $\frac{1}{2}$ the x-height above or below the line. Upper-case letters, used to start word messages, are normally of the same height as lower-case with ascender. While more space is required between lines there is some evidence to suggest that lower-case messages are more quickly recognised because of the shape of letters like b, g and l, and their position within words leads to names having a characteristic mental imprint. The way in which the memory is triggered is also important, particularly for speed of recognition or association, and it would seem that some messages are best verbalised (e.g. STOP, GO, NO ENTRY) while others are represented most effectively by symbolic displays or other abstractions (e.g. arrows to keep left or pass either side). Figures 9.15, 9.16 and 9.17 illustrate different sign layouts, lettering and spacing.

MAINTENANCE

The cleaning and repainting of signs is of the utmost importance if they are to stimulate the attention of the driver and satisfactorily perform their functions. Those mounted at low levels and in close proximity to the carriageway may be subject to mud splash if drainage at pavement edges is not good.

SITING OF SIGNS AND LETTER SIZE

Road signs are generally positioned on the driver's nearside. It has already been stated that as lateral displacement increases more time is spent in eye and head movements by the driver, with a loss of continuous forward visibility. Peripheral vision studies have indicated a marked reduction in the discrimination of detail where this angular displacement exceeds about 10°. Once the size and colour of a sign board have been determined there are three time factors which have to be taken into account when considering its siting:

(a) Reading time (t_g) of the message or symbol.

(b) Reaction period (t_r) which is a time required to act on the information presented.

(c) In most cases, an appropriate action is called for which requires a further time period, e.g. decelerating to a stop line, making a turn, etc. (t_a).

All the times are measured in seconds.

The minimum time for message perception will vary according to the individual's vision characteristics, partly on the familiarity of the information and also on the number of words on the sign. The glance reading time (t_g) is accepted in American work as a minimum of 1 s for signs with one or two words and $N/3$ s for signs with N familiar words. A factor of safety can be introduced by allowing two glances which are usually accepted as equal in time. This probably over-estimates the requirements for signs of up to four familiar words and under-estimates for those in excess of four words. However, more than four words direction signs are undesirable on high-speed routes. A suitable reaction time (t_r) of between 1 and 1·5 s is allowable in most circumstances and 1·25 m/s² as a comfortable rate of deceleration (f) taken from the operating speed (V_1) of the highway. The choice of operating speed (V_1) will depend on circumstances, but will normally be the speed limit value or the design speed. Alternatively, the spot speed distribution can be obtained and the 85th percentile value selected for design purposes. By reference to Fig. 9.18 it can be seen that the siting distance (W) is composed of two parts. The first runs from (A), where the driver commences to read the sign, to (B), where he must finish reading if the divergence angle θ

is not to be exceeded. Secondly, the sign must be sited at a sufficient distance ahead of the hazard, allowing the driver time to comfortably take the appropriate action indicated. The distance over which this can be accomplished is $(M + S \cot \theta)$, which is equivalent to the minimum stopping distance. For signs mounted over lanes the vertical angle (θ) must also be checked to ensure that the driver has read the sign before the roof line of his vehicle obscures it.

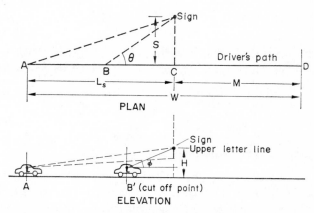

Fig. 9.18. Siting of signs.

Selecting suitable values for the parameters enables the siting distance to be determined from the following equation based on A. Mitchell and J. W. Forbes, Design of sign letters, *Proc. Amer. Soc. Civil Engrs.*, 1942:

$$ W = V_1(2t_g + t_r) + t_a\frac{(V_1 + V_2)}{2} $$

where V_1 and V_2 are the initial and final velocities (m/s) and uniform deceleration is assumed; $t_a = V_1 - V_2/f$.

Now $$ L_s = AB + BC = 2t_gV_1 + S \cot \theta $$

and hence $W - L_s = M$, the sign's distance from the hazard.

Letter size is determined from

$$H = \frac{L_s}{20l} = \frac{2t_g V_1 + S \cot \theta}{20l}$$

where H = required letter height (m) and l = legibility in metre distance per 50 mm of letter height, which is taken as the x-height for lower-case letters. To obtain the equivalent height of upper-case letters the values are multiplied by 1·33. For a displacement of $\theta = 10°$ the required letter size H

$$= \frac{4·474t_g V_1 + 18·7S}{1975}$$

Experiments at the R.R.L. have shown that a larger letter size may be needed and this can be deduced from $H = (N+6)\ 0·000568v+0·00834S$, where v is the speed in m/s.

NIGHT VISIBILITY REQUIREMENTS

Signs are as necessary to the traveller at night as in daytime and must, therefore, be suitably illuminated or reflectorised. It is important that the background boards do not warp and that the materials employed deteriorate slowly and uniformly. A standard degree of brightness over the areas of both letters and backgrounds is essential for clarity, and all lighting must avoid the production of specular reflections and patchiness. The choice between illumination and reflectorisation is often determined, particularly in rural areas, by the availability of electricity, but other factors such as mounting position, presence of street lighting and traffic conditions are important.

(i) Illumination—the following methods can be adopted:

(a) The message or symbol is set on translucent material and lit from within, or through the sign from behind.

(b) The use of luminous tubing shaped to the letters or symbols required.

(c) Floodlighting of opaque panels from external sources mounted above, at the side or below the sign.

(d) Electro-luminiscent panels which "glow" and are used to contrast either the letters or their background by insetting into the sign.

(ii) **Reflectorisation.** Reflectorisation uses incident light from vehicle headlamps to return sufficient light to the driver's eyes. Legibility again depends on the contrast between legend and background; either the background or the message can be reflectorised as follows:

(a) Button reflectors are made of either glass or plastic material set in a metal holder and mounted on the sign. They must be well made, watertight and uniform if patchiness is to be avoided.

(b) Reflective coatings of beaded material (glass spheres bonded in a hard, smooth surface medium) are used on sign backgrounds or in legends.

The reflection is required to be retrodirective, i.e. the maximum reflective brightness must occur when viewed from a point near to the source of light (see Fig. 9.3). Sign faces are usually rotated away from the carriageway by 2 to 5° to the normal, in order to avoid specular reflection.

STANDARDS

Good reflecting materials will produce an ideal brightness of 35 cd/m² when illuminated from modern upper beam headlamps or floodlighting at incident intensities of about 100 lux although a good degree of legibility is achieved at half this level. The uniformity of brightness is more important than maximum values. Sign reflectors are designed to return light from the headlamps with just sufficient spread of beam to include the driver's eyes. The narrower the incident beam, the brighter the reflector will appear, and under lower beam headlamps there is approximately a 20% reduction in legibility. The brightness requirements of the sign will also vary with location—on well-lit streets, brightness must be high if the sign is to stand out from its background. Recommendations of the Association of Public Lighting Engineers lays down a maximum and average brightness for the light coloured areas of illuminated signs as 515 cd/m² and 34 cd/m² respectively, while the ratio of the brightness variation max/min should not exceed 10:1. The higher values are suitable for use on well-lit streets, with a maximum brightness of 170 cd/m² for unlit roads.

General Emergency Signs

Because of the sudden dangers which occur from emergencies such as accidents, breakdowns, fog and icy conditions, the use of special detectors and signs is important. Signs can be installed at frequent and regular intervals with selected messages switched on by radio or cable signal, or by automatic detectors of fog, ice and traffic conditions over the dangerous sections of route. Additional portable signs, battery operated, can be carried by road patrols.

Sign Mounting

Hard shoulders with good drainage off the carriageway, reduce mud splash considerably and help the siting of reflecting signs which must, of course, be within the lighting cone of headlamps. Suitable mounting heights in rural areas are 1·5 m above the crown line and 2·1 m in urban areas measured to the base of the sign. All signs must clear the carriageway edge of footpaths by at least 0·3 m.

PRINCIPLES OF ROUTE SIGNING

Road systems are formed from a hierarchy of route types which have separate and appropriate standards. The British system is divided into motorways, primary routes and non-primary routes.

Direction signs on major routes, such as motorways, must be read without a change in vehicle speed, and any alteration in vehicle running conditions should take place off the main through lanes in the special areas provided. These requirements are met for rural motorways by erecting a preliminary sign, which acts as a brief warning, sited at between $\frac{3}{4}$ and $1\frac{1}{2}$ km ahead of the intersection. This sign allows time for the driver to move into an appropriate lane, as well as alerting drivers to a major advance direction sign ahead. It is the usual practice in European countries to include an advance direction sign in the 500–1000 m range, in addition to a main direction sign immediately before the next exit. Exit signs, or more often a simple direction arrow, are placed in the fork between the through carriageway and the slip road. Confirmatory signs are placed just beyond an intersection to indicate to through drivers, and also those who have just entered from the side road, that they are proceeding correctly on their chosen route. These signs usually list route numbers, major destinations and their distance ahead.

The signing of primary routes, in British practice, follows the principles adopted for motorways, but with fewer signs. The most important primary routes use a preliminary direction sign ahead of the junction, followed by the main direction sign at the exit with a route confirmatory sign beyond the last entry point. Local advance direction signs, which list destinations and route numbers served by junctions, are used on both primary and non-primary routes.

Special problems of signing arise on major urban routes, and the more complex interchange points of the national motorway system, particularly relating to place names. It is obviously impossible to sign all traffic destinations and it is open to question what type of grouping of areas is resorted to by drivers. Some authorities have used geographical compass points to identify a part of a city, but this leads to confusion. Once a place name has appeared on a sign it should continue to be listed until that destination is reached.

OTHER SIGNS

Whereas an offence is committed by drivers disobeying regulatory signs, warning signs are erected to advise drivers of impending hazards. If warnings are too frequently indicated for hazards which, to most drivers, do not constitute a threat calling for special action, then signs generally may be disregarded. A number of countries have introduced a new category of advisory signs, indicating safe speeds on curves, the use of lights, or the choice of particular routes. These are appropriate where uniform design standards cannot be achieved throughout a route. It is important to understand that signs cannot make up for basic deficiencies in highway design and that their use is ideally limited to the infrequently occurring exceptions.

Recent research work has indicated that the comprehension of regulatory and warning signs is often poor and that their signal value in many circumstances is low. Failure to know, or wrongly interpret, sign meanings is more than 70% in some cases and about 30% for most. Further work is undoubtedly required before signs can fully contribute to an effective control system (see Fig. 9.19).

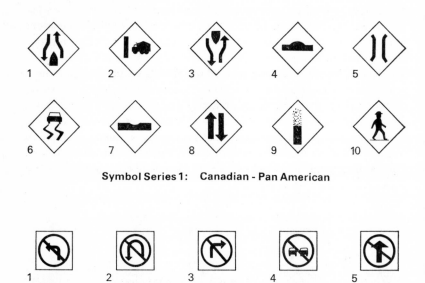

FIG. 9.19. Symbol signs (L. E. King, A laboratory comparison of symbol and word roadway signs, *Traffic Engineering and Control*, Feb. 1971).

CARRIAGEWAY MARKINGS

PURPOSE

There are various visual aids for the road user which form a necessary supplement to the information gained from road signs. They are applied to pavements, kerbs and fixed objects on or near the carriageway. Their effectiveness depends generally on their background with particular respect to colour, contrast and brightness and, because they are used by both day and night, reflectorisation is desirable. The choice of materials for durability, colour and skid resistance is also important and is determined by the study of marking purpose, location and traffic environment.

Markings are principally used to guide traffic, demark special areas of use by regulation and prohibition and provide warnings. Messages are conveyed by stripings, lines, words and symbols. Typical examples include the division of carriageways into lanes, the definition of carriageway edges, prohibition of overtaking, banned movements and waiting restrictions. Rapid identification of kerbside controls on parking, unloading, no waiting and bus stopping areas can be quickly conveyed by colour and form of lines at the edge of the pavement, but uniform standards are needed if they are to be effective and distinctive. Yellow markings are used to indicate waiting restrictions in Britain; a single solid longitudinal line parallel to the kerb shows a restriction for at least 8 hr during the period 7 a.m. to 7 p.m. on 4 or more days a week other than Sunday; a double line as for single plus any period between 7 p.m. and 7 a.m. on any day; and a single broken line any other restrictions such as unilateral, alternating, peak hours, etc. Loading restrictions are indicated by kerb marks at right angles to the road, some 0·25 m in length, painted at regular intervals in threes, pairs or singly to correspond to the waiting restriction control.

TYPES

Each category of marking must attract attention, have adequate legibility for the approach conditions and convey a clear meaning so as to provide sufficient time for the driver to respond. Occasionally, raised marks are used to supplement the visual mode and to focus further attention by affecting a driver's sensation of stability. Regulatory markings, because they may be obscured during snowfall and present reading difficulties in heavy rain, must not be used alone. Other disadvantages occur on roads carrying high traffic volumes where frequent replacement is necessary and more permanent markings than paint are required. At such sites sufficient repeat messages are needed to prevent markings being continuously obscured by traffic.

LINE TYPES

Lines may either be intermittent or continuous with normal widths (between 0·1 and 0·2 m) but for stricter lane control, in urban areas, the wider line is preferable.

(a) Continuous lines demark areas not to be crossed and are used in Britain at the approaches to junctions. Double white line markings regulate overtaking manoeuvres, both here and in most other countries, and are installed where visibility is restricted. Determination of their length is usually based on criteria relating to minimum stopping distance, selecting a value of the 85th percentile speed of the road section and an eye and target height in Britain of 1·14 m (3 ft 9 in.), although this latter standard should not logically exceed 1·05 m. Because of the serious consequences of head-on collisions while overtaking, most countries, including Britain, have made their observance mandatory. The prohibitory overtaking length may apply to both directions with a continuous double line, or to the approach direction only, on the inside of the curve. The other direction of travel has a broken line, marked adjacent to the full line, and drivers on its nearside edge are permitted to overtake, if conditions are safe to do so. Alternate offset double lines have been tried on some three-lane roads to provide regular overtaking opportunities but have invariably led to an increased accident rate. However, double line systems are often usefully applied to roads with steep gradients by, in effect, providing more lanes on the ascent.

(b) Broken lines, laid with widely spaced dashes, are used for indicating warnings or hazards and, in similar form, as centre and lane markings for guidance purposes. Warning lines are installed where visibility distances are greater than the prohibitory criteria (the latter differing from the former by 10 mph (16 km/h)). They are laid with the single broken line twice the gap length. In a speed limit of 40 mph (65 km/h) or less, the module is 18 ft (5·5 m) and for higher limits on restricted sites the module is 27 ft (8·25 m), the line width varying from 4 to 6 in. (0·1 – 0·2 m) according to site conditions. For lane markings the smaller width is used with the two modules but the marks are shorter than the gaps.

(c) Edge of carriageway markings. Two patterns are used on all-purpose roads, either broken, with gaps substantially longer than the marks, or continuous at the more hazardous sites of restricted width carriageways and bends. Broken lines are also applied to the carriageway edge where there is a doubt about its line, e.g. acceleration lanes and mouths, where alternate marks and gaps of 3 ft (0·9 m) are used.

Reflectionised edges are used for delineation on unlit rural roads and on important traffic routes.

(d) Transverse lines are mainly used at junctions to demark major and minor flows. In British practice two continuous lines are used for the stop line at stop sign controlled junctions but single lines at signals and police controlled junctions. A STOP sign is always accompanied by the word "stop" painted on the carriageway. Give-way junctions have double broken lines which may be laid alone, but where the mandatory sign is used a painted triangle is always marked as an additional warning ahead of the line. With dual approach lanes words and triangles are separately painted in each lane. In either case they are painted about 3 m from the line, but exceptionally this distance can be increased, because of visibility conditions, to not more than 15 m. With carriageways carrying single directional flows, markings are laid across the full width, but for two-way roads one central line is also laid as shown in Fig. 9·20. Transverse lines, to be readily observable because of foreshortening, must be at least 0·25 m wide and up to 0·50 m at dangerous sites, unless the double system is used as in Britain.

(e) Box markings are laid in yellow lines to form a control area, which is diagonally cross-hatched to indicate non-entry until an exit is clear.

Word Markings

Words such as STOP, SLOW, BUS STOP, SCHOOL ENTRANCE, TAXIS, etc., are often used to augment road signs. However, it is difficult to read

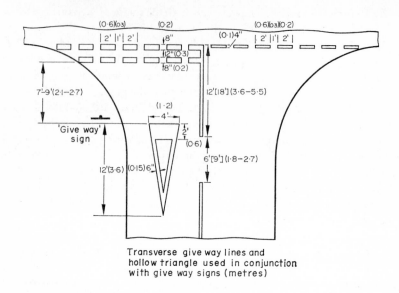

Transverse give way lines and
hollow triangle used in conjunction
with give way signs (metres)

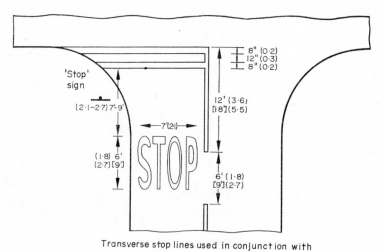

Transverse stop lines used in conjunction with
stop sign (metres)

FIG. 9.20. Transverse give-way and stop lines in conjunction with the give-way and stop signs.

pavement words unless they are of sufficiently large size. Not more than three words should be used for any one message and these should read away from the approaching driver with a spacing of between 1 and $1\frac{1}{2}$ times the letter height. Letters must also be elongated by up to a factor of five to take account of foreshortening. Siting depends on the same characteristics as for signs, though greater margins of perception time are required and repeat messages will often be desirable.

Colour

While white is the colour most used for road markings in Britain, a surface's background colour should, ideally, be taken into account in selecting an appropriate colour. Yellow is frequently used in other countries, but is reserved in British practice for waiting and unloading control lines. Colour coding, which may be used on route direction signs, can be matched by similarly coloured pavement arrows, or surfacing insets.

Materials

Over 80% of road lines are laid in Britain with thermoplastic materials which have a high durability and life of about two years in most circumstances. High-speed spraying is now used with the thermoplastic material containing a synthetic resin binder and allowing a halving of the laid thickness of line with high durability. Other materials used in road marking include plastic sheet laid with a hot bituminous adhesive. Different surface treatments, including embossing and patterning with various colours of the plastic, are available. Regular maintenance and replacement is essential if markings are to satisfactorily perform their function. Their effectiveness may be considered in terms of cost and safety (skid resistance). Greater durability reduces the relaying frequency, and ease of laying (dry-out time) is important.

AIDS TO NIGHT VISIBILITY AND REFLECTORISATION

Under good street lighting conditions reflectorisation is not necessary unless special precautions are required because of fog conditions. Glass beads, retro-reflective, are used with paint or thermoplastic as a night driving aid. Spheres, ranging in diameter from 100 mm to about 1 mm, can be dispensed onto a wet paint surface or incorporated in the mix before surface application. With the pre-mix method it is some time before the surface is abraided sufficiently to "expose" the glass surfaces. Rates of application range from 4·50 to 6 kg/litre using beads with a standard refractive index of 1·5. Generally the higher cost of glass beaded paints is off-set by their increased resistance to traffic wear thus extending the useful life of the markings. Pre-cast kerbs can also be reflectorised with paints or stud reflectors.

Road Studs

There are a number of types of stud to indicate a driver's position. These include "traffic studs" which are moulded plastic with an apoxy filled base incorporating prismatic reflectors which redirect an incident ray back to the observer. "Ghospot" markers are used with white lines and are attached to the surface by an epoxy resin adhesive; incorporating steel reinforcement they are able to withstand heavy traffic attrition. "Cats-eyes" are manufactured with a cast iron base which contains reflectors self-cleaned as they are depressed by contact with a vehicle's tyres. They are installed by cutting into the road surface and are visible, either in standard or heavy duty types, even in heavy rain, for over 90 m in dipped beams and nearly double in main beams.

The present practice on British motorways is to use a calcined flint surface dressing on the marginal edges augmenting that on the near-side by red reflecting road studs and on the off-side with yellow studs. A supplementary aid to the visual markers on the off-side is to construct the flush haunch edge as a rumble strip, thus creating a noise signal.

FURTHER READING

A.P.L.E. *Lighting of Traffic Signs*: Technical Report No. 1; *Computers in Public Lighting*: Technical Report No. 2. Association of Public Lighting Engineers.
DE BOER, J. B. (Ed.) (1967) *Public Lighting*. Philips Technical Library.
BOSTICCO, M. (1969) Street furniture. *Traff. Engng. & Control*, **10**(11).

BRITISH STANDARDS INSTITUTION. Code of Practice C.P.1004, Part 1, (1963): *General Principles*; Part 2 (1963): *Lighting for Traffic Routes*; Part 3 (1969): *Lighting for Lightly Trafficked Roads and Footways*; Part 4 (1967): *Lighting for Single-level Road Junctions including Roundabouts*; Part 6 (1967): *Lighting for Bridges and Elevated Roads*; Part 7 (1971): *Lighting of Underpasses and Bridged Roads*; Part 8 (1967): *Lighting for Roads with Special Requirements*; Part 9 (1969): *Lighting for Town and City Centres and Areas of Civic Importance*. Also BS 1788 (1964): *Street Lanterns for Use with Electric Lamps*, and C.I.E. International Recommendations for the Lighting of Public Thoroughfares, C.I.E. No. 12 (1965).

CHRISTIE, A. W. (1968) The night accident problem and the effect of public lighting. *Public Lighting*, 33(141).

CLARKE, R. H. (1970) The feasibility of holographic traffic signs. *Traff. Engng. & Control*, 12(4).

CONNORS, M. M. (1969) Luminance requirements for the identification of small targets. *Optical Soc. of America*, 59(1).

E.N.O. (1968) *Roadside Hazards*. The Eno Foundation for Highway Traffic Control, Sangatuck.

FINAL REPORT OF ADVISORY COMMITTEE (1962/63) *Traffic Signs for Motorways*, H.M.S.O. *Report of the Traffic Signs Committee, Traffic Signs 1963*, H.M.S.O.

FISHER, A. J. (1970) Visibility of objects against dark backgrounds with street and vehicle lighting. *Proc. Aust. Rd. Res. Bd.* 5(3).

GRIFFITHS, W. D. et al. (1971) Research development, design and protection of high level masts. A.P.L.E. Conference.

HIGHWAY RESEARCH BOARD (1968/70) *Vehicle Guidance, Lighting and Sign Brightness*, H.R. Record 275; *Design of Sign Supports and Structures*, H.R. Record 346.

JOHANSSON, G. and BACKLUND, F. (1970) Drivers and road signs. *Ergonomics*, 13(6).

JOHANSSON, G. and RUMAR, K. (1966) Drivers and road signs: a preliminary investigation of the capacity of car drivers to get information from road signs. *Ergonomics*, 9(1).

JOHANSSON, G. and RUMAR, K. (1968) Visible distance and safe approach speeds for night driving. *Ergonomics*, 11(3).

KETVIRTIS, A. and RAZANSKAS, S. G. (1972) *Interchange Illumination – Engineering and Economics*. Trans. I.E.S. Conf., Tulsa. Illuminating Engineering Society.

LAKE, J. R. and TYLER, J. W. (1967) The RRL reflecting kerb. RRL Report LR 89. The Road Research Laboratory.

MINISTRY OF TRANSPORT (1965) *Traffic Signs Manual*. H.M.S.O.

MINISTRY OF TRANSPORT (1967) *The Use of Headlamps*. H.M.S.O.

REID, J. A. and TYLER, J. W. (1969) Reflective devices as aids to night driving. *Highways and Traff. Engng.* 37(1715).

SUMMERFIELD, K. (1969) Road signs and signals. *Traff. Engng. & Control*, 11(1).

VARIOUS (1970, 1971, 1973) Focus on road markings, *Traff. Engng. & Control*, 11(11); Focus on signs, *ibid.* 11(10); Focus on road signs and markings, *ibid.* 12(10); Focus on road signs and markings, *ibid.* 15(3).

VARIOUS (1971) Focus on street lighting. *Traff. Engng. & Control*, 13(6).

WALDRAM, J. M. (1952) *Street Lighting*. Edward Arnold & Co. London.

CHAPTER 10

Accidents and Road Safety

THE PROBLEM

Road accidents have become a major problem in this century and increased to such an extent in developed countries that a quarter of a million deaths and 10 million injuries could occur annually on the world's road system within the next decade unless very dramatic steps are taken, in many diverse fields, to rectify this situation. World Health Organisation statistics reveal that over a third of all accidental deaths are now attributable to motor vehicle accidents in developed countries. In Germany, France, Austria, Switzerland and the Netherlands alone they account for nearly 4% of all deaths and up to 50% of deaths among young males between the ages of 15–24. However, quite marked differences occur between the statistics for one country and another and particularly the accident rate between groups of the population, as shown in Table 10.1. Smeed has shown that there is an approximate relationship between the annual road deaths (D), the number of registered motor vehicles (n) and the population (p) as follows:

$$D = 0 \cdot 0003 \, (np^2)^{\frac{1}{3}}.$$

The comparison of accident statistics between countries is made difficult because common definitions are not used. While death within thirty days is mainly accepted, as in Britain, it is only reported as such in Belgium and Portugal if it occurs at the scene, within 24 hr in Spain, within 3 days in France, 7 days in Italy and within a year in the U.S.A. Correction factors can be applied; for instance, to convert at the scene deaths to the 30-day definition requires an addition of approximately 100%, 15% in the case of death within 3 days and minus 3% for 1-year deaths.

ROAD SAFETY AND ACCIDENTS

There are many reasons for the growth in road accidents, besides

TABLE 10.1. FATALITY RATES IN DIFFERENT COUNTRIES (1966)

Country	Pedestrian fatalities	Deaths/ million population	Cars/ thousand population	Fatalities/ million cars	Fatalities m/c and motorised cycles	Deaths/ million machines
Sweden	297	38	241	337	151	607
U.S.A.	9029	46	398	435	1796	1300
Great Britain	3153	59	185	261	1134	791
France	3123	63	211	605	2928	532
West Germany	6052	105	174	677	1502	922

the increase in populations and wealth enabling more people a greater amount of individual travel, and these range from individual to collective apathy to man's physical and emotional limitations to live safely in a mechanised environment. While many of our cities have grown to their present size during the life of the motor vehicle, engineers and planners have failed to create an environment suitable for their safe and civilised use. A fuller realisation of the problems is required, and of the many factors which contribute to road accidents, before effective measures can be applied to alleviate the present situation. It needs not only a coordinated approach but a far more effective working partnership between the police, legislators, teachers, journalists, engineers, planners and doctors and, in the end, with the individual citizen. The traffic engineer can make an important contribution, from established knowledge, to the better design and control of the road system.

Well-designed roads allow greater margins of safety, enabling small errors of judgement, lack of concentration at a specific instant of time or a perception failure to be accommodated and, hence, avoid an accident by the provision of more space and time in design. Many accidents needlessly occur because the facilities provided do not adequately allow for the range of individual requirements of separate groups of road users, particularly the pedestrians. Figure 10.1 and Table 10.2 show some of the more important general statistics of road accidents. The average cost, including subjective costs, of all fatal and injury accidents are shown in Table 10.3 and are regularly updated by T.R.R.L.

ACCIDENT REPORTING AND TABULATION

Accident analysis, whether it is concerned with the detailed investigation of events at individual sites or the survey of national patterns, is dependent on the completeness and accuracy of the reporting. Because trends have to be interpreted, and significant changes detected from control and design measures, consistency in methodology is necessary for the effectiveness of improvements to be scientifically evaluated. It must be appreciated that there are generally a large number of variables present in accident analysis, but the actual event of an accident is comparatively rare in terms of the amount of travel.

Accident Reporting

In Great Britain the police authorities are the body responsible for accident reporting and the compilation of records. Similar systems and procedures are adopted, either wholly or in a modified form, in many countries of the Commonwealth. Statistical data on accidents are required by the police for law enforcement and the distribution of manpower for surveillance; by government and local authorities to determine the need for road improvement and to initiate programmes for propaganda and educational purposes; and also for accident investigation by research organisations. Unfortunately the initial recording of the factors involved in an accident lies solely in the hands of the reporting police officer whose judgement in these matters is necessarily limited by the extent and nature of his training. This is not a criticism of the police who, in this country, have consistently and effectively contributed to road safety, but it is both apparent and necessary if further measures are to be taken to reduce the accident rate that a more fundamental approach to investigations is

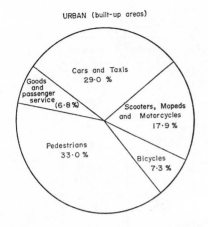

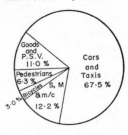

Urban Total: Fatal and Serious: 62,182

All Casualties: 252,560

Severity ratio: (%) 24·6

Rural Total: Fatal and Serious: 36,385

All Casualties: 99,467

Severity ratio: (%) 36·6

All areas: Total Casualties: 352,027

Fatalities : 7,699;   Seriously Injured : 90,868; Slight : 253,460

(2·2 %)   (25·8%)   (72·0%)

Fɪɢ. 10.1.   Road casualties in Great Britain 1971. (Source: *Road Accidents* 1971, H.M.S.O.)

Tᴀʙʟᴇ 10.2.   Rᴏᴀᴅ Dᴇᴀᴛʜs — Eᴜʀᴏᴘᴇᴀɴ Cᴏᴜɴᴛʀɪᴇs

Country	1953	1957	1961	1970
Belgium*	702	925	1079	1547
France**	7166	8517	9140	†(14,644)″
Western Germany	11,175	12,687	14,209	19,193
Italy*	4880	6936	8987	10,208‡
Sweden	921	946	1004	1307
United Kingdom	5090‡	5550	6908	7499

*Death only at scene of accident (+ 100% to 30 days).   ″1969 figure.
**Died within 3 days of accident (+15% to 30 days).
†Died within 6 days of accident (+ 90% to 30 days).
‡Died within 7 days of accident (+ 7% to 30 days).

TABLE 10.3. ESTIMATED TOTAL COSTS OF ACCIDENTS AT 1970 PRICES ($£$)
(*Road Research*, 1970. H.M.S.O., 1971)

Class of accident	Urban areas	Rural areas	Motorways	All roads
Fatal	18,000	21,000	24,000	19,000
Serious injury	1200	1800	1900	1400
Slight injury	210	380	420	250
Damage only	100	130	150	100
Total cost of all accidents divided by the number of injury accidents reported to the police.	1400	2300	3500	1600

essential. There is certainly a need for detailed research by trained and specialised observers.

Two specially coded accident sheets are used in Great Britain for accident reporting; these are known as Stats. 19 for fatal and serious injury, and Stats. 19A for slight injury. Various revisions have been made to these forms since their introduction in 1949. However, it is important that any form or card used should have precise and universally recognised terminology and contain some or all of the elements shown in Table 10.4.

ACCIDENT RECORDS

General

In common with all other traffic studies the compilation of data, its analysis and presentation in a convenient and legible form is essential. Greater use is being made of magnetic tape to store accident records for subsequent computer processing and methods of tabulating and retrieving data are now well established. Over a quarter of a million injury accident records, extracted from Stats. 19 are now annually processed at the Department of the Environment and reference tables issued in the yearly

TABLE 10.4.   ELEMENTS OF INFORMATION REQUIRED FOR ACCIDENT
RECORDS AND RESEARCH

General	Time, date (day, month and year). Locality of event and weather conditions. Holiday period. Highway classification.
Road users	*Personal Information* Age, sex, marital state, occupation, and any physical disabilities. Travel mode and journey purpose, and previous accident record. If a driver—experience. *General Information* Position of fatalities and injured. Type of injuries and property damage. If in vehicle—driver or passenger and number of passengers. Impairments—drink, drugs or illness. Interview of witnesses and statements of events.
Vehicles	Type, make, year of manufacture. External and internal features—ornaments, etc. Condition tyres, brakes, suspension (post accident investigation). Equipment check and functioning—lights and indicators. Damage sustained and position of vehicles. Seating capacity. Vehicle use at time and loading condition. Type of movement. Ancillary equipment—safety belts and crash helmets.
Road environment	*Traffic Control* Signs (directional, mandatory, warning and information) and other controls (one-way, speed, parking, loading, bus stops, laybys, etc.). Pedestrian crossings. Road markings. *Traffic* Volume, speeds and traffic composition. Public service vehicles. *Road Design Features* Grade, alignment, width and cross-sectional elements. Intersection layout, bends, crossfall, kerbs and barrier rails. Visibility distances. Street furniture. *Road Surface* State and type of surface. Skid resistance values. Defects. Drainage and lighting conditions. *Adjacent Land Use* Special buildings—schools, old people's homes, factories, etc., position of accesses. *Special Consideration* Movement of vehicles and pedestrians. Animals involved.

publication *Road Accidents*. Such records enable analysis to be undertaken for different and specialised purposes. The requirements range from:

(i) The establishment of national safety standards and the formulation of suitable legislation for educational and safety programmes and for the improvement of police patrolling of the road network and enforcement purposes.

(ii) The improvement in design and operational control measures and control equipment by vehicle manufacturers and traffic engineers.

(iii) The design of highway facilities including geometric layout, road drainage and materials used in construction.

(iv) The economic evaluation of safety measures, determining the yield of benefits against the costs imposed, and identifying their distribution within the population so that the public, through political agencies, can make decisions on investment programmes and revenue policies.

(v) The provision of emergency services, medical facilities, the rehabilitation of victims and compensation for injury.

(vi) Educational programmes to extend and improve public consciousness to road safety.

Accident Rates

In the survey of accident statistics it is usually necessary to convert them into accident rates so that useful comparisons can be made by taking into account the degree of exposure to risk that has occurred in the events. It is also necessary to monitor trends from an accurate base both to identify the relative success of policies and to detect underlying changes as soon as possible.

For general purposes accident occurrence rates are derived in relation to population, vehicle registration and vehicle travel. Stratification of the data is often required by a breakdown into urban and rural accidents, by the time of day, day of week and seasonal influences. The most useful form of accident rate is associated with vehicle travel, which relates traffic volume and length of road for a specified time period. The two indices in general international use are:

(a) Personal injury accidents
   per million vehicle
   kilometres per year

$$= \frac{\text{No. of personal injury accidents per year} \times 10^6}{\text{Length of road (km)} \times \text{traffic flow per year}}$$

(b) Fatalities per hundred
   million vehicle kilometres
   per year

$$= \frac{\text{No. of fatalities per year} \times 10^8}{\text{Length of road (km)} \times \text{traffic flow per year}}$$

Figures 10.2, 10.3 and 10.4 illustrate changes in casualty rates. Assessments are often made by averaging the number of accidents over a period of time, usually based on the preceding 3 years. Traffic flows can be determined nationally, or regionally, from sample counts or based on total fuel consumption and average vehicle consumption per vehicle kilometre. Unfortunately, when considering accident rates to pedestrians the vehicle flow is only one factor and it is necessary to add a further measure to describe the amount and type of pedestrian movement, i.e. to include a pedestrian exposure factor in the rate.

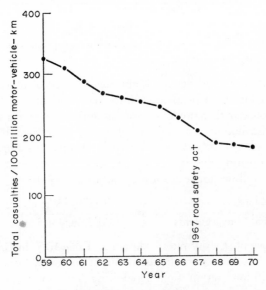

Fig. 10.2.   Total casualty rate in Great Britain.

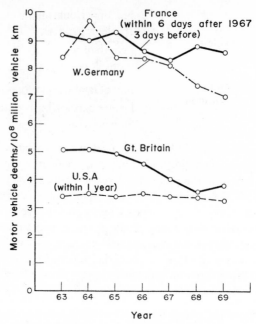

Fig. 10.3. Comparison of motor vehicle death rates in various countries.

Classification of accident rates is also made by calculating an accident involvement rate by a breakdown into road user categories, ages and sexes based on a stratification of the total population. Again problems arise over the distribution and amount of travel performed by different population groups, in total and by time. Another measure which is useful in comparing the sites of accidents, is the accident severity rate, calculated as follows for selected sites and time periods:

$$\frac{\text{Fatal accidents}}{\text{Fatal and Serious accidents}} \quad \text{or} \quad \frac{\text{Fatal and Serious accidents}}{\text{All injury accidents}}$$

An example of severity rates is shown in Table 10.5. In Great Britain reported traffic casualties are classified as slight (minor injury not requiring hospital detention), serious (injury requiring admission to hospital as an in-patient), and fatal (resulting in death within 30 days). The further group of damage-only accidents (physical damage to vehicles or property but not to a person) is a category not requiring statutory reporting in Great Britain.

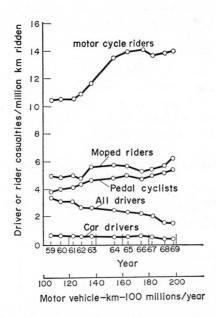

Fig. 10.4. Driver or rider casualties—rates in time.

TABLE 10.5. PERCENTAGE OF FATAL ACCIDENTS IN THE TOTAL NUMBER OF FATAL AND SERIOUS INJURY ACCIDENTS BY CLASS OF ROAD

Type of road	Class of road			All (incl. motorways)
	I	II	III and unclassified	
Roads with 30 and 40 mph speed limits	8·6	7·2	5·9	7·4
Other roads	11·8	7·8	6·1	10·1

R

Accident Surveys and Analysis

Accident surveys can be divided into two basic types.

(i) *Macro-surveys*, which yield general information on categories of road user with vehicle and location subdivided by times, types and manoeuvres as discussed later. Rates can be compared and are usually highest where mixed traffic is present, particularly on shopping streets or on older mixed residential roads with narrow rights of way, and lowest on well-designed rural roads with light traffic or on motorways as shown in Tables 10.6 and 10.7. The ratio of fatalities to personal injury categories is lowest in central areas because of congestion, but increases with vehicle speeds and is generally highest on poorly aligned rural roads and on the unrestricted roads approaching cities.

TABLE 10.6. TYPICAL PERSONAL INJURY ACCIDENT RATES (PER MILLION VEHICLE KM)

Central areas of towns	5–9
Outer areas of towns	2·5–5
Rural classified main roads	0–2·5
Rural classified main roads. Difficult sites	2·5–7·5
Rural motorways	0–1·0

Accidents are also highly correlated with vehicle manoeuvres (Table 10.8) and, as a result, are far more frequent at junctions (Tables 10.9, 10.10 and 10.11). The proportion of vehicle-to-vehicle impacts, and their magnitude, occurs with different directional frequency and is related to journey purpose and the type of area in which travel is taking place. A comparison of accident rates for different categories of user also show marked differences; the risks incurred, in descending order, are the motor cyclist, pedal cyclist, cars, commercial vehicles, and buses. However, none of these rates is static; trends change over the years due to the varying vehicle compositions, legislation, degree of motorisation and the proportion of travel in different areas. Severity rates also change due to these factors and vehicle design leading to different operating conditions

TABLE 10.7.   ACCIDENTS PER 100 MILLION VEHICLE KILOMETRES, 1968
(Notes on road accident statistics by H. D. Johnson and F. Garwood,
R.R.L. Report LR 394, 1971)

Type of area	Class of accident				Casualty rates per 10^6veh.km (all road users)	Fatality rates per 10^8veh.km
	Fatal	Serious	Slight	Total		
Urban areas:						
A roads	4·1	45	133	182	2·33	4·3
B roads	3·8	50	136	189	2·43	4·0
C and Unclassified roads	3·1	57	169	229	2·76	3·1
All roads except motorways	3·7	49	146	199	2·49	3·8
Rural areas:						
A roads	3·4	24	39	67	1·08	4·0
B roads	2·5	29	47	79	1·19	2·7
C and Unclassified roads	2·1	33	61	97	1·33	2·2
All roads except motorways	3·0	27	45	75	1·15	3·4
All motorways	1·5	6·3	12	20	0·36	2·0

such as speed and braking. Rates are also strongly influenced by age distribution of the population. Pedestrian accident rates are more difficult to compare with other categories because of the determination of exposure rates relating to distance travelled. They are, however, a major problem in Great Britain as indicated in Fig. 10.1. While accident statistics can be shown in tabular or diagrammatic form, their particular effectiveness generally depends on the purpose and nature of the study.

(ii) *Micro-surveys*, which enable particular danger points in the road system to be identified and causes evaluated. These locations are sometimes referred to as "black spots" and often require a detailed study of a local area. There are various methods in common use as outlined below.

TABLE 10.8.   DRIVER MANOEUVRES IN ACCIDENTS
(METROPOLITAN POLICE DISTRICT)

Manoeuvre	Percentage	
	1963	1971
Reversing	0·6	0·8
Parked	4·3	5·3
Starting	1·2	2·3
Stopping	4·0	4·7
Turning round	0·5	0·5
Turning left	3·4	3·3
Turning right	10·9	11·2
Going ahead but held up	4·7	4·4
Overtaking	17·9	5·1
Going ahead (other)	52·5	62·3
Entering or leaving layby or hard shoulder	–	0·1

TABLE 10.9.   JUNCTION ACCIDENTS BY TYPE OF CONTROL
(METROPOLITAN POLICE DISTRICT)

Control	Percentage
Traffic signal	19·8
"Stop" sign	1·1
"Give Way" sign	31·4
Uncontrolled	47·5
Authorised officer	0·2

TABLE 10.10   DISTRIBUTION OF FATAL AND SERIOUS ACCIDENTS BY SITE IN
GREAT BRITAIN AND OF ALL ACCIDENTS IN THE METROPOLITAN POLICE DISTRICT

Layout at accident site	Great Britain (1968)		*All* accidents Metropolitan Police District (1971) (percentage)
	Urban (percentage)	Rural (percentage)	
T and Y junctions	39·2	17·1	39·8
Cross-roads	17·5	7·9	20·7
Roundabout	1·3	1·0	2·9
Other junctions (driveways, etc.)	5·6	6·7	6·2
Total at junctions	63·6	32·7	69·6
Total non-junction	36·4	67·3	30·4
% Total accidents (1000's)	100·0	100·0	100·0
Nos.	(55)	(24)	(54)

TABLE 10.11.   MEAN ACCIDENT RATES AT JUNCTIONS WITH
NUMBERED WAYS (METROPOLITAN POLICE DISTRICT)

Type of junction	Mean accident rate per million vehicles		
	3-way	4-way	>4-way
Traffic signals	0·35	0·52	0·58
Roundabouts	0·27	0·46	0·55
Others	0·26	0·55	0·53

(Source for Metropolitan Police District Accident Tables: Annual Reports,
Road Accidents, Commissioner of Police, New Scotland Yard, London.)

Where all accident information is stored for computer analysis, routine programmes are prepared to enable records on individual locations to be extracted and tabulated in a convenient form and, if a graphical plotter is available, diagrammatic information can be displayed. Data is coded in a convenient breakdown from the detailed records from Stats. 19 forms with items as shown in Fig. 10.5 and locational information is often conveniently stored, using a grid coordinate system, based on the Ordnance Survey.

Alternatively, a comprehensive card index filing system can be employed, showing details of each accident with street and intersection locations differentiated by using colour coded cards. Each length of road between intersections is suitably divided into sectors and subdivided by type of route. It is also necessary to have a site sketch, showing the layout and principal features. Information can either be transcribed for manual extraction or punched onto the card for machine sorting.

In addition to computer and card index systems, it is essential that accident maps are also maintained with a cross-reference to the filed data. Maps quickly indicate danger points on the whole road system and should be read directly with flow, speed, lighting, traffic control and construction details of road surfacing and drainage. The engineer must also be acquainted with the effects of improvements and modifications in geometric layout together with other changes and, because these must be considered both in relation to accident rates and costs, carefully updated records must be maintained. Monitoring of before-and-after changes is thus continuously maintained and the most effective deployment of police manpower and any further detailed study work can be focused most efficiently within the total resources.

It is also important to recognise common features in accidents and to identify any chains of causal relationships that may, in order of build-up, lead to unsafe conditions. Stick diagrams can be drawn with a column for every accident and each row representing common identifiable accident factors. As accidents occur a symbol is inserted against appropriate rows and repeated factors can be detected by scanning each row. Any factor which is repeated 12 or more times in about 100 accidents, in a three-year period, is likely to occur in any other study period of the route or one with similar characteristics.

With the improved systems of data storage now in widespread use it has become possible to apply statistical techniques to accident monitoring by detecting changes as soon as they appear by continuous sample inspection. This basis of quality control seeks to ascertain causes of variation by determining which changes occur by chance and which have assignable causes. Indications that a site is moving outside predetermined statistical limits can be monitorial by using control charts for each separate attribute requiring consideration. The method enables a judgement to be made as to whether each updated set of statistics is of a different "quality" from previous ones.

Figures 10.6a–c illustrates other types of record, including a ledger record. The latter is useful but it should never replace accident maps, continuously displayed and commanding the engineer's attention as each new item of information is added to the record and control charts.

Conflict Studies

There are about ten damage-only accidents to each injury accident and a much larger number of near misses. It has been shown that irregular movements and actions are correlated with accident frequencies at the same location and can be used to study the inherent dangers and likely accident rate at a site. Simple conflicts, where one or more vehicles take evasive action, are better correlated with traffic flow. Serious conflicts arise where a driver has cause to decelerate rapidly, swerve violently or stop suddenly to avoid collision with another vehicle which leaves no time for normal manoeuvres. These serious conflicts are well correlated with accidents and 10 hours of study at a site will provide a good estimate, in most cases, of the likely accident rate, generally equivalent to 5 years of accident measurements. However, there is evidence of different injury rates for different movements and a greater conflict rate for elderly drivers.

ACCIDENT CAUSATION AND INJURY PREVENTION

There are obviously many ways in which road safety can be improved and accidents reduced, or their consequences minimised. But the most effective and appropriate measures can only be chosen after the causes of road accidents have been determined. The occurrence of an accident is not usually attributable to a single cause but to the combined effects of a

MINISTRY OF TRANSPORT
SCOTTISH DEVELOPMENT DEPARTMENT
WELSH OFFICE

REPORT OF ROAD ACCIDENT RESULTI

Form Stats. 19 (Rev. 1968)

CASUALTIES

CASUALTY CLASS　　1st 2nd 3rd 4th 5th 6th

Driver or rider	12	1
Passenger	11	
Pedestrian	0	

Of:—

Pedal cycle	1
Moped solo	2
Motor scooter solo	3
Motor cycle solo	4
Combination (m/p m/s, or m/c)	5
Car or taxi	6
Public service vehicle	7
Goods vehicle	8
Other vehicle	9

SEVERITY OF INJURY　2

Killed†	1
Seriously injured	2
Slightly injured	3

SEX OF CASUALTY

　　　　　　　　　　3-4

| Male | 12 |
| Female | 11 |

AGE in years†

CAR PASSENGER*

| In front seat | 12 |
| In rear seat | 11 |

PEDESTRIAN ACTION

| Crossing road at pedestrian crossing | 12 |
| Crossing road within 50 yds. of ped. crossing | 11 |　5
Crossing road elsewhere	0
In road, not crossing	1
Masked by stationary vehicle	2
On footpath or verge	3
On refuge or centre strip	5

PSV PASSENGER

| Boarding or alighting | 5 |

CAR OR OCCUPANT*

Safety belt in use	1
Safety belt fitted but not in use	2
Safety belt not fitted	3

VEHICLE OCCUPIED

　　　　　　　　6

First vehicle	1
Second vehicle	2
Third vehicle	3
Fourth vehicle	4
Fifth or subsequent vehicle	5

VEHICLES INVOLVED

REGISTRATION NUMBERS

1st .... 2nd ....
3rd........................... 4th ....

　　　　　　　　　　1st 2nd 3rd 4th
　　　　　　　　　　7　8　9　10
　　　　　　　　　　(7)　(7)　(7)

TYPE

MAKE　　　　11-12

MODEL OR SIZE　　13

SKIDDING

　　　　　　　　14

| Skidded | 12 |
| Jack-knifed | 11 |

TOWING & ARTICULATION

Articulated vehicle	1
Caravan	2
Other tow	3

VEHICLE DEFECTS　　15

Load	12
Tyres—report for process	11	12-0
Brakes	0	1-6
Lights, front	1
Lights, rear	2	16
Brake lights	3
Trafficators	4	12-0
Vision-glass wipers, washers	5	1-6
V.E. report requested	6	17
		12-0
		1-6

DRIVERS AND RIDERS

Vehicle: 1st 2nd 3rd 4th
SEX　　　　18

| Male | 12 |
| Female | 11 |

BREATH TEST

Positive	1
Negative	2
Not required	3
Failed to provide	4

LEARNER-DRIVER　19

| "L" driver | 11 |

DRIVER'S ACTIONS

Disobeyed junction control	1
Disobeyed double centre or offset line	2
Failed to give precedence at pedestrian crossing	3

DRIVER'S OR PASSENGER'S ACTION

| Opened door negligently | 4 |

　　　　　　　　　　1st 2nd

AGE (entered by Ministry)　20

MANOEUVRES

Entering or leaving layby	12
Entering or leaving hard shoulder	11	21
Reversing	0
Parked	1
Stopping	2
Starting	3
Turning round	4
Turning left or waiting to	5
Turning right or waiting to	6
Going ahead but held up	7
Going ahead overtaking moving or held up vehicle	8
Going ahead, other	9

OVERTURNING　　22

| Overturned | 11 |

PART DAMAGED

Front	1	23
Back	2
Left	3
Right	4
All four sides	5	24
None	6

SEATS OCCUPIED (CARS ONLY)*　25

Front Passenger	11
Rear: One passenger	1
Rear: Two passengers	2
Rear: 3 or more passengers	3

Vehicle: 1st 2nd
AGE GROUP (estimated)　26

Under 17 years	12
17 years	11
18 years	0
19 years	1
20 years	2
21 years	3
22–24	4
25–28	5
29–34	6
35–54	7
55–64	8
65 or over	9

*Report these items until 31.12.70, or at which date a review becomes operative.

Fig. 10.5.　Stats. 19 form. (Source: P. Harris, *Road accident tabulation language* (

ƏNAL INJURY

POLICE REFERENCE No.....................................

ATTENDANT CIRCUMSTANCES

E FORCE   27 28

L AUTHORITY   29 30 31

ƏF WEEK ....

32 33 34
Day Mth

35 36 37
Hour 5Min.

our clock)

ə CLASS
otorway standard 2   38
  3
  4
unclassified 5

39 40 41 42
ə NUMBER

ə LIMIT
ɔh or less 3   43
ɔh 4
ɔh 5
ɔh 6
ɔh 7

ə TYPE 44
~way in force 11
-way street 1
carriageway 2
r road 3

MARKINGS 45
ane markings 1
lanes 2
e lanes with offset
   double lines 3
nal three lanes 4
lanes 5
markings unknown 6

Ғ
ight 1
, with street lights
er 20 feet high, lit 2   46
, with street lights
der 20 feet high, lit 3
, street lights unlit 4
, no street lighting 5

WEATHER

Raining	1	47
Snowing	2	
Fog	3	
Other	4	

ROAD SURFACE CONDITION

Dry	1	
Wet	2	
Snow or ice	3	48

JUNCTION DETAIL

Roundabout	1	
'T' or staggered junction	2	
'Y' junction	3	49
Crossroads	4	
Multiple junction	5	
Other junction	6	
Using private drive or entrance	7	
Not at or within 20 yards of junction	8	

JUNCTION CONTROL

Authorized person	1	
Automatic traffic signal	2	50
Stop sign	3	
'Give Way' sign or marking	4	
Uncontrolled	5	

PEDESTRIAN CROSSING
(If on or within 50 yds.)

Manually controlled	1	51
Light-controlled at junction	2	
Light-controlled not at junction	3	
Uncontrolled	4	

MOVEMENTS BEFORE ACCIDENT   52

Stationary vehicle involved	11
One moving vehicle	1
Two moving vehicles, same direction	2
Two moving vehicles, opposite directions	3
Two moving vehicles, different roads	4
More than two moving, all same direction	5
More than two moving, same road, not all same direction	6
More than two moving, not all same road	7

CARD CLASS   53
(entered by Ministry)

SPECIAL CONDITIONS AT SITE

Dog in carriageway	12	
Other animal in carriageway	11	54 55 56
Object in carriageway	0	
Parked vehicle(s) (contributory)	1	
Automatic level crossing involved	2	
Lamp post hit	3	
Telegraph pole hit	4	

CLASS OF ACCIDENT

Fatal	1	57
Serious	2	
Slight	3	

LOCATION

58 59 60 61 62 63

†If a person under 15 is killed, attach or write below a brief account of the accident.

---

t LR 377, Road Research Laboratory, D.O.E.).

number of deficiencies or failures associated with the user, his vehicle and the road layout. Environmental conditions are also important, such as the road surface, and it is also apparent that weather and time of day will be of influence. Out of the total of road accidents about 1%, 2% and 15% occur in fog, snow and rain respectively. Night-time accident rates, for unlit streets, are about twice those of daytime; even under average street lighting conditions they are about 50% greater. In a study by the Department of Transportation and Environmental Planning of over 500 road accidents in the Birmingham area, it was found that 77% were attributable to multiple causes (environmental/vehicle/road user factors 16·4%, environmental/road user factors 48·8%, vehicle/road user factors 7·2%, and environmental/vehicle factors 4·8%) and only 23% to single causes (road user factors 12·4%, environmental factors 5·6% and vehicle factors 4·8%).

THE VEHICLE

Safety requirements for vehicles have become more specific in recent years, particularly as a result of the Federal Safety Requirements introduced in the U.S.A. The objectives of such regulations are to promote better vehicle safety by specifying component performance under impact conditions. However, vehicle factors are far less frequently the cause of accidents, although they are influential in the nature and severity of resulting injuries than either road user or environmental factors. Vehicle characteristics and defects (Table 10.12) are also contributory causes to accidents and some collisions arise as the result of vehicle breakdowns creating a hazard, even though they are not directly involved.

The principal vehicle factors directly causing accidents are due to inherent design limitations, or to defects resulting from a lack of maintenance, poor adjustment and the failure of important components, such as brakes, tyres and lighting. These lead to loss of control or hazard to other road users. Another important impediment, difficult to isolate from road user deficiencies, is visual impairment by the vehicle's body or through reduced visibility occasioned by ineffective cleansing of ice, snow, rain and dirt, and misting over of glazed areas. The frequency of junction manoeuvres increases in urban areas, and side and rear vision are of more direct consequence than in rural areas. Improved methods of cleansing and heating glazed surfaces, both cheaply and effectively, remain to be developed. All round visibility is very difficult to provide with larger and longer commercial vehicles but the cost of providing rearward closed circuit television, with an in-cab monitor, to replace mirror systems is now feasible. Whereas effective vehicle lighting has been developed it is not always installed, and undetected defects still

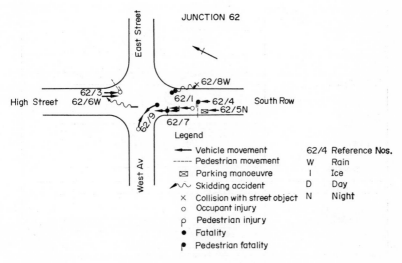

FIG. 10.6a. Spot map accident records.

occur without warning. However, accidents more often arise due to drivers using lighting inappropriate to the circumstances, for example, parking lights where headlamps are required, the authorised parking of vehicles in many areas without vehicle lighting and through glare to oncoming drivers.

Size differences between colliding vehicles affects the severity of injury, particularly in cases where heavy vehicles impact light vehicles. Night accidents frequently include cars and motor cyclists under-running the rear of heavy commercial vehicles, indicating basic deficiencies in their rear end illumination. New all-round lighting systems are being developed for heavy vehicles, and these also include repeater turning indicators

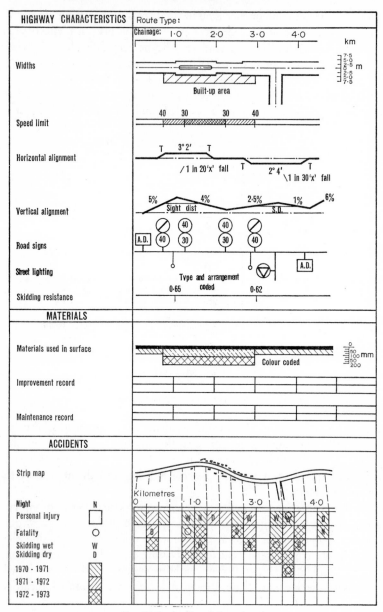

Fig. 10.6b. Accident ledger record.

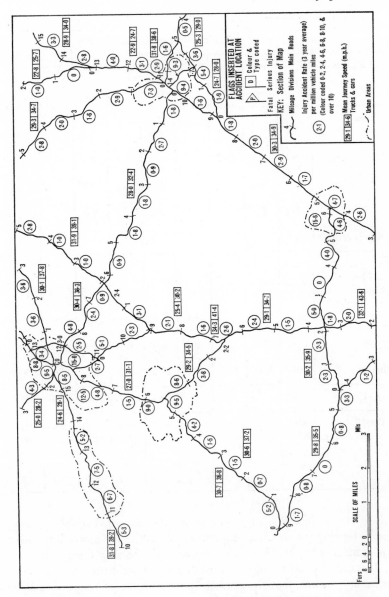

Fɪɢ. 10.6c. Accident rate map.

TABLE 10.12. REPORTED VEHICLE DEFECTS (METROPOLITAN POLICE DISTRICT)

Reported defects	Vehicle types (percentage defects)								
	Car	m/cycle, etc.	p/cycle	P.S.V.	Goods up to 1½ t	Goods 1½–3 t	Goods >3 t	Other	All
Vision:									
lights (front)	3·2	2·5	27·3		6·0	8·6	2·5	13·6	5·0
(rear)	2·9	1·3	22·7		4·3	12·1	4·9	4·5	4·5
(brake)	0·7	1·3			0·9	1·7	3·7		1·0
trafficators	2·0	1·2			3·4		1·2		1·8
wipers & other	5·3				0·9		1·2		3·3
Mechanical and body: Vehicle engineer's report	31·0	33·7		25·0	25·0	17·2	21·0	22·8	27·3
tyres	24·2	15·0	2·3	8·3	16·4	6·9	7·4	9·1	18·7
brakes	29·8	45·0	47·7	66·7	29·3	17·3	23·5	27·3	30·9
Load	0·9				13·8	36·2	34·6	22·7	7·5
Total %	100·0	100·0	100·0	100·0	100·0	100·0	100·0	100·0	100·0
No. of defects	587	80	44	12	116	58	81	22	1000

All vehicles involved in accidents = 87,667

along the vechicle's sides, obviating another hazard. Variable intensity brake lighting has been tried experimentally where the source brightness, or numbers of lights lit, is proportional to the braking force in use.

It is only by identifying the direct causes of accidents, and their contributory factors, that the correct apportionment of resources can be made, which lead to the most effective improvement in road safety. If vehicle defects have led to accidents at a particular site, no amount of road improvement will affect the situation.

Vehicle Lighting

For safe vehicle operation, a driver requires a clear view ahead, consistent with speed, and freedom from glare. Thus a compromise has to be made in the amount of off-side light directed at, or near, the horizontal in approaching headlamp beams. This is achieved by a lower beam setting; there are two principal systems in use, the Anglo-American sealed beam with a gradual cut-off and the European beam with a sharp cut-off. In most conditions, the latter specification has a superior performance. However, the sharper the cut-off the more accurately must the beam be aimed if glare is to be prevented. Tolerances are small and of the order $\pm\frac{1}{2}°$ and adjustments will be required for each load condition. This is not practical unless either self-levelling bodies or headlamps are incorporated as normal equipment.

External Vehicle Features

Pedestrians and cyclists are particularly vulnerable to certain types of injury, the extent of which is influenced by the external features of the vehicle, particularly from hard projections. Door catches, hinges, lamps, ornaments and bumpers may also entangle clothing and drag a victim forward. The mounting height of bumpers is also important in pedestrian accidents, either causing the victim to be rotated forwards, impacting the road and being run over, when set too high or, preferably, under-running with impact, absorbed by the vehicle's bonnet. While present types of bumpers do little to moderate the forces generated under high impact loads they serve to prevent excessive property damage in minor collisions. Many large vehicles, because of high body clearances, are very dangerous from the sides and rear, particularly to small cars and motor cyclists, and their high undersides should have wrap-around guard railing. External mirrors and ornaments (if permitted at all) should be rubber mounted and collapsible. Reflectorisation of further areas of the vehicle such as wheel discs and rear panels is invaluable at night, particularly on side roads and where there are parked vehicles.

Safety glass has for many years been a motor vehicle requirement. The two types in general use are laminated glass in the U.S.A. and toughened glass in Britain. The latter has a surface layer more resistant to fracture, but if damaged, the whole screen breaks up instantly into small round fragments which can cause severe eye or facial injury. As this effect is sometimes caused by sharp road chippings hitting highly stressed areas of the screen and causing complete loss of vision, manufacturers now treat the glass to produce a patch with a larger fragment pattern which allows limited forward vision. Since 1966, high penetration laminated glass has been manufactured in the U.S.A., reducing the incidence of head injuries, providing visibility without impact fragmentation and, because of its plastic interleaving, deceleration restraint when impacted. Laminated screens cost more and are far less effective overall than seat belts in reducing injury and, in any case, where seat belts are worn they prevent the majority of screen impacts.

Vehicle Tests

Improvements in the standard and design of vehicles, including auxiliary equipment, must be matched by adequate maintenance of the vehicle during its working life. Whereas vehicle testing cannot prevent sudden failures, such as lighting, the general awareness of vehicle owners to the need for adequate maintenance is emphasised by comprehensive testing of all vehicles at regular intervals. Researches have indicated that in Great Britain probably about 20–30% of personal injury accidents involve a vehicle having some deficiency present, although this is not necessarily causitive or readily apparent in statistics because of identification problems. However, some part of the estimated £320 million per annum cost of road accidents is attributable to vehicle defects and poor maintenance. Tables 10.13 and 10.14 show location of damage and severity and accident data by type of vehicle. It is apparent from these tabulations that all classes of vehicle should be regularly tested and that the costs are justifiable.

TABLE 10.13. LOCATION OF DAMAGE TO CARS IN
VARIOUS SEVERITIES OF ACCIDENT (1969)

	Severity of accident		
	Fatal	Serious injury	Slight injury
No. of cars	2551	31,063	81,818
Part damaged:			
Front (F)	31·5	30·0	23·5
Back (B)	1·6	3·7	6·3
Left (L)	4·3	5·0	5·0
Right (R)	4·0	5·5	6·1
FB	0·9	1·4	2·0
FL	12·4	9·7	8·5
FR	12·0	11·9	13·0
BL	0·7	1·1	1·4
BR	1·2	1·7	2·1
LR	0·6	0·5	0·5
FBL	0·9	0·6	0·6
FBR	0·8	0·8	0·6
FLR	5·8	3·9	2·2
BLR	0·7	0·4	0·3
All four sides	13·8	6·5	3·2
None	6·6	15·1	22·1
Not noted	2·2	2·2	2·6
Total %	100·0	100·0	100·0

(Source: *Road Research*, 1970. H.M.S.O.)

While the inspection of brakes, steering, suspension and chassis is generally required, other auxiliary equipment shows a higher defective rate, even for comparatively new cars and should be included in all comprehensive test schemes. These items include lights, direction indicators and windscreen wipers, all of which are concerned with driver visibility and affect situation perception. It would appear that a major test of all vehicles should be carried out annually and that a minor test of

TABLE 10.14.   ACCIDENTS BY VEHICLE TYPES AND REPORTED VEHICLE DEFECTS

Type of vehicle	% involved in accidents		% type reported defective	
	1962	1971	1962	1971
Goods: Up to 1½ t	7·1	8·2	1·4	1·6
1½–3 t	5·6	2·2	2·3	3·1
over 3 t	1·9	2·4	3·6	3·9
Motor-cycles, mopeds and scooters	24·3	10·2	1·8	0·9
Cars and taxis	43·3	64·4	0·7	1·0
Public service vehicles	4·6	5·9	0·3	0·2
Others	1·3	1·5	1·5	1·7
Pedal cycles	11·9	5·4	2·1	0·9

(Source: Metropolitan Police District Accident Data.)

the auxiliary equipment should be carried out more frequently or in spot checks. Testing stations need to be independent and carefully regulated and inspected.

The term *active safety* has been applied to those features of vehicle design developed for accident avoidance, e.g. brakes, steering, handling, controls, tyres, visibility and lighting. In certain circumstances these improved characteristics may lead to higher speeds and a greater range of manoeuvres, and so negate their safety advantages. As a consequence, it is difficult to determine the cost effectiveness of these developments which, in any case, probably yield diminishing returns for the next level of each improvement. There is a current acceptance that accidents will occur and resources are currently concentrated into *passive safety* improvements designed to ameliorate their consequences.

Braking

If a vehicle is suddenly stopped, any object, unless rigidly attached to the unit, will tend to continue in the original direction of travel with its initial velocity. A driver will impinge on the steering column with a force equal to the product of his mass and deceleration rate; the whole of the impact force is taken by the body without reduction of the energy absorbed in the deformation of the vehicle itself. Similar conditions occur with all passengers, although the front seat passenger who cannot absorb the shock forces by body bracing, in the same way as the driver, is the most vulnerable. Rear passengers usually escape more lightly because of the energy absorbing seat obstruction in front of them. Investigations show that for similar types of accident certain patterns of injury are repeated and these studies are embraced in a subject called the biomechanics of road accidents. Typical examples of injury are the driver's crushed thorax caused by impact with the steering wheel, fractured neck vertebrae resulting from rear end collisions, head injuries and lacerations caused by impact with car roofs, windscreens, door pillars and sun visors (see Fig. 10.7). The motor cyclist is susceptible to forehead injuries, which occur in many of their fatalities, and particularly to lower limb injuries. Table 10.15 shows, for an urban and rural environment, the distribution of injuries to body areas.

The incidence and severity of injury can be reduced by detailed study and the application of the emerging safety principles to the design of a "safe" vehicle. Human beings can survive large decelerations when the resulting forces are distributed over the body frame in a suitable way, with additional support for particularly "weak" areas. Large decelerations of $3000g$ can be withstood for periods as short as 1 or 2 ms, as shown in Fig. 10.8. In severe accidents, jerk decelerations with an onset rate of up to $300g/s$ have been survived. Figure 10.9 illustrates the deceleration/ time relationships for medium saloon cars impacting a solid object from a speed of 50 km/h.

Distribution of Injuries

Table 10.15 illustrates the general tendencies for injuries to be distributed over certain areas of the body for different categories of user.

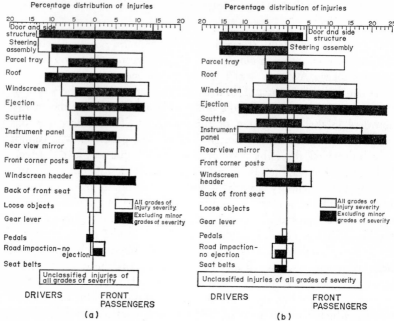

Fig. 10.7. Distribution of injuries to drivers and front seat passengers in (a) urban areas and (b) rural areas. (Source: C. P. de Fonseka, *Causes and Effects of Road Accidents*, Pt. 4. Department of Transportation and Environmental Planning, University of Birmingham, 1969.)

One of the worst features of road accidents is the high proportion of severe multiple injuries of victims, and the advanced surgical units required to restore the patient to some degree of useful health. Some part of the stabilising effect on death rates is due, in no small measure, to rapid and skilled treatment. However, motorway multiple accidents constitutes a growing problem, perhaps warranting aerial ambulance or mobile surgical facilities.

CRASH INJURY IMPROVEMENTS

In recent years an increasing amount of research work has been undertaken in the fields of crash injury relationships, and there is a greater

TABLE 10.15. TYPES OF INJURY, EXCLUDING MINOR, IN URBAN AND RURAL ACCIDENTS. (Source: C. P. de Fonseka, The injuries to road users, *Causes and Effects of Road Accidents* (Part 4). University of Birmingham, 1969)

Body area	Drivers		Front seat passengers		Motor cyclists		Pedestrians
	Urban	Rural	Urban	Rural	Urban	Rural	Urban
Head and neck	48·4	36·4	68·5	57·4	37·2	28·5	44·2
Thorax	10·6	12·2	8·5	12·8	3·2	0	3·3
Abdomen	1·5	4·1	–	6·4	2·1	0	3·3
Upper limbs	12·2	13·5	5·7	6·4	17·0	17·9	8·2
Lower limbs	27·3	33·8	17·3	17·0	40·5	53·6	41·0

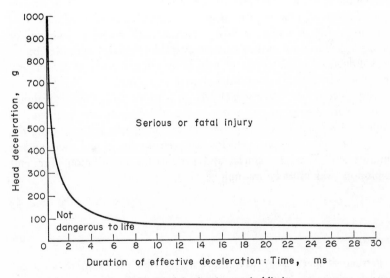

FIG. 10.8. Head deceleration survival limits.

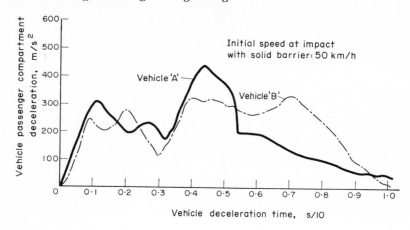

FIG. 10.9.   Deceleration pattern for vehicle impacts with solid object.

awareness among manufacturers of the part better designed vehicles can play in the reduction, and severity, of injury accidents. As vehicle owner-ship increases, so a larger proportion of all accidents involve vehicles only. It is important if design is to be drastically improved and new ideas incorporated as soon as they become available, that the individual buyer is as influenced in his choice of vehicle by the provision of these safety features, as by other such qualities as shape and power.

The objective of safety vehicle design is to improve the survivability of occupants during impact and to reduce the severity and frequency of injury. This is achieved by restraint of the occupants and absorbing the energy between colliding vehicles, between occupants and the vehicle's interior and between vehicles and pedestrians. In addition, fire and explosion risks must be minimised.

Impacts

Passenger safety is greatly improved by the provision of a strong protective passenger compartment with energy absorbing front and rear ends to produce a progressive collapse sequence at a controlled rate. The structural problem is to absorb the impact energy and reduce the decelerations of the restrained occupants to an acceptable level and rate. At the same time, the structure must maintain its integrity and limit the intrusion of the passenger compartment. The kinetic energy increases with the velocity squared; from 50 to 65 km/h represents an approximate doubling of the quantity, and thus deformation is considerably increased with each increment of speed. However, more than three-quarters of frontal injury inducing impacts are at speeds equivalent to barrier tests of up to 40 km/h. Strengthened and sloping bulkheads permit the passenger compartment to override the engine, which is now mounted well forward to absorb initial impact energy and leave a space ahead of the bulkhead for further movement. Alternatively smaller flat engines, suitable for under-floor installation beneath the rear passengers, are being developed.

In urban areas the greatly increased frequency of side impacts either with other vehicles, particularly at junctions, or street furniture requires careful design of doors and pillars to prevent excessive penetration. The main injuries from side impacts are to hips, pelvis and head and are most effectively reduced by strengthening the vehicle's outer skin and overlaying it with energy absorption padding beneath the interior facings. This must yield sufficiently to prevent injuries from the initial impact. Because vehicle bodies deform during impact it is important that occupants are protected from ejection by securing the doors integrally with the body shell with struts linking the locks and hinges.

A further cause of injury arises from vehicle collisions with structures, trees and street furniture. Severity rates are often high in such cases and all abutments, piers and trees should be set well back from the road margins, particularly on high-speed roads, or protected by guard railing. Annually more than 200 fatalities alone result from accidents involving light columns. Where there are few pedestrians light-weight columns should be installed with shear joints. These collapse under impact with little crushing of the vehicle. Similar designs are appropriate for use in road-sign gantries. Continuous wire cables linking the tops of each column have been successfully used in urban areas to reduce the risk to pedestrians of being struck by collapsible structures, but this adds to the cost and the wires are unsightly.

Passenger Compartments

The vehicle interior should be free from all sharp and projecting edges such as dashboards, parcel trays, mirrors and controls. Control buttons, switches, handles and keys must be recessed and all components and surfaces require padding. The padding materials need special energy absorption characteristics, which are achieved with moulded materials overlaying thin sheet steel to prevent the storage of energy to be subsequently applied in rebound. Yield loads are determined for particular vehicle areas and components by the threshold injury limits of limbs most likely to be involved in an impact. However, padding restraint is effectively limited to injury prevention in collisions below about 35 km/h. Steering systems should provide chest protection by absorbing energy in the steering column during collapse and this is aided by dishing and padding the hub of the steering wheel. Severe injuries can be caused by badly designed collapsible columns.

Air bag restraint systems have been developed using a sensor to detect a critical level of deceleration before triggering a high-pressure gas release, from a cylinder at 17 MN/m^2, to inflate a plastic bag stored in the dashboard or the steering boss. The bag is fully charged in less than 50 m/s (maximum 165 dBA), cushioning and enveloping the driver and nearside passenger as they move forward; deceleration and energy is absorbed by venting as the bag deflates. There are twin dangers from excessive inflation noise and the sudden rise in the pressure levels of enclosed vehicles and also the possibility of malfunction of the system causing inadvertent operation and panic reaction from the driver.

Two-wheeled Vehicles

While it is more difficult to protect the riders of motor or pedal cycles from impact injury, their general level of safety can be improved in numerous ways. Lack of stability leads to loss of control with the rider hurled into the road surface with unrestrained velocity. This problem can be partly overcome by adding small outrider wheels which operate automatically when the machine is inclined at critical angles. Improved ways of preventing the rider losing his seat, coupled with additional protection to the chest, arms and legs, can effectively limit injury severity.

Improved aids to rear vision and better methods of indicating turns are still needed. A possible system is to use an illuminated arrow head, pointing directionally as appropriate, mounted in a rectangular panel. Many pedal cycles have defective braking systems, often completely inoperable in wet weather, and lighting deficiencies. Safety standards applying to both design and operation are necessary, but to effectively improve pedal cycle equipment and reduce accidents it will probably require a licensing system with an annual inspection. It is also difficult to persuade young people to adopt safety aids even though these may be in their own best interests.

Tyres

Burst tyres give rise to widespread vehicle handling problems which are most marked with two-wheeled types. In a survey of motorway injury accidents tyre bursts, immediately prior to the accident, were present in about a tenth of car accidents but formed more than a third in the case of motor cyclists. The recent development of a total mobility tyre, by using a special lubricant and wheel rim and the self-stabilising steering systems, can do much to eradicate this danger.

SAFETY EQUIPMENT

Restraint

From a sample of 800 road accidents the R.R.L. showed that the overall ejection rate was 4%, but in fatal accidents about 30% of the victims had been ejected. In cars containing both ejected and non-ejected occupants about half of those ejected were killed compared to a fatality rate in the other groups of 27%. Injuries arise due to the ejected occupants striking parts of the vehicle, such as the windscreen, surround and the bonnet, before impacting the road surface or street furniture. Thus a considerable measure of protection is afforded to occupants by preventing ejection.

Seat Belts and Head Restraints

The most effective form of restraint is the seat belt, made up from webbing belts and straps and securely anchored to the vehicle structure through plates which distribute the loads over a sufficient area of anchorage. Connecting buckles must be simple to fix and adjust to the wearer, and rapid to release. The principal type in general use is the diagonal lap type, but full harness types and appliances for young children are also used. Lap type belts, while simpler to wear, are not satisfactory, particularly for front seat passengers, because of "jackknifing" with the wearers head likely to strike the knees or the interior with severe results. Restraint forces, which may reach a value of several thousand kilograms, must be distributed over the strongest and least vulnerable parts of the body and reach a yield condition at the threshold of severe injury. Hence limits have to be determined for all energy absorption systems, setting an average rate of load application and duration which is separately defined for different parts of the body. Test load conditions have indicated hip joint threshold injury levels from dashboard impacts of from 2–4 kN and 6 kN for chest injuries from steering assemblies. Belt stiffness is important and must be controlled to permit sufficient yield in the initial jerk, and reduce the onset deceleration rate, without permitting the dislodgement of the wearer. Nor must the belt stretch to such an extent as to cause the wearer to impact with the interior.

Seat belts have now been developed to an extent that they could, if correctly worn, halve the chance of serious injury. They also help to maintain driver control. Often initial glancing collisions are followed by serious secondary impacts, either with other vehicles or obstacles, due to the driver being thrown about the vehicle and losing control because of disorientation. However, despite the fact that well over 80% of cars are fitted with seat belts they are generally not worn. While the proportion of front seat occupants wearing seat belts has steadily increased on motorways over the last 10 years from less than a tenth to over a third, it still remains at the former figure on town roads. Because the majority of accidents occur on these shorter journeys in urban areas it is imperative that seat belts are worn at all times. Their lack of use is partly attributable to poor design and further research work is needed to improve comfort, accessibility and ease of adjustment. However, a more fundamental approach is required if user attitudes and apathy are to be overcome by voluntary methods. A marked reduction in fatal and serious accidents has resulted from the introduction of compulsory legislation, introduced in Victoria, Australia, in December 1971; legislation is also being enacted in France to be effective in 1973. It has been estimated that serious casualties in Great Britain would be reduced by between 10 and 15 thousand by similar measures. In Miami, U.S.A., drivers are encouraged to wear seat belts by having fines for driving offences reduced to a half if they are being worn at the time.

Recent developments include passive seat belts, which fit around the occupant automatically as he assumes his seated position or closes the car door, and seat belt interlock systems. The latter prevent the car being driven before the fastening of the belt unlocks the ignition circuit starter circuit, or the gear box. Load sensors may also be installed in the seats for similar purposes or to initiate a warning device.

Seats must be both secure from collapse and padded to prevent injuries to rear seat passengers in forward impact and include head support, preventing injury to occupants in rear end collisions. The maximum angle of neck distortion permitted for head-rests by U.S. and E.E.C. regulation is 45° for a 32 km/h rear impact and the head must be well supported at its centre of gravity (i.e. about eye level).

The poor performance of some such items of safety equipment as head-rests and children's restraint systems indicates the need for legislative control and carefully developed standards. Safety consciousness can only be fostered by ensuring adequate control of manufacture, sale and installation.

Crash Helmets

Head injuries are present in a major proportion of fatal and serious injury accidents to motor cyclists. These are generally skull fracture, where the injury is to the forehead or the back and sides of the head, particularly the right side facing the oncoming traffic. The design considerations for crash helmets, illustrated below, are similar to those for vehicle structures, where kinetic energy must be absorbed in a given distance by a padding material. If a motor cyclist has an impact speed of 50 km/h ($v = 13 \cdot 9$ m/s) and a head weight, w, of 5 kg, then:

$$\text{Kinetic energy} = \tfrac{1}{2}\,mv^2 = \tfrac{1}{2} \times \frac{w}{g}v^2 = \tfrac{1}{2}\,\frac{5}{9\cdot806}\,(13\cdot9)^2 = 49\cdot2 \text{ kgf/m}.$$

and, similarly, at 100 km/h ($27 \cdot 78$ m/s) K.E. $= 196 \cdot 7$ kgf/m.

Studies of survival suggest a limit of head deceleration, a, of $500g$, which is equivalent to a force of

$$F = \frac{w}{g} \times a = \frac{5 \times 500 \times g}{g} = 2500 \text{ kgf}$$

The time that this force acts is very short and measured in milliseconds. Kinetic energy absorbed by perfect padding $= (w/g)S$, where $S = $ distance moved through by the force F. Hence, the minimum ideal thickness of padding in the limiting conditions given is:

$$S_{50} = \frac{49 \cdot 2}{2500} = 0 \cdot 0197 \text{ m and } S_{100} = \frac{196 \cdot 7}{2500} = 0 \cdot 0787 \text{ m.}$$

The protective helmet consists of a hard shell with a suitable energy absorbing lining. It must also be correctly balanced, lightweight, and of good appearance so as to prevent fatigue and to encourage use. The helmet must not cause head rotation or move during impact, and for this purpose requires correctly adjusted straps. After impact, due to the compressibility of the absorbing material and possible damage to the hard shell, the helmet must be discarded.

Even at low speeds impact forces are high and the need to wear protective headgear is apparent. Unfortunately, many riders of scooters and motor cycles ignored or did not appreciate these dangers and legislation is now invoked to make the wearing of a helmet compulsory.

THE ROAD USER

All road users have an important part to play in the prevention and reduction of accidents. While accidents are unlikely to arise from a single cause, the road user is of predominant influence. In some instances, a specific lack of skill or the appropriate experience to deduce the correct significance from a series of events leads to errors, wrong decisions or actions thus indicating the importance of training and educational methods. The most frequent road-user errors are excessive speed for the conditions, failure to look, misperception and panic reactions from the inexperienced. Drivers of heavy commercial vehicles, and car drivers between the ages of 30 and 65, are less likely to make road user errors than other groups. This indicates that among young drivers it is lack of experience

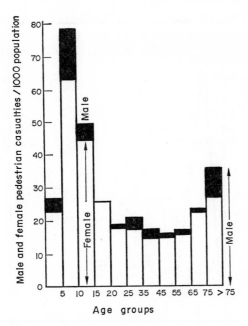

Fig. 10.10. Except for the 15 to 20 age group, the accident rate is higher for males than females (Metropolitan Police Area).

and emotional maturity that leads to speeding, exhibitionism and other traits which cause the group its high accident rate. Generally, in all accidents, males have a higher involvement rate than females, although the differences diminish with age increases above 50. Accident rates are lowest for the 30–50 age group. Alcohol is present in many of those involved in all types of accident and, again, males have a higher involvement rate than females as indicated in Fig. 10.10.

However, in any society certain categories require special attention and protection because of age and disability. Figure 10.11 shows that amongst pedestrians the young and old are particularly accident prone and similar characteristics apply to vehicle drivers. The over 65 group are more likely to meet with an accident during the winter months, whereas the summer

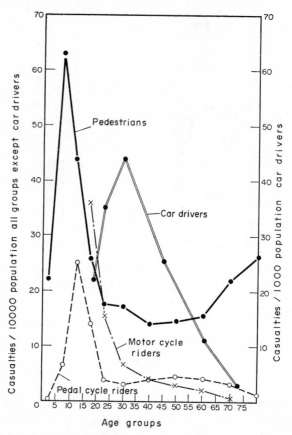

FIG. 10.11. Casualty rates for various categories of road user for total population.
(Metropolitan Police Area).

period contains the greater proportion of children's accidents. The ageing
process affects the faculties of perception, making users increasingly
susceptible to error after later middle age. Children act on impulse and
while rigorous education at school and home can do much to reduce the

tragic consequences, the traffic engineer can also assist by establishing the best routes to schools, and ensuring that adequate warning and control exists for the vehicle driver approaching crossing points. In some respects the greater problem is posed by the aged who, through inattention and physical impairment, suffer cruelly in this motor age.

As previously mentioned, town layout and design of new areas can largely overcome these problems but, as existing roads get busier, only the provision of better controlled crossing points and segregation policies can be effective. Many of the deficiencies in knowledge, erroneous practices and attitudes leading to poor performance can be improved, if not rectified, by a more thorough use of the press, radio and television. Further research is required to ascertain the type of programme that is most influential and appropriate to the many diverse groups of road users, but the costs of such work seems small in relation to the possible benefits.

Location of Accidents

The type of accident and its configuration is highly correlated to the type of route and, thus, the nature of user activities. Side collision and striking parked vehicles occur more frequently on secondary roads. As route importance increases, the frequency of rear end and multiple vehicle collisions also increases. Most accidents take place at junctions, on curves, at gaps in dual carriageways, at pedestrian crossings, private driveways and bus stops. Sight distance factors, skidding, signs and marking deficiencies are causal factors most frequently found in urban accidents and accounting for more than half the total. The incidence of involved vehicles increases in rural areas as does the number of head-on collisions, and also singly involved vehicle accidents. Head-on collisions show an increase with a decrease in route importance, i.e. with narrower roads.

Accidents are more likely at junctions than elsewhere and, in urban areas, often involve pedestrians masked by stationary and occasionally moving traffic. In rural areas, the overall severity rate increases due to the higher speed impacts, and the proportion of pedestrian accidents falls. Over three-quarters of all pedestrian accidents take place within $1\frac{1}{2}$ km of the victim's home and, for the younger than 5 age group, within less

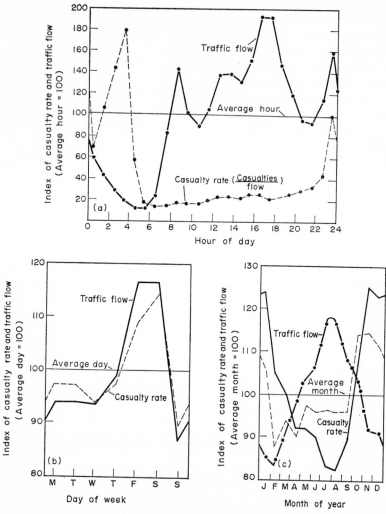

FIG. 10.12. The distribution of accidents in time and in relation to traffic flow. (Baseline values for *average* casualty rates (a) 43·2, (b) 99·8, (c) 101·3.)

than a few hundred metres of their home. About half of all accidents of other groups are within a radius of 800 m of their homes. While areas of lower social class are generally indicative of higher pedestrian accident rates, it is not so different for the group of young children, or those over 65 years, where awareness and impairment are predominant factors influencing the accident rate. After middle age there is a greater likelihood that the predestrian casualty will have been struck by a two-wheeled vehicle, indicating an increasing perceptual and dynamic visual acuity impairment with age.

The distribution of accidents is influenced by time of day, day of week and season of the year, as shown in Fig. 10.12 (a, b and c). Children of school age are more likely to have an accident between 8–9 a.m. and 3–5 p.m., and adult females in the later morning, whereas those to adult males are highest in the late evening. All of these characteristics can be expected from the type and frequency of journeys undertaken by each group.

Driving Licences

It is doubtful whether driving tests today are suitably comprehensive; a licence obtained in a lightly trafficked rural area does not necessarily indicate ability to drive in large cities or in other environments. In the establishment of test standards such conditions as driving at night, the type and power of the vehicle to be used, and vehicle control and experience in skid and motorway conditions should be assessed. In addition adequate physical standards must be ensured before the issue of a licence. It is not a matter of restricting the individual from lawful use of the road but ensuring that his experience is matched to today's conditions and not those of a quarter of a century ago. The need for revision tests at regular intervals should also be seriously considered.

The effects of disabilities on road user performance are not fully known and there is little knowledge concerning the compensations that a driver may make if his reactions, judgement, sight or hearing are impaired. There is little doubt that psychological aspects of behaviour, such as anger fear, fatigue, worry, alcohol and drugs (stimulants and depressants are contained in many medicines), considerably modify normal performance.

S

It is still difficult to include such aspects in medical or other examinations despite their potential contribution to improved safety by eliminating badly adjusted drivers. Diseases with a slow onset rate and also the detection of conditions leading to sudden failures in major body functions are not easily identified. However, more rigorous standards would perhaps result in a greater awareness in society that physical and mental fitness are important elements in a complex task like driving, and that the granting of a licence is a privilege bestowed by society.

Accident Proneness

In most fields of human activity there are persons subject to more than their fair share of accidents and it appears reasonable, from the available studies, that this is also the case in road accidents. The difficulty is that accident proneness may only occur in short time periods and if these are distributed a few hours at a time throughout the year any investigation, even if carried out with large samples over an extended time period, would run into great difficulty in detecting and determining the effect of this factor. Serious lapses and mistakes, and occasionally minor ones, sometimes occur in a chance combination of other circumstances and an accident results for which the offender is punished with a jail sentence but does not receive corrective training. Driver correction centres for accident repeaters and traffic violators should be set up with specialist medical personnel and training facilities as has been initiated in Scandinavia. If minor offenders were also to undergo a form of compulsory evening training the development of more serious or repeated offences might be prevented, or at least reduced.

Research at the R.R.L. has attempted to discriminate between safe and non-safe drivers. Four categories of driver were identified after observing their performance on a drive over a test route. The observations included near accidents, use of rear view mirror, number of manoeuvres, and overtaking and overtaken responses. Each driver was assigned to the following categories:

(i) Safe (S): very few accidents, used proper signals and made no unusual manoeuvres. Overtaken frequency equalled overtaking frequency.

(ii) Dissociated Active (DA): many near accidents and dangerous manoeuvres, casual driving, few signals and infrequent use of rear mirror. Overtaken more frequently than overtaking others.

(iii) Dissociated Passive (D.P.): a low level of awareness, driving in the centre of the road and with little speed adjustment whatever the conditions. Overtaken less frequently than overtaking others.

(iv) Injudicious (I): poor distance estimation and unusual manoeuvres, over-use of rear mirror and frequent near accidents. Poor overtaking manoeuvres.

Psychological tests have also been used to discriminate between safe and unsafe drivers and generally indicate that the former tend to come from the stable introvert (reliable) group whereas the latter lie in the extrovert neurotic (aggressive) band. Other researches have shown that accident repeaters exhibit conflict reactions to authority, again with aggression traits, and are likely to be socially maladjusted with a history of truancy and disciplinary problems in school and institutions. Unfortunately, driving is an activity that allows the maladjusted individual opportunities for overt aggressions in overcoming inner social conflicts and frustrations.

Accident repeat drivers have also been identified by reference to sociological measures; research workers have shown that as a group that they were far more likely to be known to credit agencies, social services, public health clinics and the courts. In general many of the studies have not been conclusive and in some cases the evidence has been contradictory with many anomalies indicated. Because of the unreliability of such work it is not possible to apply the methods widely to the general population, but they are of use for assessing the suitability of individuals for the professional work of driving public transport and heavy goods vehicles.

ROAD LAYOUT AND IMPROVEMENTS

Traffic Segregation

Efficient and economic road transport is largely dependent on road layout. Efficiency cannot be achieved if the road user is frequently involved in road accidents, but fortunately those design provisions that improve traffic flow often simultaneously reduce accidents. Table 10.16

indicates the main categories of road accident in relation to types of road. A traffic engineering principle of over-riding importance is the segregation of traffic categories by function and in space and time, e.g. the segregation of vehicle and pedestrian, of different classes of vehicle and of different types and purposes of vehicular movement.

TABLE 10.16.   DISTRIBUTION OF ACCIDENTS BY ROAD CLASS: LONDON, METROPOLITAN POLICE DISTRICT (Source: J. C. Cutts, The Metropolitan Police Accident Intelligence System, P.T.R.C. Conference, 1973).

Type of road	Accidents/km	Proportion of total in category	Proportion of total accidents
Motorway	6·74	0·24	0·41
Class A	17·69	13·02	56·84
Class B	9·32	4·82	11·57
Class C	5·51	7·49	10·26
Unclassified	1·11	74·43	20·92
All roads	4·63	100·00	100·00

While many of the above reasons for the application of wider segregation control may seem to lie outside road safety considerations, important benefits would nevertheless accrue because of a reduction in accidents. A central precept of traffic safety is the compatibility of user characteristics to achieve simplified operation and performance and, hence, reduce accident potential. When accidents do occur their consequences are minimised where there is a greater similarity between the elements involved.

Lighting

As has been shown in an earlier chapter, human performance, particularly visual observation, is markedly poorer at night, and the driver requires additional reaction/perception time even under good street lighting. Accident frequency increases during the hours of darkness, but considerable reductions in accident rates can be achieved after the installation of effective street lighting on traffic routes. A change from poor lighting to that recommended for traffic routes has reduced casualty accidents, in urban areas, by about one-third. The amount of light needed is based on an analysis of visual and task performance and on systems efficiency, but there would appear to be diminishing returns for investments above the recommended levels.

The decision whether to install street lighting or not can be based on the following relationship:

$$L_C \geqslant KNA_C$$

where L_C = the annual cost of an installation,

        K = the fractional reduction in accidents expected with the lighting installation (0·25 to 0·45),

        N = the average number of injury accidents before lighting installed,

        A_C = the average cost to the community of an injury accident (see Table 10.3).

For values of A_C = £1600, L_C = £550 per kilometre and K = 0·3, the value of N is equal to one injury accident per year for urban traffic routes. Similarly, a volume warrant for the lighting cost (L_C)

$$= 365 D_V V_N RKA_C S$$

where D_V = annual average daily volume,

        V_N = the fraction of the annual average daily volume carried at night,

        R = the general night injury accident rate (av. $1·7/10^6$ veh km),

        S = the length of the installations.

Visual improvements can also be made by better edge demarkation using reflectorised surfaces and markers. Better methods of adjusting headlamps to eliminate mis-aim and reduce glare are still required, but meanwhile better driver education is needed to encourage drivers to correctly use present systems and maintain them effectively. Road signs indicating the type of lighting required, might clarify current ambiguities of practice. On well-lit streets there is still an advantage in vehicles using a larger sized light source but of lower intensity than the current dipped beam. These so-called dim-dip lighting units have already been developed and are referred to as dim-dip systems. It is also technically feasible to automatically control the vehicle's lights with a device which measures the illumination from street lighting.

Speed

Investigation of mean speed in relation to accident rate tends to show that roads with a higher mean speed have a lower accident rate than roads with a low mean speed, e.g. motorways and wide open sections of two-lane rural roads. Most drivers operate their vehicle in a manner consistent with their assessment of road layout and prevailing traffic conditions and the majority correctly interpret the hazards of a particular situation by reducing speed. The fact that mean speeds are lower in itself indicates a potentially more dangerous situation likely to involve a greater risk to the driver and indeed these intrinsically more dangerous areas show a higher accident rate. A generalised expression relating accident rate and speed is shown below:

$$r = 3 \cdot 3 - 0 \cdot 027S$$

where r is a measure of all injury accidents per million vehicle kilometres on rural roads, and S is taken as the mean speed over the length of road considered (km/h). However, it can also be shown that suitably selected and enforced speed limits generally reduce both speeds and the accident rate.

Double White Lines

The prohibition of overtaking at bends and summits is indicated by double-white-line marking. They can be marked either based on the criterion for safe stopping distance, or for the time required to complete an overtaking manoeuvre at various speeds. In the latter case the T.R.R.L. chose the 65th percentile speed for overtaking instead of the 85th percentile normally used for the computation of safe stopping distance. The required visibility distance, D, in metres, can be evaluated as follows:

$$D = 1 \cdot 23\overline{V} + 0 \cdot 0173\overline{V}^2$$

where $\overline{V}$ = mean speed of vehicles (km/h). For site values less than D a prohibitory line is required; it is also suggested that the minimum gap between prohibitory sections should be not less than D, as determined above, instead of the minimum 61 m (200 ft) with the safe stopping distance used as criterion. A surprising difference in British practice is not to generally use prohibitory double line markings in urban areas and there is undoubtedly a prima facie case for their use to separate directional flows.

Alignment

The relationship of road width, curvature and sight distance all have particularly marked effects on the occurrence of accidents. In general it is more sensible to consider these factors together as they have a psychological effect on the driver and influence his selection of running speed. For instance the widening of a narrow, tortuous and badly aligned road would probably reduce accidents if speed remained the same after the improvement. However, speeds will generally increase because of a greater feeling of well being and the accident rate may then show an increase. Other improvements, such as superelevation and resurfacing taken in isolation also have a similar tendency to increase the accident rate. From considerations of safety it is wise to assess speed conditions likely to occur after each type of improvement and to check that lane widths, sight distances and surfaces are all satisfactory for any estimated increase in speed.

Road Surface

The selection of the correct road surface materials to suit traffic needs and avoid skidding accidents (see Table 10.17) is no less important than for construction purposes. Sites which have surfaces with a low sideways force coefficient are many more times liable to skidding accidents than other comparable sites which have high values. It is essential where

TABLE 10.17.   SKIDDING ACCIDENTS 1971
(METROPOLITAN POLICE DISTRICT)

Road condition	Skidding accidents as % total accidents	% total accidents in road condition	% skidding accidents in road condition
Dry	2·1	76·2	2·8
Wet	4·1	23·4	17·4
Snow/ice	0·2	0·4	53·2
Total	6·4	100·0	6·4

TABLE 10.18.   ACCIDENT STUDIES MADE ON METROPOLITAN ROAD JUNCTIONS;
41 sites treated with epoxy resin and calcined bauxite; summary of results
from October 1968 to end of September 1969*

	Before	After	Change, %
Total accidents	288	200	–31
Total casualties	337	258	–23
Accidents on wet road	105	29	–72
Accidents on dry road	183	171	– 7
Rear-end collisions	37	10	–73
Loss of control	23	7	–70
Crossing collisions	54	31	–43
Turning collisions	23	18	–22
Pedestrian accidents	76	65	–14
Other accidents	75	69	– 8

*During the same period, accidents in the Metropolitan Police District as a whole
increased by 1·5 per cent.

braking or turning is frequent, such as at roundabouts, curves and inter-sections, at approaches to bus stops, pedestrian crossings and on gradients, that suitable road surfaces are provided. Special surfacings of high skid-ding resistance have been developed for use at particularly dangerous sites, as shown in Tables 10.18 and 10.19. The objective is to produce a highly abrasive surface by using aggregate sizes of 3 mm ($\frac{1}{8}$ in.) and an epoxy resin binder. Calcined bauxite aggregates, which have favourable properties both in lightness of colour and resistance to polishing, are frequently used where the cost is justified. The regularity of surfaces also influences vehicles stability on high-speed roads and irregularities may cause the ponding of water.

Surface water run-off is critical in the avoidance of immersed aggregate surfaces and in the occurrence of mist spray. Selection of surface materials

TABLE 10.19. ACCIDENT STUDIES ON 34 PEDESTRIAN CROSSINGS TREATED WITH RESIN BAUXITE; summary of results up to June 1970 for periods of 2 to 12 m

	Before	After	Change, %
Total accidents	104	67	−36
Pedestrians on crossing	46	29	−37
Pedestrians not on crossing	7	5	−29
Rear-end collisions	30	6	−80
Loss of control	3	1	−67
Bus passenger accidents	9	9	No change
Other accidents	9	17	−89
Wet road accidents	49	19	−61
Dry road accidents	55	48	−13

(Source, Tables 10.18 and 10.19: L. W. Hatherly and D. R. Lamb, Accident preven-tion in London by road surface improvements, *Traff. Engng. and Control*, **12**(10), 1971.)

is also a factor in street lighting effectiveness. Recently developed experimental surfaces are permeable, allowing surface water to penetrate to an impermeable lower level in the pavement before passing to the outer edges, and considerably reduce mist spray and improve lighting characteristics in wet conditions.

Margins

Obstructions close to the road margins, besides reducing passing clearance distances and decreasing capacity, also cause greater accident potential and severity. Permanent obstructions which are very dangerous are street lighting columns, telegraph poles, bollards and trees. With the exception of bollards, which are now of a light-weight construction, all the other types of street furniture are frequently of large mass and produce high impact forces with rapid decelerations. Hence, fatal and severe injury risks are great, even at the relatively low speeds drivers adopt in icy conditions. The effective reduction in this type of accident can only be achieved by allowing the driver in trouble the maximum amount of time to avoid the obstructing object and to reduce impact speed. The greater cost of longspan cantilever brackets for street lighting can be offset by the reduction in numbers and severity of vehicle accidents. Trees must be planted well clear of carriageway edges, but if adjacent to shoulders or sited in narrow central reservations on existing roads they should be protected by guard railings, banks, shrubs or impenetrable thorn hedges.

Temporary obstructions, such as parked vehicles, result in many accidents to all classes of road user, particularly at night, where lights, especially those of the cyclist, are often not powerful enough to distinguish parked vehicles from their background. The opening of car doors has further perils for both cyclists and motor cyclists. Relatively high speeds are reached by pedal cyclists on down grades and their poor braking coupled with inferior lighting makes them very prone to accidents. Pedestrians shielded from view by vehicles and stepping on to the carriageway by day or night do not allow adequate time for a driver to react, even at speeds as low as 15 km/h. All main roads, especially those carrying mixed traffic and pedestrians, should have clear margins free from parked vehicles and vertical obstructions such as bridge parapets, piers, wall abutments and street furniture. These should be set back from the pavement edges by at least 3 m and, where this is not possible, special precautions in the form of deflector rails and other individually designed features should be provided.

Warning and Control Design

Information can be conveyed to the driver in many ways as explained in Chapter 9. Besides the usual visual means drivers are well alerted by vibratory and audio signals which can be induced by specially designed warning devices, set into the road surface at the approach to decision or hazard areas. The principal types are either constructed from alternating areas of rough and smooth road surface (rumble areas) or by using a sequence of raised strips (jiggle bars). Such devices are designed in relation to their intended purpose, which ranges from inducing a mild to severe sensation, dependent on the degree of warning required, the types of vehicle in the traffic stream (some types of warning for heavy vehicles may create a hazard in themselves to a motor cyclist) and site speeds of vehicles. Changes in the regularity, size and pitch of the warning may also be designed as particular manoeuvres are performed or as prohibited zones are approached. Jiggle bars usually range from 10 to 15 mm in height with a width variation of from 50 to 200 mm.

The propriety of some control devices has been questioned and this includes the speed bump or so-called "sleeping policeman". Care has to be taken that they are appropriate to the situation because the substitution of one hazard for another, albeit of lower consequence, can still have dangerous repercussions. If impacts are too high track alignment, suspension and tyres can be damaged and lead to subsequent failure. The bumps, or ridges, set across the road are usually about 100 mm high and designed to be crossed safely and without discomfort at from 10 to 20 km/h but with increasing discomfort at higher speeds. Adequate warnings, both by day and night, are required, but there is still a danger that these may fail or strangers to a district will not see the sign and be injured or unwittingly damage their vehicle in consequence. Experiments of warping the pavement to produce uncomfortable sensations at incorrect speeds have also been shown to be feasible, but are usually only applicable to single categories of vehicle because of suspension differences.

These require different wave forms to cause similar effects between different vehicle types, although some vehicles may actually be at risk in their normal operating mode even at the requisite speed.

Warning horns, bells and lights have also been used at dangerous sites where vehicles, for instance, may be cornering at too high a speed and detectors in the road surface trigger a speed comparator before switching on the warning and re-setting. Similarly sensors, mounted on the front of vehicles, have been developed to give in-cab warnings of ice-forming conditions on the road surface.

EFFECTIVE MEASURES FOR IMPROVING SAFETY

The effects of road improvements are assessed by statistical analysis of before and after studies of accident data records by comparing the number of accidents which would have been expected had no change taken place. Thus sites which have basically similar characteristics to the improved site, both in terms of geometry and traffic, are used to derive a scale of comparison known as a "control". The differences between the expected rate from the control and the actual rate are tested for statistical significance, often using the chi-squared distribution. If the observed and expected frequencies of the ith class are O_i and E_i, then

$$\chi^2 = \sum \frac{(O_i - E_i)^2}{E_i}$$

The smaller the value of χ^2 the closer is the agreement between the expected and observed frequencies and the more likely that the changes have resulted by chance.

As an example of a simple case, accidents at an improved junction, over a three-year before and after period, were 25 and 14 respectively. The accidents for all junctions in the area over the same two periods were 400 and 450 respectively. Hence

$$\chi^2 = [14 - 25(450/400)]^2/25(450/400) = 7 \cdot 09.$$

The reduction in accidents is highly unlikely to have occurred by chance as χ^2 (1 degree of freedom) is significant at the 1% level (6·64) found from tables of the χ^2 distribution.

Highway Engineering Factors

A good running surface avoids the need for sudden corrections to the vehicle's controls and consistent and stable running is maintained. It should be considered in association with surface texture with attention directed to the design requirements at dangerous sites such as roundabouts, intersections, approaches, bus stops, pedestrian crossings, sharp curves, steep gradients and also for street lighting purposes. Surface drainage must be adequate for prevailing weather conditions and crossfalls adjusted to run-off conditions and good surface regularity to prevent water ponding and the formation of ice. The carriageway cross-section must contain adequate lanes and widths for the traffic volumes, speeds and vehicle types and high-speed roads should have clear margins including shoulders and no stopping and waiting regulations. In such cases parking areas must be provided at suitable intervals on recreational routes. Pedestrian control with vertical kerbs are needed where footpaths abut carriageways and guard railing should be installed at hazard crossing points.

The general alignment must be compatible with traffic conditions by selecting appropriate horizontal and vertical curvature, and sight distances for the speeds, vehicle types and traffic volumes.

Traffic Engineering Factors

It is necessary on high-speed roads to have full access control (see Table 10.20). Driveways should have open visibility splays to protect pedestrians and other traffic. Service roads should be provided whenever possible, particularly for commercial and industrial premises. Bus routes should have laybys separated from through pavements and with speed change lanes on high-speed roads. Junctions are the most frequent site of accidents accounting for about two-thirds of fatal and serious injury accidents in urban areas. Mean rates are shown earlier in Table 10.11. At-grade intersections should have rights of way established with effective control measures, especially the absolute prohibition of parking and loading operations. Channelisation can be used to simplify drivers' choice and to separate decision points in time and space. Protected storage lanes are necessary at sites with large numbers of turning movements. Grade

TABLE.10.20.   EXAMPLES OF ACCIDENT RATES IN THE U.S.A. BY
TYPE OF ACCESS CONTROL

Type of access control	Number per 100 million vehicle kilometres (miles)			
	Accidents		Fatalities	
	Rural	Urban	Rural	Urban
None	206 (332)	846 (526)	5·4 (8·7)	2·5 (4·0)
Partial	131 (211)	798 (496)	3·8 (6·1)	2·9 (4·6)
Full	94 (151)	299 (186)	2·1 (3·3)	1·2 (2·0)

TABLE 10.21.   RATIO OF ANNUAL SAVINGS IN ACCIDENTS TO COSTS OF MINOR
IMPROVEMENTS

Type of improvement	Annual savings in accidents $(\pounds)$ / Cost of work $(\pounds)$
Improved markings and signs	19·6
Junction improvements	2·5
Installation of signals	2·3
Carriageway improvements, realignment and visibility	1·0
Provision of centre lanes for right turning vehicles	0·7

separated interchanges require adequate signs properly located and with
ramp heating on steep gradients and important turning roadways. Con-
trasting surfaces (colour or texture) should be provided for manoeuvre
areas. Full warning systems are required on important routes to indicate
breakdowns, accidents, fog, ice, etc., and should also indicate speed
limits varied to suit the circumstances. Closed circuit television can be

used for monitoring traffic behaviour at key points and information relayed to mobile police patrols or directly to variable message signs.

Good street lighting is essential on all traffic routes with reflectorised edge, lane and warning marks. High levels of illumination are needed at pedestrian crossings. Reflectorised and/or illuminated signs and street lighting must be well maintained if they are to be effective. Anti-glare planting or screening should be provided on dual carriageways without street lighting. Good road marking encourages consistency in driver performances provided that it is sited in relation to operating conditions and adequately maintained. Examples of improvements yielding high benefits for low costs are shown in Table 10.21.

Education and Road Safety

All citizens should be trained to be good road users at all stages of their lives. The training system will start at home when the young child, accompanied by his parents, learns the rudiments of kerb drill and pedestrian behaviour. This should be followed during the next 10 years of active school education, by further regular talks and demonstrations of road safety. The middle years of school instruction will concentrate on the young cyclist and time should be found in the latter stages to interest, teach and instruct in the fundamentals of driving. If special road circuits were set up to allow all learner drivers to carry out their first instruction away from the main flows of traffic much could be achieved, and senior school children could also have courses of driving on these tracks included in the curriculum. The cost may appear high but not when compared to the figure of nearly £400 million per annum in accidents on the road system, besides the untold suffering caused by the death and injury of road users. If this sum were looked upon as a profit to an individual firm then it would justify a considerable investment. The reduction of accidents is one of the most pressing problems facing society today and any improvement represents a real profit to a civilised nation. Our national accident record is not bad when compared to others, despite the often crowded and often inadequately financed road system. Worthy enough at least to receive a greater government and local contribution to road safety through positive aid. The search for solutions is sterile if all that is achieved is an attribution of blame and the punishment of some of the "guilty". Road safety must be paid for by investment in facilities and by a limitation of individual freedoms. The road user has important responsibilities to his fellow citizens when making use of the road.

Generally, in all road safety matters, compulsion is a poor substitute for public acceptance and has many attendant enforcement problems besides moral implications. While the individual may have a personal right to shoulder the consequences of injury or death, for instance by not wearing seat belts, it is not a right to impose the ensuing costs of treatment and earnings loss on society for what may have been an avoidable event. Similar arguments apply to behavioural aberrations in the driving tasks, in the upkeep and maintenance of vehicles and to authorities whose responsibility it is to provide a safe environment compatible with the circumstances. The construction of motorways with no central protection to prevent vehicles out of control crossing into the path of an innocent family is an example of the failure of authorities to shoulder the full consequences of building motorways, even though this particular danger is a well-known hazard which has occurred on such routes for more than 40 years. Responsibility for road safety lies initially with authority but finally rests on the individual.

FURTHER READING

ALLEN, T. M. (1965) *A Factor Analysis of Accident Records*, H.R. Record 7 Highway Research Board, Washington.

BAKER, R. F. (1971) *The Highway Risk Problem. Policy Issues in Highway Safety*. Wiley Interscience.

BLACKMORE, F. C. (1970) Accident risks and capacity of single-level intersections. Tenth Int. Study Wk. in Tr. & Saf. Eng., WTAO, London.

BLAIR, I. (1969) *The Traffic Environment. Causes and Effects of Road Accidents* (Part II). Dept. of Transportation and Environmental Planning, University of Birmingham.

BULL, J. P. (1968) International comparisons of road accident statistics. *J. Inst. Highway Engrs.* **15**(3).

CHRISTIE, A. W. (1968) The night accident problem and the effect of public lighting. *Pub. Ltg.* **33**(141).

COHEN, J. and PRESTON, B. (1968) *Causes and Prevention of Road Accidents*. Faber & Faber.

DAWSON, R. F. F. (1971) Current costs of road accidents in Great Britain. TRRL Report LR 396. The Transport and Road Research Laboratory.

DEPARTMENT OF SCIENTIFIC AND INDUSTRIAL RESEARCH (1963) *Research on Road Safety*. Road Research Laboratory, H.M.S.O.

DUFF, J. T. (1971) The effects of small road improvements on accidents. *Traff. Engng. & Control*, **13**(6).

ECONOMIC COMMISSION FOR EUROPE (1968) *Statistics of Road Traffic Accidents in Europe*. United Nations, New York.

FHANER, G. AND HANE, M. (1973) Seat belts: factors influencing their use. *Acc. Analysis & Prevention*, **5**(1).

GARWOOD, F. and STARKS, J. J. H. (1965) Comparison of methods of studying accident causation. Proc. Convention on Road Accidents, Inst. of Municipal Engrs., London.

GARWOOD, F. and MUNDEN, J. M. (1968) Variations in the road accidents rates in Great Britain over the last 10 years. Ninth Int. Study Wk. in Tr. & Saf. Eng., WTAO, London.

GARWOOD, F. and JOHNSON, H. D. (1971) Notes on road accident statistics. TRRL Report LR 394. The Transport and Road Research Laboratory.

GRIME, G. (1968) Accidents and injuries to car occupants wearing safety belts. *Automobile Engineer*, July.

HARRIS, P. (1971) Road accident tabulations language (RATTLE). TRRL Report LR 377. The Transport and Road Research Laboratory.

HIGHWAY RESEARCH BOARD (1971/2) *Model of Safety for Car Occupants*, H.R. Record 334; *Traffic Records*, H.R. Record 384; *Traffic Safety Barriers*, H.R. Record 386. Washington.

HIGHWAY RESEARCH BOARD. *Highway Safety*, Special Report 107; *Traffic Safety and Road Accident Research*, H.R. Record 225; *Safety and Accident Research*, H.R. Record 272; *Relationships of Highway Geometry to Traffic Accidents*, H.R. Record 312.

JORGENSEN, N. O. (1972) The statistical detection of accident black spots. Eleventh Int. Study Wk. in Tr. & Saf. Eng., WTAO, Brussels.

LEEMING, J. J. (1969) *Road Accidents—Prevent or Punish*. Cassell & Co.

LISTER, R. D. and NEILSON, I. D. (1969) *Protection of Car Occupants against Side Impacts*. Proc. 13th Stapp Car Crash Conference, Soc. Automotive Engrs. Inc., New York.

LITTLE, A. D. (1968) *Cost Effectiveness in Traffic Safety*. F. A. Praeger and Pall Mall Press.

MCFARLAND, R. A. and MOORE, R. C. (1957) Human factors in highway safety. *J. Medicine*, **256**, April and May.

NORMAN, L. G. (1962) Road traffic accidents—epidemiology, control and prevention. World Health Organisation, Public Health Paper No. 12, Geneva.

PLATT, F. N. (1958-60) Operations analysis of traffic safety. Pts. 1–4. *Int. Rd. Saf. Traff. Rev.*, **6**(2), (4), **7**(3) and **8**(4).

PRISK, C. (1967) Accident rates on USA toll roads. *Int. Rd. Saf. Traff. Rev.* **15**(2).

ROBERTSON, J. S., MCLEAN, A. J. and RYAN, G. A. (1966) *Traffic Accidents in Adelaide.* Australian Road Research Board. Special Report No. 1.

SHAW, L. and SICHEL, H. (1971) *Accident Proneness.* Pergamon Press.

SMEED, R. J. (1968) Aspects of pedestrian safety. *J. Transport Econ. and Policy,* **2**(3).

SMEED, R. J. (1968) Variations in the pattern of accident rates in different countries and their causes. Ninth Int. Study Wk. in Tr. & Saf. Eng., W.T.A.O.

SMEED, R. J. and GRIME, G. (1968) Vehicle and road design for safety. Symp. Instn. Mech. Engrs. and the Adv. Sch. Auto. Engng., Instn. Mech. Engrs.

SMEED, R. J. (1972) The usefulness of formulae in traffic engineering and road safety. *Acc. Analysis & Prevention,* **4**(4).

SPICER, B. R. (1971) A pilot study of traffic conflicts at a rural dual carriageway intersection. RRL Report L.R 410. The Road Research Laboratory.

TILLMAN, W. A. and HOBBS, G. E. (1949) The accident prone automobile driver. *Amer. J. Psychiat.* **106.**

TRANSPORT AND ROAD RESEARCH LABORATORY (1972) *Towards Safer Road Vehicles.* TRRL Report LR 481. Conference with Soc. Motor Manuf. & Traders, Crowthorne.

VARIOUS (1970) Focus on road safety. *Traff. Engng. & Control,* **12**(2).

WHITLOCK, F. A. (1971) *Death on the Road. A Study in Social Violence.* Tavistock Public and Hicks, Smith & Son.

WILKINS, H. A. (1968) Assessment of the Hope anti-jack-knife device. RRL Report LR 163. The Road Research Laboratory.

Index